In the Fever

King's Preserves

*Charles Cameron's diaries, which he kept
for almost thirty years (Royal College of Surgeons in Ireland).*

For Jack, with
love and thanks

In the Fever King's Preserves

Sir Charles Cameron
and the Dublin slums

Lydia Carroll

A. & A. Farmar

British Library Cataloguing in Publication Data
A CIP catalogue record for this book is available
from the British Library

ISBN: 978-1-906353-20-9

This edition first published in 2011
by
A. & A. Farmar Ltd
78 Ranelagh Village, Dublin 6, Ireland
Tel +353-1-496 3625 Fax +353-1-497 0107
Email afarmar@iol.ie,
Web www.aafarmar.ie

Printed and bound by GraphyCems
Typeset and designed by A. & A. Farmar
Index by the Author

Contents

Acknowledgements

In the years it has taken from my discovery of the fascinating life and career of Sir Charles Alexander Cameron—through firstly my PhD thesis, and then to the completely different format of this book—there are so many who have been generous to me with their support. I hope this acknowledgement will go some way towards expressing my sincere gratitude to all of them.

Thanks to Professor David Dickson of Trinity College, who helped me discover Cameron and generously shared his knowledge and experience. As a part-time researcher, I was lucky to have a rich store of archives convenient to my place of work, and even luckier to have helpful and knowledgeable archivists. To Robert Mills, Archivist of the Royal College of Physicians of Ireland, and to Rebecca Hayes, Archivist of the Grand Lodge of Freemasons of Ireland. Special thanks to Mary Clarke, Dublin City Archivist, who encouraged the project from the beginning and gave me an impetus to continue the work, and to Mary O'Doherty, of the Mercer Library in the Royal College of Surgeons in Ireland, who generously made the Cameron archive available whenever I requested it, and was immensely helpful and encouraging throughout my research. Thanks to Dr William Kingston of the School of Business, Trinity College, for his encouragement and advice. Particular thanks to my colleagues in the Department of Statistics in Trinity College, who, throughout my many years of research, have continued to be interested and supportive.

This book could not have come to fruition without the generous help of the Trinity Trust and the Grace Lawless Lee Fund—my sincere thanks for their support.

Particular thanks to my publishers, Tony and Anna Farmar of A. & A. Farmar, whose wise advice and inspired editing helped turn a raw PhD thesis into a polished publication.

Thanks to my extended family, in-laws, and friends, especially 'the bookworms' who have been a wonderful support throughout. Thanks to Michael, May and their families, and special thanks to Pat, who always rang to enquire, even when busy with interesting projects of his own. To my daughter-in-law Jacqueline, and my son-in-law Dermot, who always took time out from busy schedules to encourage and help. To my grandsons, Jack, Samuel, Jaydon, Cian and Ben, for being wonderful, and for keeping me on my toes, mentally and physically. To my son Jack, thanks for his support and the many interesting and helpful discussions, and for surprising (and delighting) me with his knowledge of history. To my daughter Cliodhna, whose remark (she'll know what I mean!) started me off on the great adventure. Thanks for always being there to support, cajole, and pick up the pieces after many a research session, and for being my willing accomplice in bouts of restorative retail therapy.

This book, and many other things in my life, would not have been possible without the love and support of my husband and best friend Jack. Throughout our married life, he has encouraged me to follow my dreams, and I owe a large part of anything I have achieved to his support. My love and thanks for everything, including his patience as I spent every spare moment of the past eight years thinking about 'another man'.

And finally, in remembrance of my late parents, Patrick and Elizabeth Gillis who, through the collective memories of many generations of Dubliners, who lived through the times I have researched, instilled in me a love of, and interest in, the history of my native city.

'My errors, if any, are my own. I have no man's proxy.' (Burke)

To Sir
Charles Cameron
C. B.

Enrico Caruso
Dublin

Cameron's image as a bon viveur *is captured in this flattering caricature by the famous tenor Enrico Caruso at a dinner with the Corinthian Club (Dublin City Library and Archive).*

Introduction

Sir Charles Cameron, Public Analyst and Medical Officer of Health for Dublin, died at the wrong time for posthumous acclaim. Born in Dublin in 1830, he died just short of his 91st year, on 27 February 1921, as Ireland was entering a new era as an independent nation. The new nation would put the emphasis on Catholic and National, with little interest in commemorating a Protestant unionist, particularly one who was considered to have outlived his usefulness at the time of his death.

Contemporary biographers would have been further discouraged by the fact that most of the biographical information about Cameron was, and still is, found in his own writings—two rambling volumes of reminiscences and autobiography that give the impression that the author was an old buffer, intent on proclaiming his own wit and social connections. Any interested party would have found little other information, apart from the brief biographical information in his obituaries, and his entry in two editions of a history of the Royal College of Surgeons in Ireland and of the Irish Schools of Medicine, written by himself. Fresh in the memory of contemporaries would also have been the Report, published in 1914, on the 1913 Inquiry into the Housing Conditions of the Working Classes in Dublin. This report had castigated Cameron's performance as Medical Officer of Health, accusing him of connivance with slum landlords, and of negligence in implementing legislation in respect of tenement houses.

Since his death, Cameron has languished in the footnotes of Dublin history, portrayed as an inconsequential and inefficient player in the story of the city's public health administration, his reputation besmirched with verbatim and unexamined repetitions of the findings of the 1914 Report. Only recently has that situation been reversed, as recent publications on the subject of public health in Dublin have begun to recognise his true contribution, describing him as 'the resourceful overseer of the city's public health',[1] as 'grinding down the opposition, quarter by quarter and year by year, as he relentlessly exposed the situation of the poorest of the citizens';[2] as 'the heroic

---

1 Joseph V. O'Brien, *Dear Dirty Dublin, A City in Distress, 1899–1916* (London, 1982), p. 31.
2 Jacinta Prunty, *Dublin Slums, 1800–1925, A Study in Urban Geography* (Dublin, 1998), p. 168.

Sir Charles Cameron',[3] who 'campaigned relentlessly to eliminate disease',[4] and as playing 'a key role in improving the living conditions of the Dublin poor'.[5] With the benefit of hindsight, Charles Cameron has been recognised as playing a vital role in improving the health and living conditions of the citizens of Dublin in the 19th and early 20th centuries.

In his Introduction to Cameron's *Autobiography*, Sir James Campbell, Lord Chancellor of Ireland, remarked on the absence in the memoirs of 'a single incident reflecting hostility by or to himself in the case of any person, party or creed', which was no mean feat in the political and social era in which Cameron lived and worked. He was a very public and prominent Freemason, but had the respect and friendship of many senior Roman Catholic clergy. He was a monarchist, and probably a Unionist, but worked closely with, and gained admiration for his work from all shades of Nationalists. He and his sanitary staff came under constant pressure from often powerful and influential lobby groups to tone down their sanitary efforts, but all the evidence shows that he stood firm and fulfilled his duties as far as he could under legal and other restrictions. His social life well into his late eighties and probably beyond would have exhausted a person half his age, yet he never let it interfere with his regular daily attendance at the Public Health Office and city laboratory.

However, no detailed study has been made of his life and work, and no effort has been made to ascertain the veracity or otherwise of the accusations made against him in the 1913 Inquiry and subsequent Report. While his contribution as Medical Officer of Health may have recently begun to be acknowledged, there has been little if any recognition of his significant reputation as a chemist, or of his contribution to the city's health as Public Analyst. This account of Cameron's life and times attempts to redress that situation, looking at his career as Public Analyst and Medical Officer of Health for Dublin from 1862 to 1921. An archetypal Renaissance man, Cameron had numerous professional and non-professional interests; these will also be examined, together with his often tragic private life, to give a balanced overview of his life and career.

On 30 September 1910, Dublin Corporation voted unanimously (a

---

3 Michael Corcoran, *'Our Good Health': A History of Dublin's Water and Drainage* (Dublin, 2005), front cover flap.
4 Ibid., p. 44.
5 Laurence Geary, 'Cameron, Sir Charles Alexander (1830–1921)' *Oxford Dictionary of National Biography* (Oxford University Press, 2004).

tribute in itself!) to constitute Charles Cameron an Honorary Freeman of Dublin 'for almost half a century of devoted exertion on his part to the extermination of disease and everything inimical to public health within the City'.[6] On 20 February 1911, when the honour was conferred on him, Alderman Thomas Kelly, leader of the Sinn Féin party in the Corporation—at the opposite end of the political spectrum from Cameron—remarked that his opinion of Charles Cameron had changed after he had worked with him on the Public Health Committee. He found Cameron to be a man 'whose earnest wish was to lift the city from its notoriety of having the highest death rate in Europe . . . and that he had done more than a man's part in combating disease in Dublin.'[7]

Those Trojan efforts have been largely forgotten since his death, and the only lasting monuments to Charles Cameron are a small street in the Liberties area, and a square of small houses in Kilmainham, both in Dublin 8, whose provenance is almost certainly forgotten. For a man who presided over the department which was responsible for almost halving the death rate in Dublin, who campaigned constantly for better living conditions for those for whom few others spoke; for a public servant who was acknowledged during his lifetime, not only as a key national figure in the fight against disease, but internationally as one of the foremost sanitarians of the 19th century, this is an oversight to say the least.

When added to the fact that the accusations of inefficiency made against him in the 1914 Report have never been examined, but have been allowed to adversely colour his posthumous reputation, it is more than an oversight—it is an injustice to a man who fought through public apathy, political opinion, professional dissension, and personal tragedy to leave the public health of Dublin citizens in a greatly improved state to that in which he found it.

---

6 Minutes of the Municipal Council of the City of Dublin, 1910, pp 439–40.
7 *Irish Independent*, 24 February 1911.

*Cameron's memories of his
birthplace, Magee's Court, near
Charlemont Street (seen here in
tenements in 1913), no doubt
influenced his approach to the
poor of Dublin. (Dublin City
Library and Archive)*

Chapter 1 Early life and family

Jacobite ancestors

Charles Cameron's long life completed a neat and appropriate circle for one who served Dublin city as a public servant for almost six decades. Born just off Charlotte Street in Dublin on 16 July 1830, he died over 90 years later, on 27 February 1921, two kilometres away on Raglan Road.

For details of Cameron's personal life, the only available sources are his autobiographical writing in his *Reminiscences* and his *Autobiography*, written when he was in his 80s, in the four volumes of his unpublished diaries, and in the two editions of his *History of the Royal College of Surgeons in Ireland, and of the Irish Schools of Medicine*—the first edition published in 1886 and the second in 1916.[1] He was very aware of his lineage, kept his diary on a daily basis, and was an adept record keeper in his public life. All the more remarkable then, that his accounts of his early life do not match the facts.

Cameron's own account of his birth is that he was born in Charlemont Street, the son of Ewen Cameron and Belinda Smith. His baptismal certificate, however, shows that he was born in Magee's Court, off Charlotte Street, the son of an ex-soldier called Edwin and his wife Bridget.[2] In 1851 William Wilde classified Charlotte Street as a 'mixed street', which was defined as one which contained 'small shops and the private residences of the middling classes'.[3] In 1834, the residents of this small street of 23 houses included a barrister and a brushmaker among the varied occupations.[4] Magee's Court was too small an entity to be classified by Wilde, but it is mentioned in the Dublin directories in 1840, ten years after Cameron's birth, when it is described as 'tenements';[5] it was still in tenements in 1913 and 1920 when Cameron was writing about his origins, and a photograph of

---

1 Charles A. Cameron, *Reminiscences of Sir Charles A. Cameron* (Dublin, 1913); *Autobiography of Sir Charles A. Cameron* (Dublin, 1920); *History of the Royal College of Surgeons in Ireland, and of the Irish Schools of Medicine* (Dublin, London, Edinburgh, 1886, 1916).
2 Baptismal register, 8 August 1830, St Peter's Church of Ireland.
3 William Wilde, 'Special Sanitary Report on the City of Dublin', appended to Census of Ireland, 1851.
4 Pettigrew & Oulton, *The Dublin Almanac and General Register of Ireland*, 1834, p. 31.
5 Ibid., 1840, p. 675.

it in its full dilapidation would appear in 1914 in the Report of the 1913 Housing Inquiry. As the city's foremost sanitarian, Cameron would have been fully aware of the unsanitary connotations attached to any address that contained the word 'court' or 'alley', usually a by-word for the lowest form of habitation, and he may have preferred to equivocate about his exact birthplace; Charlemont Street, adjacent to Charlotte Street, and probably better known, may have seemed a harmless compromise. There seems little other reason for Cameron to suppress the name of his birthplace; the 1911 Census shows that there were five houses set in tenements in Magee's Court, each with five rooms, and five windows to the front of each house—probably typical three-storey city-centre houses, so, while not large, they were unlikely to have been unsanitary hovels when Cameron was born there.

The discrepancy in his father's name of Ewen/Edwin might be construed from the baptismal record as a slip of the clergyman's pen were it not for the fact that Cameron's third son was named Edwin Douglas—although his youngest son was named Ewen. The change in his mother's name from Bridget to Belinda is more intriguing; unless there were two slips of the pen, twenty-one years apart, Cameron's mother is definitely named as Bridget on his baptismal certificate in 1830, and as Bridget on the 1851 Census of Dublin.[6] In Irish terms, the difference between these two names has, to put it bluntly, 'connotations'. A mother called Belinda would fit quite comfortably with Cameron's membership of the Church of Ireland, while a mother called Bridget could indicate Roman Catholic connections. Had she? Her maiden name is given as Smith—probably not a Catholic name. However, Cameron was renowned for his ecumenism. He had more Roman Catholic friends than would be usual for one of his communion in that era, and in later years, he would be a regular visitor to the North William Street convent and orphanage, just beside Portland Row where he had lived as a young man with his widowed mother. However, any ecumenical leanings must be measured against the fact that he was generally recognised as a staunch Protestant, and a private comment in his diaries where he wrote: 'I attended a meeting at church in support of the Catholic Boys Brigade. I did not like going until I heard that several other Protestants and of good position would be present.'[7]

---

6 Seán Magee, *Chart's Head of Household Surname Index*, (Dublin, 2001), CEN 1851/18/1–2, p. 88.
7 Charles Cameron, Diaries 1880–1916 (unpublished) Cameron archive, RCSI, 4 December 1898.

Whatever the exact and convoluted details of his birth, there is no doubt of the fact that Charles Cameron was a passionate Dubliner, who was fiercely protective of his city and its reputation throughout his life. He was also intensely proud of his Scottish heritage and his Jacobite ancestors. His great-grandfather, 'the amiable and unfortunate Archibald Cameron'[8] was hanged at Tyburn in 1753 for his part in the 1745 Rising; he was the last Jacobite to be executed. Archibald Cameron had qualified as a doctor, studying in Edinburgh, Paris and Leyden; for some reason his great-grandfather's profession was never mentioned by Cameron—a strange omission for a man who was himself a doctor, and who valued professional qualifications. Archibald Cameron was a somewhat reluctant Jacobite, claiming his involvement in the cause was not from commitment, 'but from compulsion of kindred'.[9] However, despite his initial reluctance, he played an active part in the Rising, was involved in concealing Prince Charles after the defeat at Culloden in 1746, and eventually went to France with the Prince and Archibald's older brother, Donald, known as 'The Gentle Lochiel'. The Prince obtained a commission for Archibald in the Spanish and later the French army,[10] where he served as physician to his brother's regiment.[11] He appears to have been chronically short of money, and made several visits to Scotland to obtain money for himself and other emigrant Jacobites.

On one such visit, in 1753, he was arrested on suspicion of being involved in the abortive Elibank plot—a plan to kidnap King George II—but was charged under the Act of Attainder with involvement in the 1745 Rising, and was sentenced to be hanged, drawn and quartered. Imprisoned in the Tower of London, he was denied the use of pen and paper, except for censored writing in the presence of prison officers, but used a blunt pencil and scraps of paper to record his thoughts before he died,[12] reiterating his support for Prince Charles and the Stuart cause. His wife, pregnant with their eighth child, travelled from Lille in Flanders to visit him before his execution.

On 7 June, 1753, he was drawn on a sledge to Tyburn, where a large crowd watched the proceedings. He prayed briefly with the clergyman who attended him and said 'I have now done with this world, and

8 Cameron, *History* (1886) op. cit., p. 443.
9 Roger Turner, 'Cameron, Archibald (1707–1753)', *Oxford Dictionary of National Biography*, (Oxford University Press, 2004).
10 John Stewart, *The Camerons: A History of Clan Cameron* (Stirling, 1974), p. 136.
11 http://www.lochiel.net/archives/arch129.html.
12 Stewart, (1974) op. cit., p. 138.

am ready to leave it'. He was forty-six years of age.[13] His body was not drawn and quartered, but his heart was removed and burnt. His remains were interred in the Savoy Chapel in London where, in 1846, a descendant was given permission by Queen Victoria to have a memorial tablet erected.[14]

Most reports of Archibald's life stress his humanity and willingness to attend to wounded opponents who were captured by the rebels. His great-grandson, Charles, would later be renowned for his humanity and lack of prejudice. Charles Cameron shares another, more unfortunate, similarity with his ancestor; shortly after Archibald's execution, his uncle, Ludovic Cameron of Torcastle, who had served with Archibald, wrote a letter accusing him of misappropriating some of Prince Charles's funds for his own use. A similar claim that Archibald had appropriated 6,000 louis d'or — a considerable amount of money — had been made by an informer, but later retracted. Before his death, Archibald wrote to one of his sons 'I have no money to leave you as a legacy . . . ' and after his execution his wife and children lived in penurious circumstances, so the claim that he was guilty of peculation is generally accepted as untrue, and described as 'the only slur on an otherwise unblemished character'.[15] The similarity with his great-grandson Charles Cameron is the Report on the 1913 Housing Inquiry, which cast aspersions on Cameron's work as Medical Officer of Health — these accusations, which will be examined in Chapter 11, were without foundation.

Archibald's descendants' allegiance to the Jacobite cause is illustrated by Charles Cameron's earliest memory of an incident where, at the age of four, he was brought to see an old woman who, as a young girl, had witnessed the withdrawal of the MacDonalds from the Battle of Culloden, so that he 'might thereafter be able to say that I had seen a spectator of the Battle of Culloden'.[16] The importance of this link with Jacobite Scotland remained — Cameron emphasized it in all his autobiographical writings. He was a founder member of the Clan Cameron Association, regularly attending their gatherings; the minutes from the first meeting of the clan in Edinburgh on 27 April 1889 show that Sir Charles Alexander Cameron of Dublin, although not present at the meeting, was appointed a member of the committee 'for carrying out the resolutions which have just been proposed and

---

13 http://www.lochiel.net/archives/arch129.html.
14 Stewart, op. cit., p. 139.
15 Ibid. p. 141.
16 Cameron, *Autobiography* (1920) op. cit., p. 3.

carried'.[17] By that time, the clan had become less warlike, but had not perhaps lost its disruptive element. Cameron recounts with some enjoyment how, in 1892, after a clan meeting in Glasgow, he returned to the Central Hotel with a group of his clansmen at three in the morning, where they noisily escorted Cameron to his room to the tune of the 'March of the Cameron Men'. Dr (later 'Sir') William Thompson, a doctor from Dublin who was staying at the hotel, was awoken by the commotion, and looked out of his room to see his compatriot 'attired in full Highland costume, slowly walking along a corridor, followed by Highland soldiers performing on the bagpipes'.[18]

Although Cameron's interest in the clan was probably mainly social, his interest in his ancestry appears to have remained undiminished over the years; in 1911, he received a confirmation of arms, with mention of descent from the family of Cameron of Lochiel; this confirmation is applied fourfold—to Sir Charles Alexander Cameron, to his father, to his mother (both deceased), and to 'Cameron of Lochiel, family of'.[19] It is unclear why, in 1911, at the age of 81, Cameron would have felt the need to look for such a confirmation. Had his lineage been questioned? Or perhaps the fact that he had been made an Honorary Freeman of Dublin prompted him to seek a formal declaration of his ancestral arms? The only family incident that occurred in 1911 was the marriage of his daughter Lucie; his younger daughter Lena had been married since 1903, and at that stage he would have had some grandchildren, so perhaps towards what he would have believed to be the end of his life Cameron wished in some way to formalise his lineage for his descendants. Whatever the reason for the formal confirmation of arms, there is no doubt that his Scottish ancestry and, more importantly, the fighting and rebellious spirit of his ancestors, was a significant factor in Cameron's upbringing and character. The fact that he mixed freely with a 'royal' set in Dublin and London, and was respectful of the British monarchy, must at some level have caused some ironic reflections.

Ewen Cameron

Cameron's link to his Jacobite ancestors was through his father, Ewen Cameron. Cameron claimed that his father, although an officer in the

---

17 http://www.lochiel.net/archives/arch023.html.
18 Cameron, *Reminiscences* (1913) op. cit., pp 109–110.
19 M111a (POS 8292), National Library of Ireland.

British army, 'always regretted the replacement of the ancient Scottish, by a German, dynasty'.[20] Ewen Cameron was born in Lochabar, Inverness, in 1787, and had a short but very active military career as a captain in the 42nd Regiment as per his wife's death certificate,[21] (or in the 79th Regiment of Foot as per confirmation of arms to Cameron in 1911) receiving eight wounds, two of which, one French, the other American, he 'carried with him to the grave'.[22] Unfortunately, the Secretary of War, Lord Palmerston, only considered six of these wounds suffered on behalf of king and country as being worthy of pension entitlement, the other two having been suffered in 'forlorn hope' sorties, and so not considered to be 'official' wounds. Cameron somewhat wryly commented that his father 'was consoled by being retired on full pay'.[23] His commission in the British army had been secured through the influence of a relative, Colonel John Cameron of Fassifern,[24] and his career had encompassed the Peninsular War, the war against the United States in 1812, and the expedition 'to aid the Queen of Spain against Don Carlos, Pretender to the throne of Spain'.[25] Fighting with the Cameron Highlanders in the Peninsular War, it was said that his name 'will live in history for all time as one of the bravest Scottish soldiers who fought at Talavera',[26] a battle which took place on 27-8 July in 1809—he would have been 22 years of age at the time.

Hyperbole aside, Ewen Cameron had certainly led an eventful life before being 'retired' at the age of 28 in 1815. He married Bridget Smith from Virginia in Co. Cavan, but there is no indication of when this marriage took place, or how and where Cameron's parents met. Cameron does state that 'after his battles were over'[27] his father, like the majority of fellow Scotsmen, did not return to Scotland, but settled, at his wife's request, in Dublin at the end of the 1820s. They lived there until 1844, when the family went to Guernsey, where his father died two years later, when Cameron was 15 years of age.[28] Cameron's parents shared a knowledge of Gaelic, and used this language when they wanted to keep the content of their conversations secret from their children. Gaelic was Ewen Cameron's native tongue, and was

20 Cameron, *Autobiography* (1920) op. cit., p. 2.
21 Death certificate of Belinda Cameron, 27 April, 1867.
22 Cameron, *Autobiography* (1920) op. cit., p. 1.
23 Ibid.
24 Cameron, *History* (1886) op. cit., p. 444.
25 Cameron, 'Some Recollections of a Long Life in Dublin' *The Lady of the House* (Christmas 1915, reprinted 15 March 1921) p. 14b.
26 *Lady's Pictorial*, 2 December 1911.
27 Cameron (Christmas 1915) op. cit., p 7.
28 Cameron, *Autobiography* (1920) op. cit., p. 18.

used by officers of the Highland Regiments in the Peninsular War.[29] When they lived in Palmerstown on the outskirts of Dublin, Cameron recalled his father speaking in Gaelic to the countrymen travelling from the west of Ireland to work in England. There was at that time no railway connection, and the labourers had to walk from the west coast to Dublin to travel to England for a few weeks' work. He was aware, therefore, of the existence of the poor from a very early age.

It is Cameron's father who figures most prominently in his childhood memories, and he is portrayed as a kind, if somewhat stern, parent. He appears to have been something of an invalid, probably as a result of his war wounds, and moved in a social circle of mainly military men in Dublin and later in Guernsey. He was friendly with Major General Sir Guy Campbell, married to the daughter of Lord Edward Fitzgerald and also, ironically, with Major Henry Charles Sirr, who had captured Lord Edward Fitzgerald[30]—perhaps Ewen Cameron passed on to his son the ability to 'be all things to all men' and 'a diplomat of the first water' as claimed of Cameron by Alderman Thomas Kelly when he was made an Honorary Freeman of Dublin.[31] Ewen Cameron knew Sir Guy from the Peninsular War, and Cameron recalled the Major General waving his whip to warn him of the danger of falling when sitting on a high wall near their house in Palmerstown.[32] The directories show that Sir Guy lived in Palmerstown from 1833 until 1836, when he moved to Drumcondra in Dublin, so this gives some idea of when Cameron and his family lived there, although Cameron also mentions living near the Earl of Mayo's house in Chapelizod.[33] There is, however, no reference to a Ewen (or Edwin) Cameron in the directories of the period in question, nor is he on the Dublin City voters' list for 1832, 1835 and 1837.[34] In the latter case, perhaps Ewen Cameron did not register as a voter, although it is unlikely that he would not have qualified. Ewen Cameron's pension was sufficient for a middle-class lifestyle; the family had some servants—Cameron

---

29 Ibid., p. 1.

30 Ibid., pp 4–5.

31 Ibid., p. 144.

32 Sir Guy Campbell was deputy quartermaster general in Ireland during the 1830s, and Cameron's memories of him were accurate; in a letter to Sir Guy's daughter after his death, Lady Pamela Campbell wrote a letter 'to shew forth the softer touches of his character . . . all animals and children loved your father, and he loved them'. Papers of Pamela Lady Campbell, National Library of Ireland MS 40,025/2.

33 Cameron, (Christmas 1915) op. cit., p. 4.

34 *Alphabetical List of the Constituency of the City of Dublin, etc. 1832, 1835, and 1837* (Dublin, 1837).

mentioned his nurse and 'a man who was occasionally employed by my father'. They appear to have moved frequently in a short space of time, and to quite unrelated areas—from Magee's Court in the centre of Dublin in the early 1830s, to Palmerstown or Chapelizod, which would have been in the countryside on the outskirts of the city in the mid 1830s, and back to the north side of Dublin city, probably around 1836[35]—he mentions going to parties as a child in Glenville, Gloucester, and North Cumberland Streets—and then to Guernsey in the Channel Islands from 1844 until Ewen Cameron's death in 1846. Like many people in Dublin at the time, they would probably have rented, rather than owned, the houses they lived in. The young Cameron was in bad health before the family moved to Guernsey,[36] and his father was an invalid, so perhaps the final move to what was probably a warmer climate may have been an effort to improve the health of both, which it appears to have done in the young Cameron's case.

Bridget (or Belinda) Smith Cameron

Very little information is available about Cameron's mother. He gives her name as Belinda Smith, daughter of John Smith from the Virginia area of Co. Cavan, and this is how she appears on her death certificate—on which the informant was Cameron. However, as we have seen, it seems more likely from Cameron's baptismal certificate and the Census of 1851 that her real name was Bridget, and that Cameron, for reasons that can only be speculated upon, decided to reinvent her as Belinda. Her father's occupation and social standing are not mentioned by Cameron—an unexpected omission for a man who had a preoccupation with lineage and social position. There is a distinct contrast, for example, with the amount of information given by Cameron about his father's family, although it is equally true that he gives us as little information about his wife's family, other than her famous cousin, the playwright W. G. Wills. Perhaps his mother's family was Roman Catholic, and Cameron did not find it socially convenient to reveal this, or perhaps all that can be fairly inferred from such omissions is that the families of his mother and wife did not distinguish themselves in any way that was worthy of historical record, unlike the fighting and rebellious Camerons. Bridget Smith was born in 1793 and died on 27 April 1867, at the age of 73, outliving her husband by 21 years. Her death certificate shows that she was

---

35   Cameron, (Christmas 1915)op. cit., p.4.
36   Cameron, *Autobiography* (1920) op. cit., p. 17.

living with her son Charles at the time of her death, at 102 Baggot Street, and that he was present at her death. It was Bridget Cameron who persuaded her husband to settle in Dublin at the end of the 1820s, but no reason is given for this preference.[37] Even with the sparse facts that are known about Cameron's mother, it is possible to piece together the pattern of her life. She was widowed at the age of 52, had lost her eldest son several years previously and, as far as can be surmised from Cameron's writings, her daughter married around the age of 18 and moved to the United States. Her return to Dublin from Guernsey in straitened circumstances after her husband's death must have been a very difficult time for her, and for the 15-year-old Cameron, now the only support of his widowed mother. These facts are borne out by the 1851 Census of Dublin, which reported the following entry for Cameron and his mother:[38]

| Charles Alexander Cameron | 15 Portland Row | St. Thomas's |
| Mrs. Bdgt. Cameron | 15 Portland Row | St. Thomas's |

The fact that Cameron was the breadwinner from the age of 15 goes some way towards explaining his determination to earn as much money as he could, from as many sources as possible, throughout his long life.

The only other fact that we know of Bridget Smith Cameron is that she spoke Irish, and could converse with her husband in his native Scottish Gaelic. She obviously felt strongly enough about the Irish language to tell Cameron that, when she was a girl, everyone, rich and poor, understood Gaelic, and that thousands were native speakers. For his part, Cameron remembered this statement, and it obviously made sufficient impression for him to recall it when writing his memoirs and to compare the situation that his mother had described with the situation that existed at the time of the 1911 Census, long after she had died.[39] There was also an interesting comment on this subject at the time of the conferring on him of the Freedom of Dublin. The Lord Mayor commented on the fact that Cameron's mother had been an Irish speaker 'which might account for his anxiety to have the Irish language a compulsory subject in the National University'.[40] The main campaigners for compulsory Irish at the time were Sinn Féin and the Gaelic League—so this comment is an insight into Cameron's interests.

---

37 Cameron, (Christmas 1915) op. cit., p. 7.
38 Magee, (2001) op. cit., p. 88.
39 Cameron, *Autobiography* (1920) op. cit., p. 1.
40 *Weekly Irish Times*, 25 February, 1911.

Although in his autobiographical writings he recalled several incidents from his childhood in which his father figured as a participant, he did not recall any childhood memories with his mother. He only mentioned her in connection with speaking Irish, with going to and returning from Guernsey, and with her efforts to find him a job on their return. When Bridget Cameron returned to Dublin she called on a family friend to use his influence to get the young Charles a job. The friend is named as John Kent Johnston, who offered Cameron his first job in his newspaper agency.

Cameron's brother and sister

Even less is known of Cameron's brother and sister. There are no records of their baptisms in the register of St Peter's Church, so the family may have lived elsewhere before Charles' birth. We know from his autobiography that his brother John was an officer in the Royal Navy, and that he was killed, according to Cameron, 'in the first Chinese war', which probably means the first Opium War, which occurred between 1839 and 1842. If that was the case, then John would have died before Ewen Cameron, and before the family left Ireland for Guernsey. He was obviously some years older than Cameron, as he always brought a present to the young Charles on his visits home, one of which, an Indian canoe, Cameron recalled sailing on the canal. Cameron appears to have been very attached to his older brother, and as a child wrote a poem about him, which included the lines:

> How long the time appears to me
> Waiting for John to come from sea.

It is a rather touching remnant of Cameron's childhood memories, and an indication of close family ties.[41]

His sister was married 'before she was quite eighteen years old'[42] and is somewhat peremptorily dismissed with the comment, written in 1920, that she 'married a literary man, emigrated to the United States', and that 'she, her husband and only child died many years ago'.[43] However, she must have been some part of his childhood, as Cameron recalls that 'on her marriage she assumed the cap, which was then the sign of matrimony'.[44] There is evidence, however, that Cameron, despite the brief mention of his sister in his autobiography,

---

41 Ibid., p. 14.
42 Cameron, (Christmas 1915) op. cit., p. 13.
43 Cameron, *Autobiography* (1920) op. cit., p. 1.
44 Cameron, (Christmas 1915) op. cit., p. 13.

kept in touch with her and her family after they went to America. When he was Professor of the Dublin Chemical Society, his brother-in-law sent him a sample of guano for analysis, the results of which Cameron presented to the Society on 12 June 1857.[45] As Cameron did not marry until 1862, this can only have referred to his sister's husband, a point reinforced by the fact that the person in question lived in San Francisco. Unfortunately, there is no mention of his name, and no further details of Cameron's sister, including no details of her name.

Cameron's childhood

The only accounts of Cameron's childhood are written by himself, in his *Reminiscences* (1913) and *Autobiography* (1920), when he was aged 83 and 90 years respectively, together with brief details in an article in 1915.[46] It is understandable, therefore, that his childhood memories are mainly pleasant anecdotes, with Cameron himself as the main protagonist, and it is also understandable that there are some minor inconsistencies. There is a distinct feeling of warmth in his memories, of a normal childhood in a close family, with freedom to indulge in boyish pranks. These anecdotes mention mainly his father, who appears to have been strict, but with some sense of humour. The young Cameron used to read a chapter of the Bible to his father every morning, and on one occasion questioned the biblical interpretation of the conversation between Balaam and his ass, proclaiming that it was not a miracle, but a vision, because Balaam did not appear to be frightened. His father told him curtly to 'Finish the chapter', but there is a definite hint that he enjoyed the repartee, and perhaps this early sign of Cameron's independent thinking. [47] This probably could not be said of the episode in which the ten-year-old Cameron and his nurse were reported to the police as being 'lost, stolen or strayed' after Cameron, unwilling to attend his first day in a new school of whose headmaster he had heard bad reports, brought the unfortunate woman on a six-mile walk out of the city, and through *terra incognita* to Clondalkin, several miles outside Dublin, claiming all the while that the school in York Street (actually about a mile from his home in the centre of Dublin), was 'further, and further, Mary.'[48] The weary woman was directed home by an amused policeman, and Cameron reported

45 *The Irish Farmers' Gazette,* 20 June 1857.
46 Cameron, (Christmas 1915) op. cit..
47 Cameron, *Autobiography* (1920) op. cit., p. 5.
48 Ibid., p. 6.

that 'as physical punishment equivalent to my offence would have made a wreck of me, I escaped severe treatment' and discovered that the headmaster, Rev. Halahan, was 'a kindly man'.[49] The long walk had no lasting effect on Mary; according to Cameron, she lived to be a very old woman, and she recounted the episode with great enjoyment to his own children. This incident is an example of the type of minor inconsistencies in the *Reminiscences* and *Autobiography*, as the nurse is described as 'Peggy Carey' in the *Reminiscences* and as 'Mary Carey' in the *Autobiography*, while the headmaster and school are described as Mr Geoghegan of Hume Street in the *Reminiscences*,[50] and the Rev. Mr Halahan of York Street in the *Autobiography*.[51] Both of these gentlemen appear in the Dublin directories during the 1830s, so perhaps Cameron attended both establishments.

The family moved to Palmerstown (or Chapelizod—the areas would have been adjacent) on the outskirts of the city in the 1830s, perhaps for a healthier environment—their previous home in Magee's Court would have been very close to some of Dublin's most unhealthy areas, and the area itself may even have been developing into a slum. The move allowed Cameron to have pets, 'dogs, rabbits, guinea pigs, pigeons' and a rather puny pig 'which bore some resemblance to a greyhound' and whose loud grunting annoyed his invalid father.[52] One day, seeing his father approach with a drawn sword with what he believed to be 'fell intent against the pig', the young Cameron hoisted the unfortunate animal into a loft by means of a rope attached to its leg, causing a rupture. It was finally driven 'with some difficulty' to Smithfield market by William, occasionally employed by Cameron's father, where it caused much amusement as a curiosity, and was sold for 1s 6d—Cameron reports that it was the only bid—the proceeds of the sale being spent on drink by William.[53]

In 1844, Cameron and his parents moved to Guernsey in the Channel Islands. Aged 14, Cameron was in bad health before the move, having 'a prolonged cold, a severe cough, and occasional haemoptysis'.[54] The move improved the young Cameron's health, partly as a result of regular exercise, and he became skilled enough at skittles to make up a team with the local infantry. His health also improved sufficiently for him to put to flight a large number of boys who shouted 'There's an Irish

49 Ibid.
50 Cameron, *Reminiscences* (1913) op. cit., p. 14.
51 Cameron, *Autobiography* (1920) op. cit., pp 5–6.
52 Ibid., p. 7.
53 Ibid., pp 7–8.
54 Ibid., pp 16–18.

Paddy!', knocking one down, and pursuing the others, encouraged by his friend shouting 'Pitch into them, Charlie!' Cameron readily admits that the presence of this friend, Mr Holland, a Yorkshireman, may have been responsible for his bravado, although he also claims that in the Dublin schools he had attended he 'had to fight—sometimes victorious, sometimes vanquished—until my fighting status was established'.[55] The same Mr Holland and his wife befriended the young Cameron, bringing him to the theatre and concerts, and putting a hunter at his disposal so that he could take part in the local hunt.[56] Cameron does not mention where his family lived in Guernsey, but he does mention a General Sir John Cameron, a relative of his father, who lived there. The Census of Guernsey for 1841 shows a Sir John Cameron and a Mr Charles Holland living in St Peter Port, so it is reasonable to assume that Cameron's family also lived there. This carefree existence only lasted two years. It came to an end with the death of Cameron's father, when the boy and his mother were obliged to return to Ireland. The family were left in straitened circumstances; they could not afford the £600 required to equip and to buy a commission in the army, so his father's death ended Cameron's ambition to follow the same career.[57] No will has been found in respect of Ewen Cameron.

---

55 Ibid., p. 2.
56 Ibid.
57 Ibid., p. 18.

*Printed in 1888, this lithograph of a youthful-looking Cameron
is from Leyland's* Contemporary Medical Men. *In that year
Cameron was 58 years old. (Author's collection)*

Chapter 2 Earning a living

Early career

When Cameron and his mother returned to Dublin, a family friend, John Kent Johnston offered the 15-year-old Cameron a job in his office—Johnston & Co., Newspaper Agents, 1 Eden Quay, Sackville Street—which advertised the supply of a large variety of newspapers and the placing of advertisements.[1] Even at this age, Cameron appears to have had strong opinions, as he did not accept the offer, finding himself 'adverse to commercial life', a brave move for a financially vulnerable young man. It was the right decision—not least because Johnston's went bankrupt in 1850, the business being taken over by the largest creditor W. H. Smith, which was bought out by Charles Eason in 1886. Johnston introduced Cameron to a friend, Henry Bewley, of Bewley & Evans, Apothecaries and Chymists, 3 Sackville Street, who gave him a job in his laboratory, and Cameron never looked back. Under the tutelage of John Aldridge, superintendent of the laboratory and also Professor of Chemistry at Apothecaries Hall medical school, Cameron became adept at chemistry, 'acquiring a good knowledge of pharmaceutical chemistry, which I subsequently found to be very useful to me'.[2] His account of his progress is worth reporting verbatim:

> I now began to read books on chemistry, physics, geology, medicine, &c. I attended lectures at the Royal Dublin Society, and subsequently received instruction in geology from Dr. Edward Hull, F.R.S., Head of the Geological Survey of Ireland. I soon began teaching chemistry myself, and had a few pupils, some of whom were subsequently amongst the founders of the Dublin Chemical Society.[3]

By the age of 19 Cameron had sufficient self-awareness to ask himself, 'What was the most congenial way of making an income?'[4] He would answer that question by resolving 'to make it in every way I could', and over the course of his long life earned his living to a

---

1 *Thom's Directory* (1846) p. 710.
2 Cameron, *Autobiography* (1920) op. cit., p. 19.
3 Ibid.
4 Ibid.

greater extent from chemistry, medicine, and public health, and, to a lesser but probably equally enjoyable extent, from geology, journalism, and as art and theatre critic. His career advancement was rapid; by 1852, six years after arriving back in Ireland as an unqualified and impecunious youth with a widowed mother, Cameron was giving the opening lecture in chemistry in the newly formed Dublin Chemical Society to an audience that included some of the most prominent intellectuals in Dublin, including his former superintendent in Bewley's laboratory, John Aldridge. The Society had elected him as its Professor of Chemistry, a title Cameron admits was 'pretentious' as he was 'a chemist and a medical student, and . . . twenty-two years old'.[5] However, this did not deter him from using the title—in 1853, aged 23, he is listed in *Thom's Directory* with the 'nobility, gentry, merchants and traders' as 'Cameron, C. A. professor of chemistry to the Dublin Chemical Society'.[6] This combination of self-confidence and modesty (which does not appear to have been false) was evident throughout Cameron's life; he regularly expressed, not only in public but privately in his diaries, surprise at the praise and honours he received, while, at the same time, having absolute confidence in his own ability, defending his views and his beliefs against his critics.

The Dublin Chemical Society

The Dublin Chemical Society's inaugural lecture, given by its newly elected Professor of Chemistry, Charles Cameron, took place on 13 December 1852, at 64 Capel Street, before an audience of about 70 people. The Society had been founded 'for the especial purpose of considering and investigating every subject connected with the advancement of Ireland in the industrial arts influenced by chemistry',[7] and expressed a hope that it would become 'an institution of national usefulness'.[8] In a deputation to the Lord Lieutenant in May 1855, members of the Society stated that 'at the time it was instituted there were no means by which persons of moderate income could study chemistry practically in connection with manufacturs [sic] and the arts. The establishment of this society has supplied this want.'[9] The deputation went on to say that: 'A considerable number of young men, belonging to very different branches of manufactures, have obtained

---

5 Ibid., p. 22.
6 *Thom's Directory* (1853), p. 1049.
7 *Irish Farmers' Gazette*, 30 August 1856.
8 Ibid.
9 *The Commercial Journal and Family Herald*, 12 May 1855.

a facility in chemical manipulation at a very trifling expense in the laboratory of the society.'[10]

This educational section of the Society was solely under the guidance of Charles Cameron; at its annual meeting in 1858 it reported that:

Dr. Cameron reports most favourably of the progress of the students in the laboratory, all of whom seem desirous of acquiring a thorough knowledge of practical chemistry.

The number of students at present attending is 15, and the various departments of the science which they cultivate, with the number studying in each, are as follow (sic), viz:-

Elementary chemistry	10
Pharmaceutical chemistry	1
Analytical chemistry	4
	15

Cameron was described as labouring

in the laboratory daily, explaining in clear and accurate language, devoid of technicalities, the mysteries of a delightful and useful science, and it was to be hoped, and, indeed, there could be no doubt, that the Dublin Chemical Society, under Dr. Cameron's able and enlightened direction, would increase in numbers, importance, and usefulness.[11]

The Society remained in existence until 1862, and reports of its meetings show that it was attended by a wide cross-section of intellectuals; for example, the previously-mentioned John Aldridge, Dominic Corrigan, President of the Royal College of Physicians, Lord Talbot de Malahide (President in 1857), and Mr John Caldwell Bloomfield, who would later found Belleek Pottery, were among the attendees. However, the lectures were also open to the public, and brought a knowledge of chemistry to a varied audience; for example, at the meeting of the Society on 19 October 1854 the corps of the sappers and miners from Mountjoy Barracks were observed 'most attentively listening to Professor Cameron's most admirable lecture'.[12] From the perspective of Cameron's subsequent career, one of the most important contacts he made in the Dublin Chemical Society was Sir John Gray, who would later be the driving force behind the Vartry water supply for Dublin, and who would recommend Cameron for his first public post.

---

10 Ibid.
11 *Irish Farmers' Gazette*, 3 April 1858.
12 *Commercial Journal and Family Herald*, 21 October, 1854.

Cameron's lectures to the Dublin Chemical Society covered a wide range of topics, such as 'The constituents of the ocean and the atmosphere', 'Urea as a direct source of nitrogen in vegetation', and 'The properties and manufacture of the new metal "Aluminium"'. The emphasis in Cameron's lectures seems to have been on innovation, on bringing what today would be described as cutting-edge scientific discoveries to his fascinated and enthusiastic Dublin audience. In December 1855, for example, he 'Exhibited the electric light by means of a battery of fifteen of Callan's cells charged with nitric and dilute sulphuric acids'.[13]

In 1857, Cameron proposed that the Society should develop a section to discuss agricultural matters—this motion was passed. It was perhaps not an altogether altruistic suggestion, but it was certainly an astute one, as much of his early lectures and publications were on agricultural matters and much of his later analytical work would be of an agricultural nature. In 1858, *The Shrewsbury Chronicle* described him as 'the most eminent agricultural chemist in the sister kingdom',[14] and he was also analyst to the Royal Agricultural Society. In 1857, he published a book, *The Chemistry of Agriculture, the Food of Plants*,[15] which received widespread and favourable publicity, and in April 1859 he became editor and part proprietor of a new newspaper, *The Weekly Agricultural Review and Irish Country Gentleman's Newspaper*, which had its offices at 7 Great Brunswick Street.[16] The new publication stated its intention to be read 'by persons of every shade of political and religious opinion', and would therefore refuse to publish anything 'having a sectarian or polemical tendency'. It would also refuse what were described as 'objectionable advertisements which too often render otherwise interesting and instructive newspapers unfit for the family circle.'[17]

Charles Cameron, as editor, and only 28 years of age, was making his non-sectarian and non-political views and beliefs plain, even to prospective advertisers in his new venture.

It was Cameron who, at a meeting of the Dublin Chemical Society in March, 1858, put forward the first suggestion for the foundation of an Irish veterinary college, stating that there were no insurmountable obstacles to founding such a college, and that he knew of a building,

---

13 *Freeman's Journal*, 14 December 1855.
14 *The Shrewsbury Chronicle*, 18 June 1858.
15 Charles A. Cameron, *The Chemistry of Agriculture, the Food of Plants* (Dublin, 1857)
16 Cameron, *Autobiography* (1920), op. cit., p. 56.
17 *The Irish Times*, 19 April, 1859.

formerly a school of medicine, in Peter Street, that was to let at a moderate rent.[18] He suggested opening a list of subscribers in the *Farmers' Gazette*. He remained committed to this cause; in 1861, as secretary to the committee of the Veterinary College, he spoke passionately of the necessity of such a college in Ireland, and announced that a limited company had been formed to further the venture.[19]

The Dublin Chemical Society would never regret bestowing the 'pretentious' title of Professor on the young Cameron. In fact, it frequently expressed, not only delight in his lectures and experiments, but also pride in having such a professor. After its first demonstration—a practical illustration of oxygen—given by Cameron, the Society's President, Surgeon Lover, said that 'Never anywhere, nor on any occasion, did he know the subject to be treated with more ability than had just been exhibited that evening'.[20]

Nor did this enthusiasm diminish as time went on; at the Society's annual meeting in March, 1857, Rev. Mr Manly, seconding a vote of thanks to Cameron, described him as 'a genuine Irishman and an accomplished chemist' and went on to comment on 'his enlarged and accurate knowledge, his playful humour, his genial warmth, his unsophisticated kindness of heart, and his unwearied and successful efforts on behalf of this society,' further stating that 'To know him is to love him'.[21]

On 27 July 1857 a deputation from the Dublin Chemical Society called on Cameron at his home in 17 Ely Place to present him with an address and testimonial.[22] This testimonial was presented, with a watch and chain, as a measure of the Society's appreciation of Cameron's 'personal worth and talent'. At the annual meeting of the Society in April 1858, one of the members, Mr Vereker, attributed its flourishing condition to 'the untiring exercions [sic] and great zeal and genius of Dr Cameron'.[23] At the same meeting, James Haughton said that the rapid progress of the Society was 'due to their Professor, Dr Cameron, whom they all loved and admired'.[24] These tributes, rather fulsome to modern ears, were obviously made with great sincerity and feeling, and the emphasis was not only on Cameron's

18 *Irish Farmers' Gazette*, 6 March 1858.
19 *The Irish Times*, 18 October 1861.
20 *The Daily Express*, 14 December, 1852.
21 *Irish Farmers' Gazette*, 28 March 1857.
22 *Freeman's Journal*, 29 July 1857.
23 Ibid., 3 April 1858.
24 Ibid.

talent and genius as a chemist, but on his personal qualities as a person who was extremely popular. That the tributes were paid to a 28 year old by those who were for the most part older, more experienced, and socially superior—an important factor in that era—and more advanced in terms of their careers than the object of their admiration, is some measure of the impact and impression that Cameron had made so early in his career. For his part, Cameron freely admitted that the Dublin Chemical Society played a major part in forwarding his career, as the 'accounts of my lectures, which appeared in the Press, made my name known to the general public'.[25] His first medical appointment in 1856 as Professor of Chemistry and Natural Philosophy in the Dublin School of Medicine was as a result of his increased fame as a chemistry lecturer with the Society,[26] and it was at the recommendation of one of its members, Sir John Gray, that he was recommended for the post of Public Analyst for Dublin, to which he was appointed in 1862.[27] It was perhaps appropriate that the Dublin Chemical Society ceased to exist the same year—according to Cameron, there was no longer a necessity for it, as chemistry was now to be taught in the Royal College of Science.[28] However, the loss of their beloved 'Professor'— 'the mainspring of its existence'[29]—who had now moved on to the next stage of his career, must have helped to hasten the end of a society that had endeavoured to make the developing science of chemistry available to a wider public.

Belleek and the 'china war'

One tangible result of the Society's endeavours was the foundation of the Belleek Pottery, which achieved world-wide fame for its parian china; Cameron's involvement with Belleek china would become the only controversial incident in his career with the Dublin Chemical Society. In 1849, John Caldwell Bloomfield inherited the Castlecaldwell estate adjacent to the village of Belleek from his father. In the aftermath of the Famine, with high rates of poverty in the area, he looked for some means of providing employment for his tenants. The records show that Bloomfield was a member of the Dublin Chemical Society— he was on its council in 1857[30]—and Cameron referred to him as 'my

25 Cameron, *Autobiography* (1920), op. cit., p. 25.
26 Ibid.
27 Ibid.
28 Ibid.
29 *The Mining Journal, Railway and Commercial Gazette*, 8 March 1856.
30 *Irish Famers' Gazette*, 11 April 1857.

dear lifelong friend'.[31] In the 1850s, Cameron spent several Christmas holidays on the Castlecaldwell estate and, on one of these occasions, discovered a patch of white clay while out shooting. His analysis of this clay led him to believe that it would prove to be suitable for the manufacture of porcelain, a fact he conveyed to his friend Mr Bloomfield.[32]

Cameron's claims for the properties of the china clay were immediately challenged by the Rev. Joseph Galbraith, a Fellow of Trinity College, Dublin, who wrote to *Saunder's News-Letter* expressing doubts that china clay existed in Co. Fermanagh. What became known as the 'china war' continued in this newspaper over several days, the weapons of choice being chemical analyses and formulae, in which Cameron appears to have dealt a fatal blow to Rev. Galbraith with the claim that 'Mr Galbraith analysed the clay in its crude state, while I examined it when perfectly freed from the pieces of undecomposed rock abundantly mixed through it'.[33]

However, with the diplomacy for which he would become renowned, Cameron went on to say that he hoped Mr Galbraith would excuse him 'for placing myself in seeming, but not real, antagonism to him' as he was sure that they were both anxious that the public should not be misled, and that if he would further investigate the matter, he would be appreciative of 'the attempts being made to introduce a new branch of manufacture into our neglected and impoverished country'.[34]

Cameron was only 25 years of age at the time—having successfully defeated in public the claims of an established academic it is possible that his politeness in victory may have been influenced by a desire to keep his professional options open so early in his career. A portion of the clay was sent to Kerr's porcelain factory in Worcester, England, to be tested in the manufacturing process, and the first article made from Belleek clay, a saucer, was presented to Charles Cameron—he still had it in his possession more than 60 years later.[35] John Caldwell Bloomfield went on to harness the power of the River Erne and campaign for a railway service to Belleek to service the new china factory, which was largely financed by David McBirney, a Dublin businessman, also a regular attendee at the meetings of the Dublin Chemical Society. The foundation

---

31 Cameron, *Autobiography* (1920), op. cit., p. 27.
32 Ibid.
33 *Saunder's News-Letter*, December 14 1855.
34 Ibid.
35 Cameron, *Autobiography* (1920), op. cit., p. 27.

stone was laid by Mrs Bloomfield on Thursday, 18 November 1858.[36]

Cameron's medical education

As one of the first Irish medical historians, Cameron is widely quoted on biographical details of 19th-century doctors, from his two editions of the *History of the Royal College of Surgeons in Ireland and of the Irish Schools of Medicine*. However, his own biographical details in both of these volumes are notably brief; in 1886, he states simply that he 'was educated in Dublin, Guernsey and Germany',[37] and that 'he has dedicated himself chiefly to the scientific branches of medicine and chemistry'.[38] If this is to be taken as a chronological indication of his education, then the implication is that, since the first two locations were during his childhood, his medical education must have taken place in Germany. This is supported by a statement in one of his obituaries, which stated that 'having received his early education in Dublin, the young Cameron went to Germany, where he graduated as a Doctor of Medicine and also as a Doctor of Philosophy in 1856'.[39] However, in the 1916 edition of his *History*, Cameron stated that he 'was educated in schools in Dublin and Guernsey. He studied Medicine in the School of the Apothecaries' Hall, the Dublin School of Medicine, the Ledwich School, and the Meath and Coombe Hospitals. He was for some time in Germany, and gained the friendship of the celebrated chemist, Baron Liebig.'[40] Further on in the same edition, Cameron elaborated on his qualifications, stating that he was 'an M.D., R.U.I., a Member and Honorary Fellow of the Royal College of Physicians; a Fellow, Hon. D.P.H., and Honorary Secretary of the College; an Honorary Licentiate, Apothecaries' Hall; a Diplomate of Public Health, Cambridge University.'[41] In his *Autobiography*, Cameron claimed 'my hospital education was carried out in the Meath Hospital and County Dublin Infirmary, but I occasionally witnessed operations in other hospitals'.[42]

Cameron was stated to be a 'Doctor of Medicine of the Royal University of Ireland' in the confirmation of arms that he received in 1911.[43] However, the records for this institution show that Cameron's

36 http://www.belleek.ie/profile.asp.
37 Cameron, *History* (1886) op. cit., p. 444.
38 Ibid.
39 *The Irish Times*, 28 February 1921.
40 Cameron (1916), op. cit., p. 510.
41 Ibid., p. 511.
42 Cameron Autobiography (1920), op. cit., p. 55.
43 M111a (POS 8292), National Library of Ireland.

medical degree was awarded *honoris causa* in 1896. This would seem to rule out this provenance for his MD, together with the fact that the Royal University did not receive its charter until 1880, long after Cameron first began to use a doctoral title.

The evidence of its origins is further complicated by another account of his career which states that Cameron took his first medical qualification in 1868 from the King and Queen's College of Physicians in Ireland (later the Royal College of Physicians of Ireland).[44] This reference appears to refer to his licentiate from this college, which he received in 1868. However, he would have had to provide proof that he already held a medical degree in order to become a licentiate. He would later become a member (1880) and an honorary Fellow (1898) of the college.

Cameron's obituary in *The Lancet* appears to corroborate the fact that his medical degree came from another institution: it claims that he received a medical degree from the Coombe Hospital in 1868;[45] however, the medical registers[46] show that his qualification from the Coombe was LM—licensed midwife—a qualification that was common to most licentiates of the King and Queen's College; besides, Cameron had begun to use the letters MD in the late 1850s. Feeney claims that in 1868 Charles Cameron was appointed as Analyst to the Coombe, where 'his job . . . was "to make analyses and to examine food"'.[47] Cameron would be associated with the Coombe as a member of the board from 1876 to 1912, and again from 1917,[48] and Feeney records him as 'a Coombe man' and 'a consultant' in filling the post of President of the Irish Medical Association in 1891–2. He also records that Cameron 'later on . . . became a pathologist'.[49] In his history of the Society of Public Analysts, Dyer, a contemporary of Cameron who would have known him and his qualifications well, claims yet another skill for Cameron, stating that he 'had considerable reputation as a toxicologist',[50] which was evident in Cameron's role as government expert in poisoning cases (see Chapter 5). The most contemporaneous biography with Cameron's own 1886 account of his education is that of Leyland, in 1888; it was also the most expansive, stating that 'Mr

44 *The Medical Press and Circular*, 9 March 1921.
45 *The Lancet*, 5 March 1921.
46 Various, from 1859 in Royal College of Physicians archive.
47 J. K. Feeney, *The Coombe Lying-in Hospital* (Dublin, 1983), p. 50.
48 Ibid., p. 274.
49 Ibid., p. 294.
50 Bernard Dyer, *The Society of Public Analysts and other Analytical Chemists: Some Reminiscences of its First Fifty Years,* (Cambridge, 1932), p. 37.

Cameron studied medicine and surgery in the School of Medicine of the Apothecaries' Hall, the Dublin School of Medicine, the Original (now Ledwich) School of Medicine, the Meath Hospital, and the Coombe Hospital. In 1854 he went to Germany (where he graduated in philosophy and medicine), and where he acquired the friendship of Liebig'.[51]

Leyland gives Cameron's qualifications at the time (1888) as MD, MKQCPI, FRCSI, PhD, DPH Cambridge. This account would therefore appear to corroborate some of the conflicting details in the obituaries and Cameron's writings, but does not clarify the date and location of Cameron's medical degree.

In his *Autobiography*, Cameron states that, after he commenced work in Bewley's laboratories, he 'now began to read books on chemistry, physics, geology, medicine, &c. I attended lectures at the Royal Dublin Society, and subsequently received instruction in geology from Dr. Edward Hull, F.R.S., Head of the Geological Survey of Ireland. I soon began teaching chemistry myself'. [52]

According to Dyer:

> When the position of the Public Analyst was created by law, it was not easy for local authorities in many cases to select for appointment real expert chemists; and, as the earlier Act had mentioned "medical" knowledge as one of the necessary qualifications, the appointments most frequently, and very naturally, were thrust into the hands of Medical Officers of Health. Some of these—among whom as examples may be mentioned Dr. Letheby, Dr. Meymott Tidy, Dr. Hassall . . . and Dr. (later Sir) Charles A. Cameron—were essentially chemists who had taken medical qualifications to devote themselves to general questions of public health, because there had been so little opportunity of success in the practice of purely professional chemistry, and such men had already done good pioneering work in the chemistry of food and drugs.[53]

In his *Autobiography*, Cameron states that, at the time of his appointment as Professor to the Dublin Chemical Society in 1852, he was 'a chemist and a medical student',[54] while elsewhere in the volume he speaks of translating poems from the German 'on my return from Germany'.[55] This book—*Short Poems Translated from the*

51 John Leyland, *Contemporary Medical Men*, vol. ii, (Leicester, 1888).
52 Cameron, *Autobiography* (1920) op. cit., p. 19.
53 Dyer (1932) op. cit., p. 5.
54 Cameron, *Autobiography* (1920) op. cit., p. 22.
55 Ibid., p. 15.

German—was not published until 1876.[56] Cameron mentions that he returned to Germany 'shortly before the Franco-German War' [1870–71], and that during this visit he stayed with 'my old friend Baron von Liebig'.[57] This friendship, together with what was obviously some fluency in German, and the statement that 'when I was in Germany the purchasing power of money was much greater than it is now, and a student could live respectably upon a very moderate income',[58] indicates a stay of some time as a student in Germany. Justus von Liebig was a world-renowned agricultural chemist, and was attached to Munich University from 1852. Cameron mentioned visiting him years later in Munich, and it would appear fairly certain that Cameron's German education took place in that university; however, it has not been possible to prove this connection. It is most likely that his first stay in Germany was in 1854, as reported by Leyland, as Cameron's collection of newspaper cuttings suggest that he was almost constantly in Ireland throughout the 1850s, except for a gap between July 1853 and October 1854. A possible conjecture is that he received a doctoral qualification during his first stay in Germany, probably in agricultural chemistry, the subject for which Liebig was famous and the subject upon which much of Cameron's early writings and career was based. It is likely that during this period he also bought a medical degree, as was possible at the time in Germany, on the production of a thesis, based on knowledge that he had gained through lectures in Dublin. Although this was common practice at the time, it would not perhaps have compared favourably with the qualifications of other Dublin doctors, a fact that could explain Cameron's uncharacteristic reticence about its provenance. Of possible significance in this regard is the fact that Cameron did not take the Diploma in Public Health that was available in Trinity College, Dublin from 1870—the first examination for the new diploma took place on 12 June 1871.[59] One of the requirements of this qualification was that the candidates should have taken 'the higher degrees in Medicine'.[60] Cameron was awarded a Diploma in Public Health from Cambridge, probably in 1887, the year Cambridge received the licence (it is mentioned by Leyland as one of Cameron's qualifications in 1888).[61] It could be speculated that Cameron did not

56 Charles Cameron, *Short Poems Translated from the German* (Edinburgh, 1876).
57 Cameron, *Autobiography* (1920) op. cit., pp 73–4.
58 Ibid., p. 74.
59 Dr Ninian M. Falkiner 'The evolution of the Diploma of Public Health', JSSISI Vol. XIV, No 3, 1923-5, pp 158–65
60 Ibid.
61 Leyland (1888), op. cit.

have the qualification required to sit the Trinity diploma; on the other hand, it could equally well be speculated that, in 1887, with his career and reputation established, he took the Cambridge diploma as an adjunct to his position as Examiner in Sanitary Science at the college.

What is certain is that Cameron started to use the title MD in the late 1850s. The earliest documentation found of his use of the title appeared in 1857, in a report of a meeting of the Dublin Chemical Society, where he is described as 'Professor Cameron, M.D.'[62] The title MD is added to his title of 'Professor' in *Thom's Directory* for 1859;[63] until then, this directory had only used the title 'Professor', so it must be assumed that Cameron informed them of this addition to his title at this time. Cameron also used the title MD in his application for the job of Public Analyst for Dublin in 1862. He also used the letters MD after his name when he joined the Freemason's Lodge No. XXV in 1866, as shown in an extract from a meeting of that year quoted in an article by him.[64]

However, Cameron did not enter his name in the Medical Register for Ireland until 1874, and he did not then include the title MD. He only used the title of MD (Hon.) RUI from 1896—his *honoris causa* MD. However, his obituary in the *British Medical Journal* claims that he was a past President of the Irish Medical Schools' and Graduates' Association.[65] There is no record of him practising formally as a medical doctor—he himself said that he specialised in the scientific branches of medicine. His diaries show that he often treated friends in a minor way, but called an outside doctor for his family; there is one instance where his very good friend, Willie Gregg, was dying and, while Cameron was constantly at his bedside, two other doctors attended him.[66] Despite a thorough check of all sources, the exact provenance of Charles Cameron's MD remains something of a mystery.

Lecturer

On his return to Dublin from Germany, and throughout the rest of the 1850s, Cameron continued his association with the Dublin Chemical Society and began to consolidate his position in the medical world. The *Mining Journal* on 15 March 1856 reported that he was a candidate

62 *Irish Farmers' Gazette*, April 11 1857.
63 *Thom's Directory* (1859) p. 1071.
64 Charles A. Cameron, 'A History of Lodge No. XXV' in *Irish Masonry Illustrated*, October 1901.
65 *British Medical Journal*, 12 March, 1921.
66 Cameron, Diaries, 17–26 March 1901.

for the vacant professorship of chemistry in the Queen's College in Galway, but his first foothold into an academic career came when, in 1856, Dr Edward Hamilton offered him the professorship of chemistry and natural philosophy in the Dublin School of Medicine in Peter Street. The school closed in 1857, transferring its activities to Dr Steevens' Hospital, with the school renamed Dr Steevens' Hospital Medical College. The Chair of Chemistry in Dr Steevens' Hospital School had an erratic history before Cameron was offered the post. James William Warren was appointed in 1857, but resigned after his first lecture! His successor, John Aldridge, was appointed immediately after Warren's resignation, but his position was declared vacant in 1859 due to the irregularity of his attendance at lectures, but he 'continued to be named in the school lists as the Professor of Chemistry and Natural Philosophy till 1867'.[67] Cameron, however, was appointed in 1859 and continued to lecture at the school until he resigned in 1875. It was noted that, during his tenure, 'a good deal was done to develop the chemical department, and to make it more efficient'.[68] In 1875, Cameron was asked to hand over the teaching of the subject to Chichester Bell, and according to Kirkpatrick, he readily acceded to this request. By this time he was well established in his career, and probably had more than enough to do. An interesting footnote to the mixed history of this Chair is that Chichester Bell resigned two years later, and would eventually work in the laboratory of the Bell Telephone Company with his cousin, Alexander Graham Bell, the inventor of the telephone. In 1858 Cameron was offered the lectureship in chemistry in the 'Original School of Medicine', later known as the Ledwich School of Medicine, Peter Street. He reported with some satisfaction that 'for many years I was connected with three medical schools which were practically rival institutions. I lectured on chemistry and physics in the Ledwich School of Medicine and in Dr. Steevens' Hospital and Medical College, and on Public Health in the Royal College of Surgeons.'[69]

He would continue to lecture at the Ledwich for 20 years, and at Dr Steevens' for 16 years, while his association with the Royal College of Surgeons lasted a record 52 years from his appointment as Professor of Hygiene or Political Medicine in 1868 and his appointment as Professor of Chemistry and Physics in 1875, and both positions were held until his retirement in 1920, when he became Professor Emeritus. The occasion of the first of these appointments is worth looking at in

67 T. Percy Kirkpatrick, *The History of Dr Steevens Hospital Dublin* (Dublin 1924) p 257
68 Ibid. p 68
69 Cameron, *Autobiography* (1920) op. cit., p. 25.

some detail, as it indicates the esteem in which Cameron was held by his contemporaries. There were four candidates for the position, and the election 'was regarded with some interest'[70] as Cameron and another candidate were not members of the college, while of the two other candidates, one was a fellow and the other a licentiate. A panel of seven council members, chosen at random from a box by the Junior Fellow of the college, considered the applications and, 'after a prolonged absence'[71] selected Cameron, described as a 'Chemist and Lecturer of attainments and position'.[72]

Cameron claimed that he never lectured on a subject unless he had a good knowledge of it, and was proud of the fact that, in a lecture career that spanned 68 years and 'not less than eight thousand lectures'[73] he had never used notes, and could make his words heard even in the largest room. He claimed that 'many of my happiest hours were spent in lecturing',[74] and his confidence in his ability as a lecturer does not appear to have been overstated; Leyland reports that, when his lectures on 'Hygiene' were opened to the public, 'people came at two o'clock to secure seats for a lecture which was not to be delivered until two hours later'.[75] Cameron gave these lectures 'without remuneration', and was amused to be informed by night policemen that his exhortations to open bedroom windows in the interests of better hygiene had the desired effect, as 'an unusual number of bedroom windows were open which before my lectures had been closed'.[76] These lectures were published by Cameron in 1868 and dedicated to Baron von Liebig,[77] and Cameron may not have been amused at a footnote in the margin of the copy in the National Library of Ireland. In the lecture dealing with the ventilation of houses to improve health, Cameron is quoted as saying 'Every day the windows and doors of each apartment should be left open for several hours'—and a contemporary (it must be assumed) has written in pencil in the margin 'Your own windows are never open!!'[78]

70 Kirkpatrick Archive, Royal College of Physicians of Ireland.
71 Ibid.
72 Ibid.
73 Cameron, *Autobiography* (1920), op. cit., pp 26–7.
74 Ibid., p. 25.
75 Leyland, (1888), op. cit.
76 Cameron, *Autobiography* (1920), op. cit., p. 78.
77 Charles A. Cameron, *Lectures on the Preservation of Health* (London and New York, 1868).
78 Ibid., p. 147.

A turning point

The year 1862 marked a turning point in Cameron's life. On 16 October, in St Mary's Church in Donnybrook, he married Lucie McNamara, the only daughter of a Dublin solicitor. On the same day, Major General Sir Thomas Larcom wrote to the Lord Lieutenant confirming the appointment of Charles A. Cameron as analyst 'of all articles of Food and Drink purchased within the City of Dublin'.[79] It was his first public appointment to the service of Dublin citizens, and despite many other responsibilities and interests, he would remain committed to this job over the next six decades.

---

79 Minutes of the Municipal Council of the City of Dublin, vol. 23, p. 75.

Cameron lived at 51 Pembroke Road from 1890 to 1916. He left the elegant neighbourhood of 'The Roads' every day to go to the Public Health laboratory and his work in the slums. (Author's collection)

Chapter 3 In the Fever King's preserves[1]

Cameron's return to Dublin from Guernsey in 1846 coincided with the Famine, when thousands of starving people thronged to the city in a desperate struggle for survival. He returned to a city that had severe unemployment, execrable housing conditions and an exceptionally high death rate—a city whose already overcrowded housing conditions and labour pool were being exacerbated by the migration to Dublin of those affected by the Famine. A great deal is known about the housing conditions and mortality rates in the city at that time, mainly due to the work carried out by the surgeon William Wilde, based on the 1841 Census figures,[2] and revised after the 1851 Census, and to the pamphlet by Thomas Willis, *Facts connected with the Social and Sanitary Condition of the Working Classes in the City of Dublin*, published in Dublin in 1845.

Willis revealed that in 1841 the habitations of the 49,511 families living in Dublin were as follows: 5,605 families in first-class accommodation; 8,412 families in second-class accommodation; 12,297 families in third-class accommodation, and 'the enormous number of 23,197, or very near one-half of the entire number of families, have the wretched and pestiferous accommodation of a single room'.[3] In 1841, of this 23,197, 12,050 were housed in first-class houses, and 10,151 in second-class houses. This one-room accommodation was in what, due to their size, number of windows, etc., could technically be termed first- or second-class houses, but which were deemed to be fourth class due to the number of families living in accommodation originally designed to cater for one family or, as Thomas Jordan stated, 'the same style of house affords very different accommodation according as it is occupied solely by one family or by several'.[4]

All over Dublin, the old mansions of the rich were becoming the death-traps of the poor. Charles Cameron, even as a young man in his teens, must have been aware of this problem when he returned to Dublin. There is an entry in the 1846 *Thom's Directory* for a Charles

---

1 Title of article in the *Freeman's Journal*, 15 September 1871.
2 William Wilde, *Special Sanitary Report on the City of Dublin*, appended to the Census of Ireland 1841.
3 Ibid., p. 31.
4 Rev. Thomas Jordan, 'The present state of the Dwellings of the Poor, chiefly in Dublin' in *Jn. SSISI*, (1857) ii, p. 12.

Cameron at 32 Clanbrassil Street, in the section 'nobility, gentry, merchants and traders', and he is also named as the householder.[5] However, no occupation is given, and Cameron would have been only 16 at the time, so this cannot be identified as the younger Cameron. The earliest residence that can definitely be attributed to Cameron following his return to Dublin is in the 1851 Census for Dublin, in which he appeared with his mother, living at 15 Portland Row, which was in Summer-hill, in the north of the city.[6] In 1853, aged 23, Cameron, as 'Professor of Chemistry to the Dublin Chemical Society' is listed in *Thom's Directory* with the 'nobility, gentry, merchants and traders' as living at the same address;[7] however, the householder is given as John Williams, letter carrier.[8] In *Thom's Directory* for 1854, Cameron appears at the same address, listed as the householder, so it would appear that he may have first lived in the house as a tenant, and later became the householder as his financial situation improved. The house had a valuation of £14, and neighbouring householders included a clerk and a coachmaker, while there were two tenements at numbers 17 and 19.[9]

An indication of Cameron's early social status, and of how far up the social ladder his career would bring him, can be gauged from the same *Thom's Directory*, which showed that houses in Pembroke Road, where he would spend most of his later life, had valuations of between £63 and £78.[10] The area of north Dublin city in which he lived in the 1850s was fast disintegrating into notorious slums, so the young Cameron, starting off on his career, would have seen at first hand the early descent of the great city town houses into tenements. In his *Autobiography* he wrote: 'Had I been absent from Dublin since the days of my childhood until the present year, I would hardly have recognised a large part of north-east Dublin'.[11] He noted that in many of the houses 'eight or ten families have replaced one family'.[12] His own early family circumstances—an abrupt drop in economic status after his father's death—echoed, albeit on a higher social level, the fate of many of Dublin's skilled workers. While Cameron found a foothold in the labour market thanks to the intervention of a family friend, he

5 *Thom's Directory* (1846) p. 472 and p. 689.
6 Magee, (2001) op. cit., p. 88.
7 *Thom's Directory*, (1853) p. 1049.
8 Ibid., p. 922.
9 *Thom's Directory*, (1854) p. 936.
10 Ibid., p. 931.
11 Cameron, *Autobiography* (1920) op. cit., p. 11.
12 Ibid., p. 11.

must have been fully aware that Dublin was no place to be poor, and this knowledge, for one of his disposition, would have sharpened his ambition to succeed and survive in an increasingly impoverished city; it is also likely that it gave him a deeper understanding of the plight of the poor: he was always aware that, for most of the poor, their circumstances were not of their own making, and in his public capacity he often spoke forcefully of the poverty and hardship which afflicted, not only the unemployed, but many hard-working people in low-paid work. This knowledge of, and empathy with, the plight of the poor was one of the hallmarks of his approach to the problems he encountered as Medical Officer of Health.

The death rate in Dublin between 1851 and 1860 averaged 25.01 per thousand;[13] by 1880, the year before Cameron took over 'the entire control of and responsibility for the working of the Public Health Department under the Public Health Committee'[14] this had risen to 37.7 per thousand, one of the highest in Europe. By the time he died in 1921, still in office, this had been halved—to 17.6 in the metropolitan area and 18.6 in the city area.[15] The number of tenements had also been halved. In order to evaluate Cameron's contribution to public health, it is necessary to understand the state of the city in which he grew up, studied, started his career, and eventually took control of its public health defences.

The genesis of the problem

When the subject of Dublin's atrocious housing conditions and resultant public health problems in the 19th century are discussed, the genesis has more often than not been seen as the Act of Union in 1801. This Act, which demoted Dublin from a centre of political activity to a purely administrative centre, is viewed as precipitating many of the city's problems during the following century. This argument is true to some extent—many of Dublin's most prosperous industries were affected by the aristocratic retreat from the city—carriage making, for example, was no longer required to the same extent, while the former mansions of the aristocracy deteriorated, becoming institutions, being divided up; many, later in the century, became the tenement dwellings of the poor. Eventually, throughout the 19th century, many of the

13   Mary E. Daly, *Dublin: The Deposed Capital: A Social and Economic History, 1860–1914* (Cork, 1985) p. 242.
14   Charles A. Cameron, *A Brief History of Municipal Public Health Administration in Dublin* (Dublin and London, 1914), p. 41.
15   Corporation of Dublin, *Report of the Public Health Committee*, vol. 1, no. 88 (1922), p. 491.

middle classes moved to the suburbs, and their houses also became tenements—this was the case with Cameron's childhood home in Magee's Court, which had become tenements by 1840. However, Dublin's economic problems were more widespread than those caused by the exodus of the political elite and the fallout of the Act of Union; surveys, notably that of James Whitelaw, carried out in 1798,[16] show that a housing and health problem existed before the effects of the Act of Union could be claimed to have been the cause.

By the second quarter of the 19th century, increasing industrialisation and the growth of large cities had led to a common problem of overcrowding and high mortality rates in every large city in the British Isles. In 1800, no city in England or Scotland, except London, had a population of 100,000: Dublin had a population of 182,000. This demographic pre-eminence was lost during the course of the century, during which Dublin's population remained relatively static—only reaching a figure of 245,001 in 1891,[17] while the population of other cities in the British Isles increased substantially during the same period. However, unlike those other cities, where, as the population grew, 'the appropriate dwellings for the different classes of society increased *pari passu*',[18] Dublin's housing stock inside the canals did not keep pace even with its marginally increased population.

What new houses were built within the metropolitan area were at the higher end of the market, with the growth of new middle-class housing, while the increasing numbers of poorer citizens were housed in the cast-off houses of the rich, who had either left the city after the Act of Union in 1801, or moved to more salubrious suburbs. The *Irish Builder* claimed that 'whole streets of houses once occupied by single families are now inhabited by several families, from basement to attic . . .',[19] while Charles Cameron, giving evidence to the 1884–5 Inquiry into the Housing of the Working Classes, stated bluntly that Dublin 'does not in the least resemble Belfast, Liverpool, Manchester, Glasgow and other British cities . . . their working population live in houses specially built for them, and adapted to their wants, whilst the Dublin artisans and labourers live chiefly in the decayed houses of former generations of people of superior rank.'[20]

---

16 James Whitelaw, *An Essay on the Population of Dublin, being the Result of an Actual Survey taken in 1798, with great care and precision, and arranged in a manner entirely new* (Dublin, 1805).
17 Daly, (1985) op. cit., p. 3.
18 Cameron, *Brief History* (1914), op. cit., p. 7.
19 *Irish Builder*, 1 July 1872, p. 179, also 1 November 1880, pp 297–8.
20 PP1884–85 Cd.4547–1 xxxi, *Minutes of evidence of the 3rd Report of Her Majesty's Commissioners for inquiring into the Housing of the Working Classes* f.304.

Dublin's economy

Moreover, while the overcrowding in most British cities and in Belfast was caused by increased industrialisation, Dublin's industries, such as fine textiles and carriage-making, declined during the course of the 19th century, and were not replaced by any labour-intensive industries. By the first quarter of the 20th century, most of the employment in Dublin was casual and seasonal, in brewing, biscuit making, in transport or on the docks—industries that employed workers during busy seasons, and let them go during slack seasons. What manufacturing industry did exist tended to be capital-intensive, rather than labour-intensive—for example, Guinness's brewery had a capital value of £5 million, and employed 2,000 staff, compared with the York Street Spinning Company in Belfast, which had a capital value of £500,000, but employed 4–5,000.[21] Moreover, while large-scale industries, such as spinning and weaving, provided employment for women in other cities, the large industries in Dublin (apart from biscuit-making) provided mostly male employment—work for women in Dublin was mainly in dressmaking and domestic service. With a largely male workforce, and a high rate of male tuberculosis, many families could therefore drop very quickly from working-class to pauper status by the death of a male breadwinner. As a result, a large proportion of Dublin citizens lived an insecure, hand-to-mouth existence, surviving 'by employing every mode which industry can prompt or human ingenuity devise in order to procure even the meanest supply of the common necessaries of life'.[22]

The situation was exacerbated by the fact that native Dubliners had to share the precarious employment opportunities with an incoming stream of immigrants, both from the great European migrations, and from a hinterland which was shedding labour throughout the 19th century, which was exacerbated by the Famine. However, even before the catastrophe of the Famine, Francis White reported that the number of poor in Dublin fluctuated due to 'the number of paupers transmitted from England and Scotland, without means of even a day's subsistence'.[23] During the latter part of the 19th century, many native Dubliners, who had previously been classed as skilled tradesmen, found that they and their descendants had sunk to the lower socio-economic category of unskilled workers, with a

21 Mary E. Daly, 'Late Nineteenth and Early Twentieth Century Dublin', in D. Harkness and M. O'Dowd (eds) *The Town in Ireland*, (Belfast, 1979), p. 223.
22 Report of the Sick and Indigent Roomkeepers' Society, 1857, p. 14.
23 Francis White, *Report and Observations on the State of the Poor of Dublin*, (Dublin, 1833) p. 9.

consequent loss of income and status.

By 1911, the Census showed that almost a third of the residents of Dublin (29.67 per cent) had not been born in the city.[24]

Dublin's housing

Dublin's housing problems reflected its economic situation as the city's overcrowded living space was worsened by an increased demand for a static and deteriorating housing stock by a more and more impoverished population. An influx of new and mostly needy new residents settled beside natives who had a lower than average emigration rate, and a higher than average fertility rate, in a city with little regular employment, and even less new housing, and thus increased the density of the population in the poorest areas.

The city, confined between the two canals until the inclusion of some of the new townships (Drumcondra, Clontarf and Kilmainham) in 1900, had a stock of houses that had hardly increased since the 18th century, colonised by middle-class landlords, who let and sub-let them in as many units as possible. Georgian houses, built to house one family in comfort, eventually became tenements, each housing many families in great discomfort, with no running water, and the only means of waste disposal a constant and malodorous ash-pit in the back-yard, and the only sanitary facility a common privy in the same location.

Many of the yards and courts of the city were further colonised for makeshift housing, and became, according to Dr Thomas Grimshaw, Registrar General, some of the worst slums in the city,[25] described graphically by Charles Dickens as 'possessing vomitoria seemingly innumerable, in the shape of lanes, back streets, courts and blind alleys . . . with an almost indescribable aspect of dirt and confusion'.[26] Tenements where families lived in one-roomed squalor were in nearly every area of the city, even 'the lanes at the rere of the Squares and most highly rented houses contain them'.[27] Cameron, a man who had travelled quite extensively for the time, stated that 'I have never been in any city in which the purlieus are so widely distributed as is the case in Dublin'.[28] Cameron did not fully accept the general consensus

24 Cameron *Brief History* (1914), op. cit., p. 7.
25 T. W. Grimshaw, *The House Accommodation of the Artisan and Labouring Classes in Ireland* (Dublin, 1885), p. 25.
26 Jim Cooke, 'Charles Dickens, A Dublin Chronicler' in *Dublin Historical Record*, 1989, XLII, No. 3, pp 97–8.
27 Cameron, *Brief History* (1914), op. cit., p. 60.
28 Ibid., p. 60.

that Dublin's housing problems could be explained simply by the fact that the well-to-do had abandoned their homes, which had then deteriorated into tenements. While he agreed that this was partly true, he compared the situation in Dublin with that in other cities, such as London, where whole districts formerly occupied by the wealthy were now occupied by the poor claiming that 'in London only 6.7 per cent of the population [lived in] one–room dwellings' and with Belfast, where 'there are only a few hundreds of one-room tenements'. He believed that, if the state of Dublin were to be fairly compared with that of Belfast, then the suburbs of Dublin, to which many of the wealthy had moved from the city centre, should be taken into the equation, as Belfast had 'no townships like Rathmines, Pembroke, &c., in which the richer classes chiefly reside'.

Cameron correctly attributed the worse state of housing in Dublin to the fact that employment in the city was largely for unskilled workers, whose low wages and intermittent employment left them unable to pay high rents, and maintained that 'if all the working classes in Dublin could afford to pay 4s 6d and upwards for their dwellings, there would be a very limited, if any, slum area'. The increasing pauperisation of the population resulted in an inability to pay for adequate housing, and an increased tolerance of substandard accommodation provided by opportunistic landlords.[29]

However, this situation was an exacerbation of a long-standing crisis; the evidence shows that the problems of substandard accommodation, unscrupulous landlords, and uncaring ratepayers, had existed in Dublin for generations, and, throughout the 19th century had been brought to the attention of the authorities by concerned citizens.

The evidence

In 1805, Rev. James Whitelaw, a clergyman in St Catherine's parish in the Liberties area of Dublin, published an account of a survey he had carried out in 1798 on housing conditions in the city, stating that: 'My assistants and I undeterred by the dread of infectious diseases . . . explored in the burning months of 1798 every room of these wretched dwellings, from the cellar to the garret, and on the spot ascertained the population.'[30]

Whitelaw described in graphic detail 'degrees of filth, stench, and

---

29   Ibid., pp. 62, 14, 62, 59.
30   Whitelaw, (1805), op. cit., p. 4.

darkness inconceivable by those who have not experienced them'.[31] Whitelaw had been moved to make his survey by the human suffering he saw in the course of his ministry in the parish, like the 'family of a poor working shoemaker, seven in number, lying in a fever, without a human being to administer to their wants'.[32] The family's plight was worsened by the fact that the landlord had removed the door to force them to abandon the room, because the family had been unable to pay the rent due to the father's illness.[33]

Whitelaw's survey, carried out at 'my own private expense and toil',[34] amounted to nearly five hundred tables in folio,[35] of which he published in 1805 an epitome which was presented to the Lord Lieutenant. [36] The picture which emerged of the poorer areas of Dublin was one of destitution, disease and despair, of living conditions where humans lived cheek by jowl with slaughter-houses and their detritus,[37] and where human waste was flung from the windows into the back yards, often reaching the windows of the first floor.[38] He wrote of many who had seen better days, and whose 'apartment bespoke a recollection of former decency, which even poverty could not obliterate'.[39] On presenting his findings to the Lord Lieutenant, Whitelaw wrote that 'should they be the means of rescuing one son of wretchedness from filth and poverty . . . I shall not consider that I have toiled in vain'.[40] He hoped that his work 'may be considered as a correct and faithful picture of the actual state of Dublin in 1798, and may, at any future period, be compared as such with its then existing state, in order to discover . . . the changes, whether for better or worse, which have taken place in the lapse of time.'[41]

It is doubtful if Whitelaw's conscientious efforts resulted in alleviating the plight of many unfortunate slum dwellers, because we can, as he had hoped, compare them with subsequent reports.

In March and April of 1832, Francis White carried out a similar survey in the parishes of Dublin's Liberties at the request of the Mansion House relief committee, and reported that:

---

31 Ibid., p. 4.
32 Ibid., p. 54.
33 Ibid.
34 Ibid., p. 3.
35 Ibid., 'Advertisement' at front of Essay.
36 Ibid.
37 Ibid., p. 53.
38 Ibid., p. 52.
39 Ibid., p. 58.
40 Ibid., p. 3.
41 Ibid., p. 12.

No perceptible change has taken place in the neglected and unhappy state of the Poor: their condition appears not improved, and their habitations seem as crowded as ever, with the calamitous addition of about 1,000 orphans thrown completely destitute by the ravages of contagion, many of whom are compelled to wander from house to house without any settled place of residence, and can constantly be found at midnight sleeping in the filthiest halls and passages[42]

White's report was as graphic and unrelenting as Whitelaw's, and showed no obvious improvement in the living conditions of the Dublin poor. He told of a house in Elbow Lane in Whitelaw's old parish of St Catherine's, where there were four cases of cholera in the same room 'which was crowded to excess, there being eleven straw litters for fifteen individuals, who occupied the room at night'.[43] He claimed that there were several such cases in the parish, while the situation in St Michan's parish was even worse, where he reported a population of nearly 24,000 living in about 1,612 houses 'of which three-fourths are in such a state of filth as, in itself, would be sufficient to generate disease [and that] upwards of 1,600 cases of cholera occurred in this parish alone'.[44]

White blamed much of the poverty on a largely unemployed population, exacerbated by an influx of poor from other parts of the city and country seeking cheap lodgings, while Mr Clarke, an officer of health, told White that much of the misery of the Dublin poor could be ascribed to 'the rapacity of their landlords, who exact their rent with great severity, compelling the inmates to pawn their clothing to satisfy the weekly demands, while no attention is paid to repairing the premises, or keeping the ash-pits or sewers in a proper state.'[45]

White corroborated this statement with the example of a Mr Caffrey, a porter living with his family in Chatham Street. Unable to work due to an inflammation of the lungs, the family had pawned all their furniture, bedding and clothes to pay the rent— 'they had no food and their means were exhausted'.[46] White found Caffrey in a small room with his wife and four children, covered by an old cloak belonging to his wife. White reported that the family were given 'five shillings a week, some mutton broth, and medicine, which in

---

42 White, *Report* (1833), op. cit., p. 21.
43 Ibid., p. 8.
44 Ibid., p. 10.
45 Ibid., pp 18–19.
46 Ibid., p. 19.

three weeks entirely altered their condition'.[47] The man recovered his health, 'the little property was recovered from the pawnbroker, and I had the pleasure of beholding him again employed and supporting his family'.[48]

Francis White recounted several such heartening incidents, but they were obviously mere drops in the ocean of Dublin's distressing condition, as was obvious from a further survey carried out in 1845, when Dr Thomas Willis's account of the slums of St Michan's parish[49] confirmed that housing conditions for the Dublin poor had worsened rather than improved in the intervening years, and that the inhabitants had 'sunk into that state of abject misery for which there is no parallel in any country in Europe'.[50] Willis claimed that accommodation for nearly half the families in Dublin consisted of one room.[51] Even worse were cellar dwellings, where a troglodyte population lived a subterranean and subhuman existence—cellars which, according to Willis, 'at all times bring better rents than single rooms, and many of them are crowded with lodging beds'.[52] These cellars were totally without windows, 'dark, wet … into which every kind of filth drained',[53] and many could only be entered 'by descending backwards, as a wild animal descends from the top of a tree'.[54] Although constant efforts were made to eliminate these, efforts to totally close cellar dwellings could not keep pace with the desperate need for accommodation. In 1852, it was reported that, out of 2,100 cellars in the city, 1,740 were being used as sleeping places. By-laws for the regulation of lodging houses were approved in 1851, but despite the Corporation taking legal advice 'on proceedings in reference to the cellars . . . in 1852 and 1853, there seems to have been great difficulty in enforcing [them]'.[55] From 1851 up until 1877, a period of more than twenty years, only about 200 houses were closed as unsanitary.[56]

Willis's report varied little from those of previous surveys, and recounted the recurring story of Dublin's poor, unchanged from Whitelaw's account almost fifty years previously: 'In one tenement I

47 Ibid.
48 Ibid.
49 Thomas Willis, *Facts connected with the social and Sanitary Condition of the Working Classes in the City of Dublin* (Dublin, 1845).
50 Ibid., p. 21.
51 Ibid., p. 31.
52 Ibid., p. 33.
53 Prunty, *Dublin Slums* (1998) op. cit. p. 37.
54 Jordan, (1857) op. cit., p. 17.
55 Cameron (1914), op. cit., p. 23.
56 Ibid., p. 67.

found five young children huddled around a small fire. Their mother was dead; their father was a labourer earning 14s a week. The rent of their single room was 2s. The weekly consumption of a bag of coal cost 1s 6d.'[57]

He continued:

> The stench and disgusting filth of these places are inconceivable . . . in some rooms in these situations it is not an infrequent occurrence to see above a dozen human beings crowded into a space not fifteen feet square . . . within this space they must eat and drink; men, women and children must strip, dress, sleep. In cases of illness the calls of nature must be relieved; and when death releases one of the inmates, the corpse must of necessity remain for days within the room . . . I am speaking of an entire district, and state facts incontrovertible.[58]

Fighting the Fever King

It was not until Cameron was appointed Superintendent Medical Officer of Health in August 1879 that any significant closure of houses and cellars took place. With the energy and determination that were to be his trademark, he immediately on his appointment 'prepared a handbook for the Inspectors giving them full instructions for the discharge of their duties',[59] and 'resolved to personally inspect every tenement house in the city, and also some hundreds of small cottages occupied by very poor people'.[60] He also quickly set about improving their wider surroundings, in particular the hundreds of unhygienic and unregulated slaughter-houses and dairy-yards, whose effluvia added to the general offensiveness and contributed to the spread of disease. He and Edward Mapother, his predecessor as Medical Officer of Health, wrote a strongly worded report in 1879 which stated that 'There should be established two public abattoirs, one at the north, the other at the south side of the city . . . we consider this one of the most important sanitary improvements that could be effected in Dublin.'[61]

Cameron, like many before him, was aware of the execrable state of Dublin—in 1849, the newly appointed City Engineer reported that the city streets were a total of 108 miles in length, while the total length of

---

57 Willis, (1845) op. cit., p. 67.
58 Ibid., p. 45.
59 Ibid., p. 67.
60 Ibid., p. 66.
61 Charles A. Cameron and Edward D. Mapother, *Report on the Means for the Prevention of Disease in Dublin*, RPDCD, vol. 1, no. 63, (1879), pp 341–3.

the sewers was only 39 miles in length.[62] Nine more miles of sewers were added by 1855, but at its first meeting for the 1857–8 session, the Dublin Chemical Society heard a paper from a Mr Gregg, which informed them that the outlets of all the sewers in Dublin were discharged into the river Liffey, from which the 'pestiferous inhalations . . . are wafted into every house and street in the vicinity of the river.' As a result, according to Gregg, the valuation of property along the quays had been decreased by 22 per cent, compared to an average depreciation of 18 per cent throughout the rest of the city. He reported, moreover, that the north side of Merrion Square still had cess-pool drainage, as had many other streets, including Sackville Street. More importantly, however, was the effect on public health, and Gregg pointed out that epidemics were too readily attributed to Divine Providence, instead of to 'our total disregard of the simplest sanitary laws'.[63]

The effects on public health in Dublin

The correlation between overcrowded, unsanitary dwellings and public health was increasingly brought to public attention in the course of the 19th century. While giving a description of housing conditions similar, and probably worse than those described by Whitelaw and White, Willis went one step further, and pointed out that of the many inmates of the workhouses and hospitals of Dublin, 'there are few . . . who cannot trace much of their present destitution to the . . . diseases having their origin in the unhealthy condition of their habitations'.[64] Willis paid tribute to the contribution to knowledge made by the 1841 Census, whose commissioners believed that a census 'ought to be a social survey, not a bare enumeration'.[65] Sir William Wilde, now better known as the father of Oscar, was a renowned Dublin surgeon, with an interest in the use of statistics as a tool for social reform. The 1841 Census, widely regarded as the first 'scientific' census, gave him an ideal opportunity; using the details contained in the census, Wilde created a unique street classification, based on the 'wealth, character, more or less healthy position, and the occupations of their population'.[66] Wilde's correlation of street classification with the death rates of the inhabitants showed unequivocally that the mortality rates in poorer

---

62 Cameron *Brief History* (1914), op. cit., p. 32.
63 Dublin Chemical Society, report of first meeting for the session 1857–8, reprinted from the *Farmers' Gazette*.
64 Willis, (1845) op. cit., p. 53.
65 Ibid., p. 23.
66 Wilde, (1841) op. cit., pp lxviii.

areas were significantly greater than those in wealthier areas. This was particularly applicable to the 'zymotic', or infectious diseases, as revealed by Wilde when he examined the figures in the 1851 Census:

> In the first-class private streets, south side, with a population of 8,232, the number of deaths from small-pox was but 1 in 1,646, whilst in Merchants'-quay ward, with a population of 22,389, the deaths were 199, or 1 in 113. Again, the total deaths from fever in the first-class private streets on the north side were but 6, or 1 in 508, while in Arran-quay ward, upon the same side of the Liffey, with a population of 18,258, the deaths were 279, or 1 in 65 . . . These results of locality, in influencing disease and mortality, extend throughout the whole class of zymotic diseases.[67]

Thomas Jordan, in a paper to the Statistical and Social Inquiry Society of Ireland in 1851, claimed that the numbers living in poor housing conditions had increased between the 1841 and 1851 Census, due to 'the very large numbers that have been driven into these towns [Dublin and Belfast] from the country by distress of various kinds'.[68] Conditions had hardly improved by 1891, when Charles Eason claimed that 19,342 families, or 37.3 per cent of the population of Dublin, lived in this class of housing.[69]

The realisation that poorer areas of housing were hotbeds of disease as well as poverty caused a significant rise in concern, not so much for the inhabitants of the slums, as for the potential spread of the disease to other parts of the city. Although the theory of contagion would not be fully accepted until the 1880s, it was obvious many years previously that contact with the poor could seriously damage the health of those who were better-off. According to Willis, statistics showed that those who ministered to the poor, such as doctors and clergymen, had a significantly lower life expectancy than their peers who did not.[70] William Wilde estimated that the life of medical men who attended the poor was shortened by at least twenty years, 42 per cent of their deaths being caused by epidemic diseases.[71]

Others relied on the labour of the poor to provide many of their needs, such as domestic service, food supplies, and clothes. Cameron, for example, discovered that constant outbreaks of scarlet fever among the Royal Irish Constabulary in Dublin were caused by the

---

67 Wilde, 'Special Sanitary Report' (1851) op. cit., Par. V, p. 488.
68 Jordan, op. cit., p. 17.
69 Charles Eason, 'The Tenement Houses of Dublin. Their Condition and Regulation', *Jn.. SSISI*, Vol. X, Part LXXIX, (1898) p. 384.
70 Willis, *Facts* (1845) op. cit., p. 54.
71 Ibid., p. 54.

making of uniforms 'in tenement houses where there had been cases of scarlet fever',[72] and that residents of Fitzwilliam Square in 1877 and of Clontarf in 1908 had been infected by typhoid fever from milk supplied by carriers of the disease.[73] Three of Cameron's own sons, living in circumstances far removed from the slums, would be tragically affected by contagious diseases. That Cameron was acutely aware of the effects of the slum problem on the rest of the city is obvious from many of his statements—for example, in 1879, he and Edward Mapother stated that 'everything that lessens contagious disease in the humbler part of the city, is an additional precaution against the spread of it to the houses of the rich',[74] while at the 1884–5 Housing Inquiry, Cameron gave evidence to the effect that 'A man going about with insufficient clothing would probably only injure himself,whereas if his house is in a filthy condition it may injure me, and as a means of protection I get his house put into a proper sanitary state.'[75]

Cameron's reports to the Corporation throughout his long tenure as Medical Officer of Health revealed the same litany of diseases month after month, year after year, with the occasional upsurge caused by epidemics, such as influenza, measles or dysentery. It was increasingly obvious that the genesis of most of the diseases, and the majority of their victims, lay in the Dublin slums. Cameron and Mapother's report in 1879 repeated exactly the same findings as Wilde and Willis a quarter of a century previously: 'a high death rate is the almost constant corollary of great density of population'.[76]

The most prevalent diseases were those caused by overcrowded and unsanitary living conditions, aggravated by poverty, insufficient heating and clothing, and malnutrition: diseases such as typhus, typhoid, smallpox, dysentery, tuberculosis, and the dreaded cholera, all had one thing in common—they found an easy and deadly foothold in the poverty-weakened bodies of the inhabitants of the Dublin slums.

Typhus, caused by the body louse, was an inevitable consequence of unwashed clothes and bedclothes in habitations with no running water, and a lack of adequate supplies.

Typhoid was endemic from contaminated water, and outbreaks of the disease erupted frequently, not only in poorer areas; many middle-class areas found that newly-installed water closets had been

---

72 Cameron, *Autobiography* (1920), op. cit., p. 139.
73 Cameron, *Brief History* (1914), op. cit., pp 39–40.
74 Cameron and Mapother, (1879), op. cit., p. 344.
75 PP.1884-85, Cd.4547-1, xxxi, op. cit., ff 223.
76 Cameron and Mapother, (1879), op. cit., p. 344.

inefficiently connected to the main sewer, and the resultant polluted sewage caused outbreaks outside of the slums. The disease was also spread through contaminated milk, and Cameron published a paper 'On an Epidemic of Fever caused by Infected Milk' in 1879.[77] He discovered another cause of the disease in the polluted oyster beds on the outskirts of the city; at his request, the licences for the oyster beds were withdrawn.[78]

As a busy port, Dublin had frequent cholera scares, and several devastating outbreaks of the disease. Cameron reported that in 1873, when there was a threat of cholera to Dublin, he, together with Edward Mapother, then Medical Officer of Health, Dr Burne and Dr Minchin, 'were stationed for several weeks each, for 6 hours day and night, at the North Wall to examine the crews of vessels entering the Port with the yellow flag (signal of illness) flying.'[79] This appears to have been the 'floating cholera hospital' ordered by the South Dublin Union from Messrs. Bewley, Webb & Co. of North Wall, to which the above four doctors were assigned.[80] When a similar threat occurred in 1884 during his term of office as Medical Officer of Health, Cameron acted swiftly, requesting fifteen temporary sanitary sub-officers, who were employed in reconstructing defective sanitary accommodation in preparation for a possible epidemic.

That cholera was a recurring threat is obvious; Cameron's diary recorded that in September 1892 he was woken at three in the morning to examine a ship just arrived from Hamburg with a suspected case of cholera. He ordered the ship to be quarantined.[81]

Smallpox posed a constant threat, and the large workhouses of the North and South Dublin Unions provided regular starting points for epidemics. These were used as a last resort, not only by the Dublin poor, but by the desperate poor of surrounding counties, a factor which added to the death-rate in Dublin. In his diaries, Cameron recorded one such investigation of a smallpox outbreak in the North Dublin Union and Hardwicke Fever Hospital in 1894, in which, having spent a long time with five smallpox patients, he was obliged to send home for a change of clothes, having sent those he was wearing to be disinfected—a reminder of the constant risks run by medical

---

77 Charles A. Cameron, *The Dublin Journal of Medical Science*, 1 July 1879, Vol. LXVIII, No. 91, Third Series, pp 1–25.
78 Cameron, *Autobiography* (1920), op. cit., p. 139.
79 Cameron *Brief History* (1914), op. cit., p. 37.
80 *Irish Builder*, 1873, Vol. XV, p. 305.
81 Cameron, Diaries, 8 September 1892.

practitioners in their daily duties.[82]

Tuberculosis remained one of the deadliest killers, claiming twice as many victims as other contagious diseases; it was the most difficult disease to eradicate, retaining its hold long into the 20th century. Erroneously believed to be hereditary, it was one of the most easily spread by contagion, and most quickly to those who were malnourished and poorly clad and housed. In poorer areas, the infected person usually shared the same room, and often the same bed as others, which resulted in whole families being wiped out by the disease. Cameron campaigned for, and was successful in seeing established, an isolation hospital at the Pigeon House Road and a sanatorium outside the city at Crooksling.

One of the most potent diseases — syphilis — remained unmentionable in the public arena, its victims' posthumous reputations often protected by officially recording the cause of death as some other contributory cause. Some accurate details of these deaths were recorded, however, and O'Brien notes that 'Of the recorded deaths from venereal disease (mainly syphilis) in Ireland between 1899 and 1916 — a total of 1,984 — over 69 per cent were of children under five years.'[83]

Dublin's status as a garrison city ensured a constant stream of cross-infection between soldiers and prostitutes. A lock hospital had been established in Townsend Street in 1792, and Cameron's diaries record regular attendance at its meetings during his term of office as Medical Officer of Health. Many of the prostitutes resorted to the occupation out of desperation, as the only means of survival, and there appears to have been an acceptance of them as part of poorer communities until the churches launched a moral campaign of eradication in the 20th century.

All of the above diseases were added to by frequent epidemics of influenza, measles and dysentery which killed large numbers, particularly children, at regular intervals throughout the century, constantly bringing an upsurge in the death rate, and undoing almost overnight years of work by the health authorities, who faced a Sisyphean task in lowering the mortality statistics. Moreover, the male death rate in Dublin was particularly high, mainly from tuberculosis, leaving many families destitute, as employment for women was limited. Nor did epidemics affect only the poor, although the figures showed that, already weakened by poor living conditions, they were

---

82 Ibid., 31 May 1894.
83 O'Brien, *Dear Dirty Dublin* (1982) op. cit., p. 116.

Figure 3.1 *Death rates per 1,000 in city of Dublin, 1879–1913*

1879	37.5
1884	30.3
1889	27.9
1894	26.6
1899	36.6.[1]
1904	24.9
1909	22.3
1913	20.3

1. The downward trend reversed by outbreaks of infectious measles, whooping cough and diarrhoea which caused considerable deaths of children under two years of age.

Source: Charles A. Cameron *A Brief History of Municipal Public Health Administration in Dublin* (Dublin 1914), p. 13.

more susceptible to illness; all classes could be affected by the contagion that spread through human contact. Willis pointed out that Dr Hagan had warned the affluent 'that their riches cannot exclude infection, which will insinuate itself into the inmost recesses of their dwellings, attached to their furniture, clothes, and bedding; all these articles being supplied by the labouring poor',[84] and that disease, which originated in the homes of the poor, 'not unfrequently stalks within the threshold of the wealthy'—a fact which was still true a generation later.

Throughout most of the 19th century, Dublin had one of the highest death-rates of any city in the British Isles and, while mortality in cities like London, Liverpool and Birmingham began to decline after the 1870s, all having a death rate under 20 per thousand in 1905, Dublin's mortality still stood at 22.3 per thousand.[85] However, this masks the great inroads made by Charles Cameron and his staff into Dublin's death rate, helping to reduce it from 37.5 per thousand in 1879, the year Cameron took over responsibility from Mapother, to 17.6 in 1920, the year before he died. Comparison with other cities should not mask the improvements in the mortality figures for Dublin, improvements that were hard-won, in conditions that were worse than in other cities; improvements that could be wiped out almost overnight with an unexpected and uncontrollable epidemic. Figure 3.1 shows this clearly, as a falling death rate soared in the years when epidemics occurred.

The Dublin that Charles Cameron returned to as a teenager, and in

84   Willis, *Facts* (1845) op. cit., p. 52.
85   Cameron *Brief History* (1914), op. cit., p. 13.

which he began his career, was little improved from the city he had left as a young boy; in fact, it is probable that the state of the city, and the health of its people, particularly the poor, had declined greatly in the intervening years. The problems were enormous, and posed a challenge both for those starting on a medical career and for an organisation whose early years coincided with Cameron's early career—the reformed Dublin Corporation, on whose shoulders responsibility for the heaving mass of humanity within the city boundaries devolved in 1840.

Chapter 4 A problem inherited—the reformed Dublin Corporation

Financial difficulties

The difficulties faced by Dublin Corporation continued for much of the 19th century. The Municipal Corporations (Ireland) Act 1840, (3 & 4 *Vic. c. cviii*), reformed Dublin Corporation, allowing all freeholders to stand for election and become Corporation officers. Catholics, previously excluded from the old franchise, were allowed to vote in civic elections, but the Bill took the precaution of restricting the civic franchise to householders with a rateable valuation of £10 in an effort to allow Protestant property holders not to be overwhelmed. Whether this was successful or not is debatable, but the fight for votes meant that, from the beginning of the reformed Corporation, there was a sectarian element to civic politics. However, as far as the daily life of Dublin's citizens was concerned, it was immaterial which religious faction had power, as the Corporation had limited involvement with everyday matters such as sanitation, housing, lighting, etc. From the late 18th century, these tasks had been carried out, not by the Corporation, but by bodies appointed by the Lord Lieutenant. As a newspaper of the day noted: 'Whether Roman Catholics or Protestants would best manage the lighting, watching, and paving of the city, it is unnecessary to determine . . . in spite of the new corporation, the citizens of Dublin will still have clean flags, bright lamps, and an efficient night watch, that no inconvenience or discomfort will be felt from the existence of that body.'[1]

However, the old Corporation had left debts of over £300,000,[2] substantially higher than most other cities in the United Kingdom. In 1849 an Act for the Improvement of the City of Dublin, (12 & 13 *Vic. c. 97*), was passed, transferring the duties of the paving board to the Corporation, and when the duties of the Wide Streets Commission passed to the Corporation in 1851, they inherited not only the duties,

---

1 Oliver McDonagh, *O'Connell: The Life of Daniel O'Connell, 1775–1847* (London, 1991), pp 432–3.

2 'Report of the Finance Committee', Minutes of the Municipal Council of the City of Dublin, 1 December 1841.

but a further debt of £36,263 12s 0d.[3] A revaluation of the deteriorating city in 1852 put the rateable valuation of Dublin at £541,000, a reduction of £120,000,[4] a factor which decreased its borrowing powers.

The Corporation endeavoured to make the best of the bad hand they had been dealt. When the Lord Lieutenant drew to their attention the provisions of the Nuisances Removal and Diseases Prevention Act, 1848 (*11 & 12 Vic. c. 123*), a special meeting was called to consider these, and a 'Health of the City Preservation Committee' was formed.[5] The committee's plans to carry out the provisions of the Act received a set-back when they were unable to obtain a government grant or loan.[6] However, in 1851, the Corporation appointed an inspector of nuisances and an *ad interim* inspector, who returned the first details of nuisances and fines to the Corporation. Charles Cameron reports that for the rest of the decade, up until 1859, 'sanitation was enforced by the very limited Corporation sanitary staff of three officers, but aided by the Police.'[7] This lack of resources resulted in no unsanitary houses being closed and no water closets being installed.[8]

Vested interests

The Corporation's problems were only partly financial because, as well as substantial debts and sectarian divides, there were miscellaneous outside factions, with strong opinions on how to administer the city, lined up and ready to obstruct the Corporation if they felt it against their own interests. The aldermen and councillors were reliant on a limited franchise base within the city wards, so were vulnerable to influence and lobbying from vested interest groups, such as landlords, shopkeepers, cattle-men and assorted recalcitrant rate-payers. Most tenement landlords were not sympathetic to the plight of their tenants, and saw the housing of the poor strictly as a business. The belief in the inviolability of private property, immune from interference from the state and its minions, remained paramount. Enid Gauldie claims that it was the idea as much as the reality of private ownership that had 'almost a sanctity',[9] that private property had long 'stood as a defence between the state and the individual,' and that not much had changed

---

3 Cameron, *Brief History* (1914), op. cit., p. 19.
4 O'Brien, *Dear Dirty Dublin* (1982) op. cit., p. 12.
5 Cameron, *Brief History* (1914), op. cit., p. 19.
6 Ibid., p. 20.
7 Ibid., p. 22.
8 Ibid., p. 22.
9 Enid Gauldie, *Cruel Habitations, A History of Working-Class Housing 1780–1918* (London, 1974), p. 117.

since William Pitt had proclaimed to the House of Commons that 'The poorest man may in his cottage bid defiance to all the forces of the Crown . . . the King of England cannot enter—all his force dares not cross the threshold of the ruined tenement'![10]

The bulk of appeals against the Buildings Regulations Bill in 1842 were, according to Gauldie, based on the fact that this Bill was 'highly injurious to rights and property'.[11] The Shaftesbury Act of 1851 (*14 & 15 Vic. c. xxxiv*), which permitted the purchase of land on which to build working-class dwellings, remained a dead letter due to such interests. Although the Act was supported by medical officers of health, it was made unworkable by the opposition of property owners, who believed that the provision of housing for the working classes would compete directly with their interests as slum landlords.[12] A few years earlier, in Dublin, Thomas Willis had been aware of this problem:

> When landlords not only neglect their duty but grossly abuse the power they possess, it is imperative on the government to legislate on the subject, and to protect the great majority of the people from such selfish and heartless cruelty.[13]

Unhygienic dairy-yards and slaughter-houses had long added to the misery of the Dublin slums, and the owners formed a powerful lobby to resist any attempts to reform their *modi operandi*. The ratepayers of Dublin were no different to their equivalent in other cities, and resisted any increase in their taxation. However, whereas in the rest of the United Kingdom it was usual to absorb new suburbs (and hence additional ratepayers) into the existing city, attempts by Dublin Corporation to incorporate the wealthy townships surrounding the city to their administration were resisted forcefully, primarily on the grounds of the increased rates they would incur; for example, in 1878, the residents of Upper Leeson Street in the Rathmines township paid rates of 3s 8d in the pound, whereas just across the canal bridge, their neighbours in Lower Leeson Street paid Dublin Corporation rates of 6s 10d.[14]

As the 19th century progressed, most wealthy businessmen moved their residences to the suburbs while retaining their business interests in the city, and the townships were regularly condemned for their use of

10   Ibid., p. 118.
11   Ibid.
12   Anthony Wohl, *The Eternal Slum, Housing and Social Policy in Victorian London* (London, 1977), p. 78.
13   Willis, *Facts* op. cit., p. 32.
14   O'Brien, (1982) op. cit., p. 15.

the city's facilities, while evading any contribution to its upkeep. The township residents used the facilities of the city, without contributing to its rates—for example the ratepayers of Dublin city, through Dublin Corporation, contributed £4,000 a year to city hospitals, £7,900 to industrial schools and reformatories, and £7,000 to lunatic asylums, while the townships, many of whose citizens used these institutions, contributed nothing.[15]

Edward Mapother urged that Rathmines and Pembroke townships should contribute to the city in 'which they employ but never house their working people'.[16] On the recommendation of a select committee on taxation, a commission to investigate extending the boundaries of Dublin to take in the surrounding townships was set up in October 1878. The main purpose of this commission, from Dublin Corporation's point of view, was to force the townships to be part of the city and to pay rates. This would not only contribute much-needed funds to the Corporations's municipal commitments, but the inclusion of the more affluent suburbs would increase the city's valuation, and hence its potential borrowing powers, essential to improve the fabric of the city.

The committee heard evidence in Dublin between April and July 1879, and Cameron was one of the first witnesses to be questioned, in his capacity as Medical Officer of Health for Dublin. His evidence started somewhat mildly; when asked if he approved of the extension of the boundaries, Cameron replied, 'I strongly approve of it, although I am living in one of the townships you have named yourself'.[17] He elaborated his reasons in further questions: on the question of the spread of disease, he believed that a centralised sanitary authority would be more efficient, giving the following reasons: 'We have got what they have not got in the townships. We have a disinfecting chamber erected at considerable expense in the city of Dublin; it is quite available for all the districts proposed to be annexed.'[18] He continued: 'We have the necessary powers to destroy infected clothing, and to compensate the owners. All that could be done by one central authority or organisation better than by a number of small sanitary authorities, each having jurisdiction over four, five, or

15   Séamus Ó Maitiú, *Dublin's Suburban Towns, 1834–1930* (Dublin and Portland, Oregon, 2003), p. 111.

16   E. D. Mapother, 'Address at the opening of the thirty-fourth session of the Statistical and Social Inquiry Society of Ireland', JSSISI, Vol. VIII, Part LVII 1880/1881, pp 85–106.

17   PP.1880, xxx, c. 2725, Municipal Boundaries Commission (Ireland) Part 1, evidence from Dublin, Rathmines, etc., par. 839.

18   Ibid., par. 843.

10,000 inhabitants.'[19] Cameron soon launched into the real complaint against the townships—that their citizens placed a burden on the city's facilities, adding to the public health problems:

> With respect to the area for registration purposes, I wish to state that I think Dublin is rather unfairly placed, because all the eleemosynary institutions and the two workhouses, and nearly all the hospitals and places of that kind are within the city; and the suburbs—and the northern suburbs especially—contribute [inmates] to all these institutions, and the deaths which occur in them are placed as a rule, or with very few exceptions, to the credit of the city, and in that way the city is made to appear, so far as the death rate is concerned, worse than it really is.[20]

Asked about the death rate of Dublin, Cameron said that the annual rate was 28 to 28.5 per 1,000,

> ... but it has risen last winter to a very high degree, especially in some districts—to fifty and sixty per thousand—especially in the two districts where the union workhouses are situated, which are more healthy naturally than some of the central districts of the city, and that shows that a large number of deaths were unduly charged to the districts in which the poorhouses are situated.[21] My experience is that broken down people from all parts of the country take refuge in the poorer parts of the city, and remain in such places, finding their way ultimately to the hospitals, workhouses, or charities of various kinds that exist in the city; that is my experience, and it may be taken as one of the causes of the gradual increase of the death-rate of the city.[22]

The townships, however, remained outside the Corporation's pool of revenue until the Dublin Boundaries Act (*An Act to extend the City of Dublin and for other purposes—63 & 64 Vic. c. 264*), compelled the annexation of the northern townships in 1900. Until then, Dublin remained a 'cribbed, cabined and confined'[23] city between the Royal and Grand Canals, with an increasingly impoverished population housed in ever deteriorating buildings. The reason behind the townships' resistance to being absorbed into the Corporation area throughout the Victorian period was political as well as financial. The townships, at least those south of the city, were predominantly Protestant or Protestant-controlled and unionist, while Dublin

19 Ibid., par. 845.
20 Ibid., par. 859.
21 Ibid., par. 857.
22 Ibid., par. 860.
23 O'Brien, (1982) op. cit., p. 15.

Corporation from 1840 was quite the reverse, being mainly Catholic and nationalist.

Clean water and mains drainage

One of the earliest battles fought (and won) by the reformed Corporation was for the provision of a supply of clean water to Dublin. In 1806, the Corporation had entered into sixty-year contracts with the Grand Canal and Royal Canal companies to provide a water supply to the city.[24] In 1854, dissatisfied with the quality and inadequacy of the supply from the canal companies, the Corporation decided to find its own source.

Thomas Hawksley, a London engineer, and Parke Neville, Dublin City Engineer, recommended the Coyford scheme, which would supply water from the Liffey near Newbridge, and in the 1859–60 parliamentary session the Corporation sought powers to put this scheme in place. After much negotiation and objections from the canal companies and railway interests, the Corporation was forced to abandon the plan, and the groups opposing the scheme called for a royal commissioner to examine the issue, his decision to be binding on all parties.[25] The commissioner appointed was John (later Sir John) Hawkshaw, who recommended the best source of supply as the river Vartry. However, despite the prior agreement to accept the decision of the appointed commissioner, his recommendation was vigorously opposed by the canal companies.

The Corporation was forced to defend its support of the Vartry scheme in 'a severe Parliamentary contest — extending over five weeks in the House of Commons, and afterwards for six days in the House of Lords'[26] before the Bill was eventually carried. Sir John Gray, Chairman of the water-works committee, and two aldermen, George Roe and W. H. Kinahan, defended the Bill in London, and Alderman Kinahan could be said to have died in the attempt. He insisted on staying in London to support the Bill, refusing to return to Dublin on doctor's advice; he took ill in the Committee Room of the House of Commons, and died in London.[27] However, the most fervent campaigner for a new water supply for Dublin was Sir John Gray.

---

24 Parke Neville, *A Description of the Dublin Corporation Water Works* (Dublin, 1875), p. 4.
25 Ibid., pp 5–6.
26 Ibid., p. 7.
27 Ibid.

Sir John Gray

Sir John Gray was born in Claremorris, Co. Mayo in 1816. He qualified as a doctor in Glasgow, and practised in Dublin. He was imprisoned for several months in 1843 for conspiracy against British rule as a supporter of Daniel O'Connell, and helped organise the Tenant League's founding conference in 1850. He was sole proprietor of the *Freeman's Journal* from 1850, and through this paper campaigned 'for the disestablishment of the Anglican church in Ireland, land reform, and the educational aspirations of Irish Catholicism'.[28] In 1852 he became a Dublin councillor and embarked on a campaign to provide Dublin with a clean and abundant water supply. Dirty and contaminated water was a major cause of disease, including typhoid and cholera, and the absence of running water made already unhygienic living conditions even more intolerable.

Parke Neville, in his contemporary description of the Vartry water scheme, wrote that it was to Sir John Gray's 'great ability, scientific knowledge, and indomitable energy and perseverance, [that] the citizens of Dublin are mainly indebted for obtaining the great boon of an abundant supply of pure water. From the year 1860 he devoted a large portion of his valuable time, working late and early, to promote the success of the scheme.'

As soon as permission for the Vartry scheme was obtained, Gray 'pre-empted any possibility of land speculation in the Roundwood area. He bought the land that would be needed for the scheme and transferred it to the corporation at no profit to himself'.[29]

A statue to Sir John Gray was erected on O'Connell Street in 1879.

Parke Neville

Parke Neville, who wrote such glowing praise of Sir John Gray, is somewhat reticent on his own contribution to the improvement of living conditions in Dublin. He mentioned that he had 'the whole responsibility, as Engineer-in-Chief, of preparing the working drawings, and subsequently superintending the construction of the [Vartry] works.'[30]

Born in 1812, he was the third generation of his family to serve Dublin city as surveyors, following his grandfather Arthur Richards Neville

---

28 David Steele, 'Sir John Gray (1816–1875)', *Oxford Dictionary of National Biography*, (Oxford University Press, 2004).

29 Corcoran, *Our Good Health* (2005) op. cit,, p. 48.

30 Neville, (1875) op. cit., p. 27.

(Surveyor 1801–28) and his father Arthur Neville (Surveyor 1828–45). Arthur and Parke Neville were joint City Surveyors from 1845 to 1851, when Parke resigned the post on being appointed Borough Engineer and Local Surveyor: he became City Engineer in 1851, and when his father died in 1856, he combined it with the post of City Surveyor.[31] A contemporary described Neville as being 'most conscientious in the performance of his public duties, which were discharged with unswerving fidelity'.[32] This was clearly demonstrated in 1867, when he and his staff fought for several months to plug a serious leak in a tunnel leading from the reservoir to the filter beds. A contemporary described how, on 10 February, working at night to repair the leak, Neville fell, and was 'much cut on the head, full 20 ft we had to carry him up to bed and send for the carriage, 1 a.m.'.[33] Neville would have had close associations with Cameron and Mapother in their work, supporting the clearance of the twelve unsanitary areas identified by Mapother in his report in 1876, and corroborating the evidence given by Cameron to the Commission of Inquiry into the Sewerage and Drainage System of Dublin in 1879.[34] Neville worked constantly on efforts to improve Dublin's drainage, drawing up a plan as early as 1853, going on a fact-finding mission to investigate sewage disposal in British cities such as Birmingham, Manchester, Glasgow and Edinburgh, and drawing up, with the noted Sir Joseph Bazalgette, recommendations for a main drainage scheme in 1866 which was approved by the Corporation in 1869 but never implemented.[35] A revised proposal by Neville, based on his earlier 1853 plan, would eventually be recommended by the Royal Commission of 1879, but was not implemented for many years.[36] A trained architect, he designed Dublin's fruit and vegetable market in Mary's Lane, and the cattle market in Prussia Street. Both facilities had been vigorously campaigned for by Charles Cameron, and were important contributions to an improvement in hygiene conditions in the city.[37] Parke Neville died on 30 November 1886 at his home in 58

31 Corcoran, (2005) op. cit., pp 39–41, p. 212.
32 Ibid., p. 39.
33 Richard Walsh, 'Construction of the Vartry Waterworks', National Library Ms. 19814.
34 RPDCD, *Report of the City Engineer to the Chairman and Gentlemen of the Committee nominated 4th September, 1879, to lay all necessary evidence before the Royal Commission of Inquiry into the Sewerage and Drainage System of the City of Dublin, and their Effects on the Sanitary Condition of the City, etc.*, (1879), vol. 3, no. 184, pp 163–94.
35 Corcoran, (2005) op. cit., p. 75.
36 Ibid., p. 91.
37 Christine Casey, *Dublin: The City within the Grand and Royal Canals and the Circular Road with the Phoenix Park* (New Haven and London, 2005), p. 100 and p. 269.

Pembroke Road,[38] and appears to have gone unrewarded in terms of public recognition.

Spencer Harty

This was not the case with his deputy and successor, Spencer Harty, who worked with Neville on the Vartry water scheme, and to whom the task of continuing Neville's work fell; he would bring to fulfilment several of Neville's plans, including the fruit and vegetable market and most importantly, the completion of the Dublin main drainage scheme in 1906. This scheme was a vital weapon in the battle to improve living conditions in the city, enabling the efficient disposal of sewage from the water closets which had replaced the old privies, largely through the efforts of Cameron. Spencer Harty was made a Freeman of Dublin in 1907, four years before Cameron—they are the only two Dublin Corporation officials to have received the honour. They are also both mentioned in James Joyce's *Ulysses*.

The Dublin Statistical Society

The lack of interest and recalcitrance of vested interests and city ratepayers was somewhat offset by the involvement in health and housing issues of voluntary organisations. One of the most influential bodies on public health and housing reform was the Dublin Statistical Society and its closely related organisation, the Dublin Sanitary Association. The idea of a Dublin Statistical Society was first proposed in the rooms of William Neilson Hancock, the then Whately Professor of Political Economy, in No. 16 Trinity College. The society (later the Statistical and Social Inquiry Society of Ireland), was founded on 23 November 1847 following a public meeting in the Royal Irish Academy, and its first president was Richard Whately, founder of the Whately chair, and head of the Irish Commission at the time of the New Poor Law.

From its inception, and throughout the 19th and early 20th centuries, members with an interest in public health and housing used the Society's meetings as a forum for research on Dublin's problems, and their papers, many of which were aimed at instigating social reform, provide much of the contemporary eye-witness accounts of the state of the city. For example, Edward Mapother, first Medical Officer of Health for Dublin, presented four papers on public health and public health

---

38 Cameron lived at No. 15, and would move to No. 51 Pembroke Road in 1889.

legislation.[39] When William Lawson read his paper entitled 'Remedies for Overcrowding in the City of Dublin' to the Society in January 1909, he began his paper with the statement 'This question is no new one; it has been discussed in and out of this Society'.[40] This is clearly evident in the list of papers read to the Society during the years when the problems of overcrowding and public health became of increasing concern. From the Rev. Thomas Jordan's paper in 1856, 'The Present State of the Dwellings of the Poor',[41] through John Norwood in 1873, 'On the Working of the Sanitary Laws in Dublin, with Suggestions for their Amendment',[42] to Charles Eason in 1898, 'The Tenement Houses of Dublin, Their Condition and Regulation'.[43] The papers continued into the new century with William Lawson, as mentioned above in 1909, and Charles Dawson in 1913, still considering 'The Dublin Housing Question'.[44] Dawson was fully conversant with the plight of the poor by virtue of 'his long connection with the Corporation' and his connection with the Association for the Housing of the Very Poor, which was founded by Cameron—an illustration of the network of connections between people concerned with the problems caused by bad housing in Dublin at the time. Cameron himself was a member of the Society, although he never gave a paper.

It would appear from the occupations of members that the Dublin Statistical Society and later the Statistical and Social Inquiry Society of Ireland (SSISI) had intimate links with those who mattered in the Irish administration, and that this nexus of concerned people discussed, decided on, and eventually brought to the attention of those in power, the reforms that needed to be made in public health and housing legislation. In Edward Mapother's paper in February 1865, he stated that he enjoyed in the SSISI 'the cooperation of its legal and other members expert in the construction of acts of Parliament',[45] and Daly claims that it was due to Mapother's efforts that Irish public health law was brought into line with that in the rest of the United

---

39 Mapother, 'Address' op. cit. pp 85–106; 'The sanitary state of Dublin', in *JSSISI* Vol IV, Part XXVII, 1864 pp 62–76; 'The differences between the statutes bearing on public health for England and Ireland', in *JSSISI* Vol IV, Part XXX, 1865, pp 203–211; 'The unhealthiness of Irish towns, and the want of sanitary legislation', in *JSSISI* Vol IV, Part XXVI, 1865/1866, pp 250–75.

40 *JSSISI*, Vol XII, Part LXXXIX 1908/1909, pp 230–248.

41 *JSSISI* Vol. II, Part VIII, 1857 pp 12–19.

42 *JSSISI*, Vol VI, Part XLIII 1872/3, pp 230–42.

43 *JSSISI* Vol X Part LXXIX, 1898/1899 pp 383–98.

44 *JSSISI* Vol. VIII, Part XCIII, 1912/1913 pp .90–5.

45 Mapother, 'The differences between the statutes bearing on public health for England and Ireland', in *JSSISI* Vol IV, Part XXX, 1865, pp 203–211.

Kingdom.[46] The SSISI claimed to be above politics, but it would appear that, while it may ostensibly have eschewed political opinions, many of its members and their associates had strong opinions on matters of public health, and disseminated these views to those whom they thought could implement them. This point of view becomes more obvious when one examines an early offshoot of the Dublin Statistical Society—the Dublin Sanitary Association.

The Dublin Sanitary Association

The Dublin Sanitary Association was formed shortly after the Dublin Statistical Society, on 3 June 1848, with the stated purpose 'to lighten, as much as possible, the physical deprivations of their fellow citizens'. There was a marked overlap in the membership of the two associations—the list of founding members of the Dublin Sanitary Association included William Wilde, James Haughton and John Aldridge, all prominent members of the Dublin Statistical Society. And while the Dublin Statistical Society may have professed to avoid politics, the Dublin Sanitary Association had no such reservations and was much more militant in its activities. When the Nuisance Removal and Disease Prevention Act (*11 & 12 Vic. c. 123*), was enacted in 1848, the Dublin Sanitary Association immediately convened to discuss it and set up a sanitary court to support the Act. The purpose of this self-styled tribunal was to try offenders if the Dublin courts were too busy to do so. The *Dublin Medical Press* was doubtful of their motives, and referred to them as 'a kind of provisional government of cess-pools and privies, to carry this act into operation'.[47]

The driving force behind this tribunal (which was, incidentally, supported by the Lord Mayor and held in the city assembly house) was Sir Edward Borough, President of the Dublin Sanitary Association.[48] In 1849, the Lord Mayor, Sir Timothy O'Brien, praised 'the extraordinary exertions that had been made by Sir Edward Borough in connection with the Sanatory [sic] Court'.[49] The court lasted until 1850, when it was forced to disband after 'a question of its legal status was raised.[50] The association was also involved more widely with legislation—the report of its transactions for 1848–9 stated that 'circumstances have

46 Mary E. Daly, *The Spirit of Earnest Inquiry* (Dublin, 1997), p. 33.
47 *Dublin Medical Press*, XX (1848), p. 395, cited in Stephanie Jones, 'Dublin reformed: the transformation of the municipal governance of a Victorian city, 1840–60' Ph.D. dissertation, University of Dublin (2002) Ref. 267 p. 243.
48 Jones, (2002) op. cit., p. 255.
49 *Saunder's News-Letter*, 10 Oct. 1849.
50 Cameron (1914), op. cit., p. 22.

enabled the Association to interfere more directly in the progress of sanitary legislation than it would, of itself, have sought to do'.[51] Despite this apparent demurring, the Dublin Sanitary Association sent delegates to a committee which drew up alternative Bills to be introduced in the House of Commons, in opposition to 'rival bills previously introduced' and claimed that these rival bills 'have been withdrawn, to the saving of expense and annoyance of the citizens'.[52]

The aims of the Dublin Sanitary Association were almost identical to the aims of the Health of Towns Association in England, an association closely connected with Edwin Chadwick, who was, in his turn, a lifelong friend of Archbishop Richard Whately, closely connected, as we have seen, with the Dublin Statistical Society. These connections and similarities are interesting; both the Dublin Sanitary Association and the Health of Towns Association put the major emphasis on sanitation as the solution to health problems, and were part of the great debate about the real cause of disease, but they largely ignored the underlying cause of poverty and the contagion caused by overcrowding in unsanitary housing. Chadwick, the most influential force in public health in the British Isles until the mid-1850s, believed that the solution to improving public health lay with engineers rather than with medical men, and most mid-19th century reforms concentrated on the environment outside the home, such as sewerage and clean water supplies. Chadwick and his associates believed that the source of high mortality was 'not due to want of food and greater misery . . . but in the generation of effluvial poisons'.[53]

Many anti-contagionists were doctors, some in prominent positions, and their views influenced public health policy for much of the 19th century. Dr Thomas Southwood Smith and Dr Neil Arnott, close associates of Edwin Chadwick, 'projected a closed circle of causation which avoided the moral questions of deprivation and redistribution'.[54] In Ireland, one of the most influential anti-contagionists was Sir Dominic Corrigan, five times President of the Irish College of Physicians. An example of his views was evidenced during the 1853–4 cholera outbreak, when Corrigan and his colleagues in the Hardwicke and Whitworth hospitals admitted cholera patients to wards containing non-infected patients, in the belief that this would

51 *Report of the Transactions of the Dublin Sanitary Association from 4 June 1848 to 30 April 1849*, pp 24–5.
52 Ibid.
53 F. B. Smith, *The People's Health 1830–1910* (Hampshire, England, 1993), p. 232.
54 Ibid., p. 232.

allay 'the unfounded fears of contagion', believing that 'the fear of contagion demoralises the mind and extinguishes the best affections of the heart',[55] the practice only ceasing on the orders of the Irish Poor Law commissioners.[56] Corrigan was of the opinion that Dr Mapother 'described a blue mist accompanying cholera cases which was believed to arise from myriads of spores of fungi in the air'.[57] Others in the Irish medical establishment disagreed, believing that contagion was responsible—for example, Dr Robert Graves claimed that, in his experience of fever 'its transmissibility from individual to individual is a truth which it is idle to gainsay'.[58]

Dr W. P. Alison, a leading Scottish expert on social medicine, published a significant study on poverty in 1840 in which he argued that poverty and destitution were the primary sources of disease.[59] In 1842, Alison 'explicitly criticised the miasma theories of the Chadwickians'.[60] These reports were ignored by Chadwick. This debate continued until the 1880s, when contagion was finally accepted as the real cause of disease, and some attention began to be paid to the living conditions of the poor. Connections, therefore, between the Irish group and their Chadwickian counterparts in England indicate a pro-sanitation/anti-contagionist bias in the Dublin organisation.

Although it has been stated that the Dublin Sanitary Association ceased to exist in the 1860s, [61] the Association was in fact re-formed on 17 May 1872, following a smallpox epidemic,[62] and remained in existence—based on the number of annual reports—until 1910. This re-formed Association shows an undimmed concern with sanitation, stating as its first objective: 'To create an educated public opinion with regard to sanitary matters in general', and three other objectives: the sanitary condition of the city, sanitary legislation in the city, and the formation of a body which could act on behalf of the citizens if necessary.

The Dublin Sanitary Association lived up to its objectives, constantly bringing public health violations to the attention of the authorities, campaigning for legislation and official inquiries, and haranguing

---

55 Dominic Corrigan, *Cholera map of Ireland with Observations* (Dublin, 1886), p. 12.
56 Joseph Robins, *Miasma: Epidemic and Panic in Nineteenth Century Ireland* (Dublin 1995), p. 210.
57 Ibid., p. 211.
58 Ibid., p. 210.
59 M. J. Cullen, *The Statistical Movement in Early Victorian Britain* (New York, 1975), pp 56–7.
60 Ibid.
61 Jones, (2002) op. cit., p. 242.
62 O'Brien, (1982) op. cit., p. 22.

Dublin Corporation and its sanitary officers. The minute book of the Association for 1883–94 reveals continuous correspondence between its committee and the official custodians of public health in Dublin, the Public Health Office; it also reveals that Thomas Wrigley Grimshaw, Registrar General, and former President of the SSISI, was an active member of the Dublin Sanitary Association. The correspondence deals with reports of 'nuisances'—either discovered by members of the association, or reported to them by members of the public. While one can sympathise with the concern and aims of the Dublin Sanitary Association, given the state of public health in Dublin, one can also appreciate the exasperation of Dublin's hard-pressed medical officers, who were themselves outspoken campaigners on public health matters. There was a long-running history of animosity between the Dublin Sanitary Association and the official guardians of the city's public health. As far back as 1850, Sir Edward Borough had told the *Freeman's Journal* that 'he was of the opinion that much activity or energy could not be expected in that quarter [Dublin Corporation] in carrying out arrangements calculated to benefit the poorer classes.'[63]

Stephanie Jones claims that the Association 'often made peculiar recommendations to the Corporation, such as a water works scheme without engineering plans and a sewerage system based on unproven and faulty techniques'.[64]

The animosity still existed over a quarter of a century later: in 1878, for example, Edward Mapother described members of the Dublin Sanitary Association as 'self-constituted and irresponsible persons, who might possibly be actuated by such motives as greed of notoriety or of employment'.[65] In 1883, a complaint from the Association about Cameron's 'plurality of offices' when he was appointed Deputy Coroner for Dublin, received a quick and acerbic reply from him to the effect that there was nothing in the terms of his contract to prevent him from temporarily discharging the duties of a colleague.[66]

The Dublin Artisans' Dwellings Company

The Dublin Sanitary Association itself had an offshoot, as it was the main instigator of the Dublin Artisans' Dwellings Company (DADC). This Association was formed after a housing conference which the

---

63 *Freeman's Journal*, 15 May 1850.
64 Jones, (2002) op. cit., p. 245.
65 *Report on death rate in Dublin*, 1878, no. 71.
66 Dublin Sanitary Association Minute Book, 1 Nov. 1883.

Dublin Sanitary Association held in 1876,[67] and became one of the foremost housing societies in the city. From the beginning it was run as a business, paying 4–5 per cent to its shareholders. Cameron claimed that, while the type of housing provided by organisations such as the DADC fulfilled some need, they did little to help the overcrowding that caused public health problems, as the rents charged were beyond the reach of those who were causing the problems, the lowest paid and unemployed,[68] the type of people who were dying in such great numbers in tenements. In 1881, Cameron claimed that artisans' dwellings were as inaccessible to the very poor 'as are the houses in Fitzwilliam Square to ordinary mechanics'.[69]

It is interesting to note that, when Cameron finally succeeded in persuading Dublin Corporation to build its first public housing scheme in Benburb Street, the scheme was objected to by the DADC on the grounds that it competed unfairly with semi-philanthropic housing,[70] despite the fact that the Artisans' Dwellings Company had obtained almost half its funding from public loans at interest rates that were lower than the market rate and the fact that Dublin Corporation had leased it sites for building at a financial loss to themselves.[71] The DADC, although a commercial organisation with an eye to the dividends for its members, justified its claim to semi-philanthropic status by asserting that the people who moved into their dwellings vacated lower standard dwellings that were then available to, and affordable by, the poorer sections of the community. Up to 1925, the DADC built 3,415 dwellings.[72]

Philanthropic housing

Several other organisations could claim to have provided philanthropic housing, although most were on a smaller scale than the DADC—for example, the Industrial Tenement Company, the City and Suburban Workmen's Dwellings Company, the Association for Housing the Very Poor (founded by Cameron—see Chapter 9), the Alexandra Guild from Alexandra College, and the Social Service (Tenements) Co. Ltd, which refurbished existing tenements and let them at the lowest rents.

---

67 Murray Fraser, *John Bull's Other Homes: State Housing and British Policy in Ireland, 1883–1922* (Liverpool, 1996), p. 71.

68 *Report of the Royal Commission on Sewerage and Drainage of the City of Dublin 1880* (c. 2605) xxxi, evidence of Dr Cameron, qs. 1386.

69 RPDCD (1881), Vol. 2, No. 94, p.68

70 Fraser, (1996) op. cit., p. 76.

71 Ibid., p. 71.

72 Prunty, (1998), op. cit., p. 177.

The Guinness Trust (Dublin Fund), which amalgamated with the Bull Alley Area Trust in 1903 to become the Iveagh Trust, provided the largest number of dwellings built by a philanthropic enterprise. Between 1891 and 1915, the Trust built a total of 1,224 dwellings[73] mainly in large blocks of self-contained or semi-self-contained flats; in 1907 the rents ranged from 2s to 6s 3d per week, depending on the number of bedrooms in the flat.[74] The Bull Alley building scheme cleared some of the worst slum areas in Dublin's Liberties. Small, unsanitary streets, lanes and alleys and their substandard dwellings were replaced with new blocks of dwellings on wider roads; the new St Patrick's Park provided much-needed green space; there was space for shops, a public swimming baths, a recreation hall and concert hall; the old street markets in Patrick Street were replaced with the Iveagh Market in Francis Street, which also provided facilities for washing clothes, and a hostel was built for single men. Cameron's diaries show that he was closely connected with members of the Guinness family, and almost certainly had discussions with them in connection with their philanthropic work. However, the rents in these buildings were still beyond the reach of the very poor, as the following table shows:

Figure 4.1 *Accommodation and rents, Bull Alley, 1903*

    32 three-room self-contained tenements at 5s 9d per week
    80 two-room self-contained tenements at 4s 3d per week
    32 three-room associated tenements at 5s 0d per week
    80 two-room associated tenements at 3s 6d per week
    20 single-room tenements at 2s 6d per week

Source: F. H. A. Aalen, *The Iveagh Trust, the first hundred years, 1890–1990* (Dublin, 1990), p. 39.

Legislation, 1848–66

In his paper to the SSISI in 1873, John Norwood quoted a judge of the Court of the Queen's Bench in Westminster as stating that the difficulty with legislation 'arose from the practice of repealing parts of acts and incorporating parts, and thus making up an act of bits and fragments out of other acts, instead of clearly and simply stating what was enacted.' (The result, according to Norwood, was 'a . . . chaotic

---

73 Ibid.
74 F. H. A. Aalen in Michael J. Bannon, (ed.), *A Hundred Years of Irish Planning, Vol. 1, The Emergence of Irish Planning, 1880–1920* (Dublin, 1985), p. 156.

jumble of sanitary statutes.'[75])

A possible explanation for this 'chaotic jumble' is that most Victorian health and housing legislation appears to have been formulated in response to a crisis, an official report or a public outcry of some kind, and was brought in as an emergency response to a particular issue without much consideration of the wider causes. Norwood, however, quoting the same judge, Mr Justice Blackburn, states that the latter was of the opinion that government 'did not wish to take the plain and simple course,' but preferred to formulate legislation that was not simple, thus 'throwing upon the judges the onus of interpreting it.'[76]

In the case of Ireland, there was the further difficulty of translating legislation designed for the problems that existed in British cities to those that existed in Ireland, in particular the largest centre of population, Dublin, whose health and housing problems were unique in their origins and in their characteristics. This difficulty would appear to have been resolved, depending on the legislation, in one of three ways:

1) by neglecting to apply the legislation to Ireland at all;

2) by applying the legislation, and leaving the Irish authorities to interpret and implement it as best as they could in the Irish situation;

3) by introducing legislation that was specific to Ireland: while this was often designed with an Irish situation in mind e.g. An Act for the Improvement of Dublin, 1849 (12 & 13 Vic. c. 97), there were other instances where the Acts applied to Ireland were an amendment of existing English legislation, and were implemented in Ireland as a patchwork of earlier English statutes, leading to the scenario described above by Norwood where 'there had arisen a practice of repealing parts of some acts and incorporating parts of others, so as to create the greatest possible difficulty'.[77] An example of this is the Public Health Act (Ireland) 1866, which incorporated all of the English public health statutes up to 1855, many of which had been found to be unworkable in England.

While no one public health Act could be said to have had a great effect on public health legislation, the cumulative effects of the various health and housing Acts enacted between 1849 and 1874 increased awareness of the problems that existed and the measures that needed to be brought to bear on them. Even though many of the pieces of

---

75 John Norwood, 'On the Working of the Sanitary Laws in Dublin, with Suggestions for their Amendment', *Jn. SSISI* Part XLIII, (1873), Vol. 6, pp 230–42.

76 Ibid.

77 Ibid.

legislation were unworkable, their very inadequacy accentuated the increasing urgency of implementing effective legislation.

The Public Health Act, 1848 (*11 & 12 Vic., c. 62, 63*), created a Central Board of Health although 'the confusion of authorities that hindered the progress of sanitary reform remained intact until 1855'.[78] Nevertheless, the Public Health Act, 1848 was the first piece of legislation by which the health of the public was considered to be the responsibility of government, and led to public debate about the best methods of improving public health. As Gauldie states, in an age of individualism 'to have the welfare of the community considered as the responsibility of government was a not inconsiderable step'.[79]

The Act, however, was not compulsory, and only applied to England and Wales—its provisions did not apply to Ireland.[80] The implications of Ireland's exclusion from this piece of legislation are evident from contemporary commentators. Edward Mapother, in his paper to the SSISI on 21 February 1865,[81] includes the Public Health Act, 1848 under the heading of 'Laws for England only', and claims that this Act '[rendered] legislation for any town inexpensive', a factor that would have been of considerable use to an increasingly impoverished Dublin. Mapother pointed out a provision of the 1848 Act which would have allowed public inquiries to be held under certain conditions. The Act stated that public inquiries into such matters as the 'sanitary condition of the Inhabitants', as well as the sewerage and drainage, could be called by the general board of health on the petition of 'one tenth of the [rated] Inhabitants' or where the 'number of deaths . . . exceeded the proportion of twenty-three to a thousand of the population'.[82] He emphasised the difference such a provision would have made in many towns in Ireland, including Dublin, where the death rate would have exceeded that number, and where, despite reservations about higher rates, there would doubtless have been sufficient concerned ratepayers to constitute the tenth required for a petition.

Charles Cameron endorsed Mapother's views in *A Brief History of Municipal Public Health Administration in Dublin* (1914) when he claimed that 'the Corporation were practically devoid of authority in relation

78 Henry Jephson, 'The Sanitary Evolution of London', pp. 12–13, cited in Wohl (1977), op. cit., p. 17, ref No. 60.
79 Gauldie, (1974) op. cit., p. 133.
80 *11 & 12 Vic., c. 63*.
81 E. D. Mapother, 'The differences between the statutes bearing on Public Health in England and Ireland', *Jn. SSISI* (1865), Vol. iv, Part XXVI, 203–10.
82 *11 & 12 Vic., c. 63*, VIII.

to public health until after the Sanitary Act of 1848'.[83] This Act, (*11 &*
12 Vic. c. 123), was also known, according to Finer[84] as the Cholera Bill,
due to its importance in preparing for the incipient threat of cholera.
The Act was passed on 4 September 1848, and was officially known
as the Nuisance Removal and Disease Prevention Act. Its provisions,
which did apply to Ireland, were brought to the attention of Dublin
Corporation by the Lord Lieutenant, and Cameron states that,
following a special meeting of the Corporation on 22 September 1848
a Health of the City Preservation Committee was formed to consider
the provisions of the Act.[85] This committee made an application to
the government for funds to enable them to put the sanitary laws
as outlined in the Act into place. However, in December 1848, the
committee informed the Corporation that they had been unable to
obtain a grant or loan, and that the Queen's Bench had refused to
allow them to use the borough fund to carry out the provisions of the
Act.[86] In order to do so, the Corporation would need to recover the
cost from the person guilty of causing the nuisance—an insuperable
task in the labyrinthine maze of Dublin property ownership, where
'in the case of our ancient houses we have frequently a succession of
owners between the occupier and the fee'.[87]

Finer claims that the Nuisances Removal and Diseases Prevention
Act, 1848 'was sloppily drawn and badly conceived [and did nothing]
to consolidate the local cleansing functions under one authority', and
that in some areas, for example, London, 'rival bodies squabbled like
cats and dogs'.[88] The Act, with its amendment in 1849, was deemed
to be defective, and An Act to Consolidate and Amend the Nuisances
Removal and Diseases Prevention Acts, 1848 and 1849 (*18 & 19 Vic. c.
120*), was passed on 14 August 1855. Under this new Act, the previous
two Acts were repealed 'as far as relates to England'. Ireland, however,
still laboured under the provisions of the old laws until the Sanitary
Act of 1866 (*29 & 30 Vic. c. 90*) incorporated all English legislation up
to 1855 and made the provisions applicable to Ireland.

In addressing the members of the SSISI in 1865, Edward Mapother
bemoaned the fact that Ireland was excluded from the Nuisance
Removal Acts of 1855 and 1860, which he claimed 'render the local

83 Cameron (1914) op. cit., p. 19.
84 S. E. Finer, *The Life and Times of Sir Edwin Chadwick* (London, 1997), p. 336.
85 Cameron (1914), op. cit., p. 19.
86 Ibid., p. 20.
87 Hon. F. R. Falkiner, 'Report on Homes of the Poor', *JSSISI* Vol. VIII, Part LIX 1882/1882, pp 261–71.
88 Finer, (1997) op. cit., p. 336.

authorities more general than do similar acts bearing on Ireland'.[89]
Section VI of the 1855 Act (*18 & 19 Vic. c. 121*), allowed the inhabitants
of any place with a population of more than 200 to elect a 'Nuisances
Removal Committee', while Section XXIX allowed proceedings against
overcrowding, if evidence of overcrowding was certified by a medical
officer of health or two medical practitioners. Mapother maintained
that, because these provisions did not extend to Ireland 'there are
hundreds of dwellings in our "Sanitary Register" . . . in which overcrowding exists to the utmost, and yet no amendment is possible
under any act the legislature has thought of conferring on us.'[90]

Among other legislation that Mapother viewed as desirable, but
not extended to Ireland, was The Registration of Births, Deaths and
Marriages Act, 1836, a plea for which had also been made in 1853 by
the No. 2 Committee of Dublin Corporation. This important legislation
was not applied to Ireland until 1864, and did not become fully
effective until notification of deaths became compulsory in 1879. The
lack of civil registration was a significant disadvantage in Ireland, as
registration in England had shown up the areas of highest mortality —
Ireland relied for this information on the voluntary research of men
such as Sir William Wilde, working from the Census figures.

On 28 June 1866, the first piece of housing legislation for Ireland
was passed — The Labouring Classes Lodging Houses and Dwellings
Act (Ireland), 1866. Under the provisions of this Act, companies and
municipalities could be granted a loan at 4 per cent interest over forty
years by the Board of Works for up to half the cost of a housing scheme.
This Act was little used, except by the Dublin Industrial Tenements
Company. While the Act gave local authorities some power to deal
with overcrowding, most authorities and their medical officers of
health were reluctant to evict people from overcrowded dwellings
if they had no alternative housing — this would have simply moved
the overcrowding to another area. The Act was not used by Dublin
Corporation until 1881, when 'a strong recommendation . . . for its
adoption and immediate application' was made to the Corporation by
Charles Cameron and accepted by them on 7 November 1881.[91] In the
meantime, two Acts specifically designed to deal with overcrowding
were introduced to little effect — these were known as the Torrens Act
and the Cross Act. The Torrens Act was first introduced to parliament
by William McCullagh Torrens in 1866, and contained provisions that

89 Mapother, (1865), op. cit., pp. 203–10.
90 Ibid.
91 Cameron (1914), op. cit., p. 52.

would allow local authorities to demolish unsanitary housing where owners had failed to maintain them, and to build improved housing on the site. This version of the Act caused a furore in parliament, as the idea of using public funds to build housing for the poor was anathema to most MPs, one member declaring, 'If such a principle were admitted he did not know where it would stop. The next demand upon them might be to provide clothing if not carriages and horses for the poor.'[92]

After much acrimonious discussion, and several versions, the Torrens Act was passed in an emasculated form by parliament in 1868—the Artisans' and Labourers' Dwellings Act (*31 & 32 Vic. c. cxxx*). All provision for municipal housing had been removed, and the overcrowding problem remained virtually unchanged, other than that 'a few foetid houses were demolished at the expense of increased overcrowding elsewhere'.[93] In 1875, another effort was made to deal with overcrowding with the introduction of the Artisans' and Labourers' Dwellings Improvement Act (*38 & 39 Vic. c. xxxvi*), usually known as the Cross Act. Under this Act, local authorities would be offered loans at 3½ per cent to enable them to clear unsanitary sites, which they could then sell or lease to private builders for housing. In Dublin, this Act was used by the DADC to build houses on two sites that had been cleared by Dublin Corporation in the Coombe and Plunket Street, and then leased to the company. At the request of the Corporation, Edward Mapother, then Medical Officer of Health, earmarked twelve sites as 'unhealthy areas' which should be cleared and redeveloped under the terms of the Cross Act. Mapother had been careful to choose areas that would involve the least disruption to existing tenants, and also to involve the Corporation in the least amount of compensation. In the event, the expense of compensation, mainly as a result of arbitration decisions in favour of the sitting tenants, resulted in only two areas of the twelve being developed—the Coombe and Plunket Street. Parke Neville, the City Engineer, had no illusions about the compensation implications of clearing such spaces:

> It is almost impossible in practice to take down a house between two others, or one that is attached to another, without having claims real or alleged made by the adjoining owners or occupiers, and the more rotten the property, the more loss will be sustained by claims of this sort, as it will be attempted to be proved that buildings are good and sound which

---

92 Wohl, (1977), op. cit., p. 87.
93 Ibid., p. 90.

are the very reverse, and in all cases of this kind Corporations and Public Companies are generally victimised without mercy[94]

Neville's views were proved correct—the original estimate of £8,513 15s

> . . . was increased by Mr. Fitzgerald (who made the revised valuation for arbitration purposes) to £10,869 7s 9d, which was further increased by the arbitrator in his final award to £14,421 9s 4d., and still further increased before the juries to £15,983 19s 8d., including costs . . . The [eventual] total cost to the Corporation was £24,367 12s 10d.[95]

The development of the Plunket Street site was equally expensive—the original estimate of £12,470 would eventually more than double, to cost £27,000. The cleared sites were let at £340 per annum to the DADC, which built 354 dwellings.[96] The experience and the expense put on hold any development of the other sites listed by Mapother, and discouraged Dublin Corporation from becoming involved in similar ventures for many years. In many instances, those displaced by redevelopment could not return to the cleared area—'they could not pay the increased rents which prevailed in it, and they secured new dwellings at their former rents'.[97] Cameron maintained that 'as every scheme in connection with the dwellings for the Working Classes has resulted in some loss it is better that the loss should be incurred in keeping people out of the slums'.[98] Over the course of his tenure, Cameron campaigned for low-rent housing to be provided by the Corporation, an unfashionable and politically unpopular attitude at the time, pointing out that rents for housing of the type built by the DADC was beyond the reach of those who were living in unhealthy, overcrowded tenements, and who badly needed to be re-housed.

There was, however, one piece of public health legislation which was immediately successful, the Sanitary Act, 1866 (29 & 30 Vic. c. 90). The Times of 11 August 1866 declared that 'seldom has an enactment been received with more general approbation or with milder criticism'. John Norwood, addressing the SSISI on 18 February 1873, believed that 'from that date the history and operation of effective sanitary legislation

---

94 Quoted in Spencer Harty, 'Some considerations on the working of the Artisans' Dwellings Acts, as illustrated in the case of the Coombe Area, Dublin' in *JSSISI* Vol. VIII, Part LXII, 1883/1884, p. 508-522.
95 Ibid., pp 511–12.
96 Cameron (1914), op. cit., p. 62.
97 Ibid., p. 65.
98 Ibid.

in Ireland practically commenced',[99] but added a cautionary note that the circumstances under which the Act had been introduced 'rendered it especially complex and difficult in working'—it was discussed in committee until 2 August 'rushed through the Lords on 6 August and became law next day'.[100] Clause 20 of the 1866 Act made it a duty of the nuisance authority 'to make . . . inspection of the District, with a view to ascertain what nuisances exist calling for abatement'.[101]

Norwood stated that '[Dublin] Town Council lost no time in putting its provisions into operation',[102] and, on 22 August 1866, constituted a public health committee. The committee was formed in the middle of a cholera outbreak in Dublin, and it was 'at once necessitated to adopt energetic action in carrying into effect this new and important statute'.[103] The committee framed notices and orders which 'after being subjected to the trying ordeal of judicial decision' were now [1873] used 'by other local authorities in this and the sister country'.[104]

Two other pieces of legislation were particularly taken up with effect in Dublin. One was enacted specifically for Dublin—the Dublin Waterworks Act (24 & 25 Vic. c. 172), which was passed on 22 July 1861. Norwood claimed that the passing of this Act was achieved 'in the face of vigorous, though . . . conscientious, opposition on the part of the citizens', and that 'No city in the kingdom is better supplied with this chiefest necessity in life'.[105] The Dublin Main Drainage Act (34 & 35 Vic. c. 28), passed on 30 July 1871, and 'An Act to Amend the 'Sanitary Act, 1866', so far as it relates to the City of Dublin' were enacted to deal with the drainage of the city, and Norwood looked forward to Dublin being 'in as favourable a condition as any in her Majesty's dominions'.

One piece of legislation that was enacted throughout the British Isles, but which was used to effect solely in Ireland, was the Adulteration of Foods Act, 1860 (23 & 24 Vic., c. 84). The person appointed to put this Act into effect as Public Analyst for Dublin was Charles Cameron.

---

99   Norwood, (1873) op. cit., pp 230–42.
100   Royston Lambert, *Sir John Simon 1816–1904 and English Social Administration* (London, 1963), p. 383.
101   29 & 30 Vict., c. 90.
102   Norwood, (1873) op. cit.
103   Ibid.
104   Ibid.
105   Ibid.

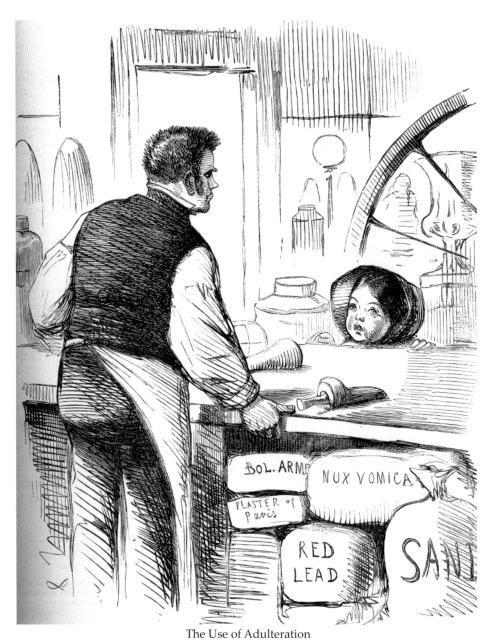

The Use of Adulteration

Little Girl: If you please, Mother says, will you let her have a quarter of a pound of your best black tea to kill the rats with, and a ounce of chocolate as would get rid of the black beadles.
Punch 4 August 1855

The availability of basic chemcials made adulteration of basic foodstuffs easy, and a scandal of the age. The fear that the neighbourhood grocer was quietly poisoning your family with additives did not improve the middle-class Victorian's opinion of those in 'trade'.

Chapter 5 'Death in the Pot':[1] Charles Cameron as Public Analyst

> The paupers of the South Dublin Union are unfortunate in the matter of milk. We believe it was the poor of this union who discovered a vivacious pinkeen in the milk pail one Sunday morning . . .[2]

This anecdote was no doubt designed to amuse the breakfast tables of *Irish Times* readers, while at the same time fulfilling a journalistic quota of concern for the poor. However, for the residents, and indeed the Board of Guardians of the South Dublin Union, the discovery of a pinkeen in their milk, vivacious though it might be, was no laughing matter. The milk in question had been analysed by Dr Charles Cameron, Public Analyst, and found to contain '16 per cent of water above the natural proportion, while the proper weight of the fluid was cleverly made up by a liberal addition of salt'.[3] The point at issue was not the introduction of wildlife into the workhouse milk, which might have been a welcome diversion in the miserable lives of the inmates, but rather the addition of water to the milk, water that not only reduced the nourishment of the drink, but which was very likely to be contaminated, with the risk of transmitting dysentery, typhoid, or even cholera. The addition of a large amount of salt would also have had serious implications for infants in the workhouse.

The adulteration of food and drink was widespread for much of the 19th century, and was a major contributor to public health problems. It was common practice to adulterate milk with water taken from contaminated sources—perhaps from the canals, the cattle drinking trough or the farmyard pump, often referred to as 'the cow with the iron tail'. This contamination was compounded by overcrowded and unhygienic cowsheds, the belief at the time being that the more cows were immobilised, the less food they consumed and the more milk they produced. The result was that a high percentage of the milk produced already contained the tubercular bacillus before being further adulterated with contaminated water, while milk stored in unhygienic conditions often carried typhoid.

---

1   F. Accum, *A Treatise on Adulterations of Food and Culinary Poisons* (London, 1820).
2   *The Irish Times*, 25 March 1871.
3   Ibid.

Milk was only one of numerous items of food and drink that were adulterated. A contemporary cartoon from *Punch* summed up the situation fairly well, showing a grocer's shop with some unexpected commodities, such as red lead, sand, plaster of paris, and *nux vomica*, better known as strychnine, under the counter.[4]

As far back as 1831, *The Lancet* had commented that 'people are allowed to poison themselves with adulterated food, without the slightest concern being manifested by the rulers of the land'.[5] This situation worsened with the increased anonymity and mass production brought about by growing urbanisation. Sir John Simon, Medical Officer of Health for London, claimed that 'Pennyworths of poison [were] being handed over the counter as nonchalantly as cakes of soap'.[6]

Sweets often contained mercury and Venetian lead. Ice cream, commonly sold by Italian immigrants, was regularly found to contain extra 'ingredients' such as 'cocci, bacilli, torulae, cotton fibre, lice, bed bugs, bugs' legs, fleas, straw, human hair, cat and dog hair'[7] and was responsible for many outbreaks of diphtheria, scarlet fever, diarrhoea and enteric fever—so much so that severe warnings against lack of hygiene were posted in English and Italian.[8] Alum and sawdust were added to bread, and bakers, working in basement bakeries in temperatures of between 80° and 110°F, kneaded the dough with hands and feet, sweating profusely, and washing in the water used to mix the next batch of dough.

Cheap meat usually came from diseased animals—beef with pleuropneumonia, or bacon, cheapest when pockmarked with the black spots of anthrax, or painted with creosote to make it appear well smoked. Tape-worm was endemic among the working classes due to eating diseased meat. There was virtually no supervision of slaughterhouses, most of which were in private hands, in backyards and sheds in already overcrowded city areas. In 1860, Dr Letheby, Public Analyst for the City of London, confiscated and destroyed half a ton of diseased meat from city slaughterhouses.[9] Dr Letheby was of the opinion that, as most diseased meat seemed to have very little fat, this fat had already been melted down and used to adulterate butter.

4 *Punch*, 4 August, 1855.
5 *The Lancet*, 9 July 1831, p. 449.
6 Cited in Lambert, op. cit., p. 235.
7 Anthony Wohl, *Endangered Lives, Public Health in Victorian Britain* (London, Melbourne, Toronto, 1983), p. 53.
8 Ibid., p. 54.
9 F. B. Smith, *The People's Health 1830–1910* (Hampshire, England, 1993), p. 206.

Many of the poor sought solace in drink, but it was unlikely to improve their health; brewers added *cocculus indicus*, a narcotic that contained *pycrotoxin*, and strychnine, which in small doses was a hallucinogen, to strengthen beer already diluted with water. It has been argued that this practice may have been responsible for much of the degradation and brutality of lower-class Victorian life.[10] Moreover, it was common practice among the poor to give infants alcohol and opiates to pacify them; Rev. J. Clay, 'on the basis of an enquiry among the chemists and druggists of Preston [reported] that more than 1,600 families used Godfrey's Cordial, a popular compound containing opium, and that on average each family consumed about half an ounce per week'.[11]

While the adulteration of items like ice cream, confectionery and milk could affect all social classes, those on the higher rungs of the social ladder could usually compensate with better nourishment from a plentiful and varied diet, purchased from reputable sources. The poor, however, with their limited diet of milk, bread, cheap cuts of meat and beer, were more vulnerable, and the children of the poor even more so. Although proprietary baby foods were introduced in 1867, the cost was prohibitive for the poor, and it was usual to feed children with the same diet as adults from about one year old, with the unfortunate results of impurities magnified in small digestive systems. Writing in 1817, John Bunnell Davis, 'who established a Universal Dispensary for Children in London, attributed the high mortality rate among the infants and children who had attended the Dispensary over a period of fifteen years to improper feeding after weaning'.[12]

The first person to raise the alarm about food adulteration in Britain was Frederick Accum, in *A Treatise on Adulterations of Food and Culinary Poisons*, published in 1820. However, efforts to introduce legislation to deal with the problem were unsuccessful until Thomas Wakely, Editor of *The Lancet*, started a campaign against adulteration. He formed the Analytical Sanitary Commission, and invited Arthur Hill Hassall, who had been working on the adulteration of coffee, to be the Commission's analyst.[13] Hassall, who had received his medical education in Dublin in the original School of Medicine in Peter Street, published several papers on the dangers of unsound food in *The Lancet* between 1851

10 Ibid., p. 211.
11 George Rosen, 'Disease, Debility, and Death' in H. J. Dyos and Michael Wolff (eds), *The Victorian City*, Volume 2 (London and New York, 1973), pp 625–67.
12 Ibid.
13 http://www.rsc.org/Education/EiC/issues/2005Mar/Thefightagainstfoodadulteration.asp.

and 1855, and his book, *Food and its Adulterations*, published in 1855, led to an increased public concern about food regulation. Hassall's work was a major factor in the enactment, on 6 August 1860, of An Act for Preventing the Adulteration of Articles of Food and Drink *(23 & 24 Vic. c. 84)*. Under the Act, town councils could appoint one or more persons 'possessing competent medical, chemical, and microscopical Knowledge' as public analysts. However, the Act was not compulsory, and in the ten years up until 1872 only seven public analysts were appointed. Until the amendment of the Adulteration of Food, Drink and Drugs Act of 1872, the analysts could not initiate an investigation into suspect food, but could analyse a sample only if brought to them by a complainant, who paid for the service. At the time of Cameron's appointment as Public Analyst in Dublin in October 1862, only two other public analysts had been appointed, Dr Letheby in London, and Dr Hill in Birmingham.[14]

The Public Analyst for Dublin

When Dublin Corporation appointed a Public Analyst (or City Analyst as he was also known), it was a significant step in the fight to improve public health. The Corporation, however, were not the original instigators of the appointment—the request to appoint a Public Analyst came in the form of a letter from the clerk of the South Dublin Union, at the behest of the Board of Guardians. They requested the Corporation to appoint 'a practical chemist to analyse food and other articles sold in the Borough of Dublin for the protection of the public'.[15] The Town Clerk put an advertisement in the morning papers of 22 September 1862, declaring that

> The Municipal Council of the City of Dublin will, upon MONDAY, the 6th day of OCTOBER NEXT . . . proceed to elect . . . a person possess-ing competent Medical, Chemical, and Microscopical knowledge, to be Public Analyst of all articles of Food and Drink purchased in the City of Dublin [16]

Four applications were received: from John Aldridge MD; Charles Cameron, MD, PhD, MRIA, Professor of Chemistry; Edmund Davy, MB, MRIA, Professor of Chemistry; and John Dowling.

The votes of the Council were: Professor Cameron, 34 votes and Professor Davy, 7 votes. There were no votes for the other two

14 Cameron, *Autobiography* (1920), op. cit., p. 138.
15 Minutes of the Municipal Council of the City of Dublin, Vol. 23, p. 75.
16 Ibid., p. 113.

applicants, and the Lord Mayor declared Cameron duly elected 'under and in pursuance of the provisions of the Act 23 and 24 Vic. c. 84'.[17] On 16 October 1862, Major General Sir Thomas Larcom wrote to the Lord Lieutenant confirming the appointment of Charles A. Cameron as analyst 'of all articles of Food and Drink purchased within the City of Dublin'.[18] Cameron got married on the same day.

However, he had no honeymoon period as Public Analyst, because, while his election may have been almost unanimous, Cameron's initial experience of the post was of division rather than harmony. From contemporary newspaper reports and the municipal council minutes, it seems that his appointment was regarded by the Corporation as something of a sop to public health campaigners; they appointed a Public Analyst, but did not publicly advertise that he had been appointed, nor did they allocate a salary for his work. He was to receive a statutory fee of between 2s 6d and 10s for each analysis that he carried out, bearing the cost of any chemicals and equipment himself—he would presumably receive the perceived status of a public post, and work *pro bono publico*. The result, by the time Cameron first reported to Committee No. 2 in a letter dated 6 May 1863, was that only 23 suspect food items had been brought to him for analysis, for which he had been paid fees of £3, while the cost to him of carrying out the analyses was £20! A letter from Cameron, which was discussed by the Corporation at its meeting on 7 July 1863, pointed out that 'very few persons appear to be aware that the fees .. . are purely nominal', and that 'were the nature of the office of public analyst popularly known' his services would be requested to such an extent 'as to oblige me to limit my labours solely to the detection of food sophistication'.[19]

The meeting of 7 July was not the first time this issue had been aired in public. On 8 May 1863, a newspaper had reported on a meeting of the South Dublin Union at which Cameron had reported on adulterated milk. The paper condemned the adulteration of one of the main sources of nourishment for poor children, stating that it was as 'cruel and destructive in effect as manslaughter', and went on to blame the Corporation for failing to publicise the fact that the services of a Public Analyst were now available for a mere 2s 6d, when previously an analysis had cost £4, thus keeping those most

17 Ibid., p. 114.
18 Ibid., p. 160.
19 Ibid., pp 411–12.

in need of this service 'in cimerian darkness as to his existence'.[20] In
the light of his subsequent dealings with the Corporation, one can
detect Cameron's voice in the newspaper report, which pointed out
the public's right to be aware of the appointment of a Public Analyst,
and calls for 'the present absurd system . . . of no remuneration . . .
by which the officer is expected to incur daily loss out of pocket, *pro
bono publico*', to be ended, because 'the services of a Public Analyst are
worth paying for'.[21] Cameron, who had dabbled in journalism himself
as editor and part proprietor of *The Weekly Agricultural Review and Irish
Country Gentleman's Newspaper*, was throughout his career an astute
user of the press. He was a shrewd man, well aware of his commercial
worth, and while he may have taken on the role of Public Analyst on
the understanding that there was no salary attached, there appears
to be little doubt that, when his outgoings in the role began to exceed
his incomings, he expected some financial return for the energy and
enthusiasm he brought to the position.

The question of whether or not the position of Public Analyst
was to have a salary attached became a serious matter of contention,
not only between Cameron and the Corporation, but also between
members of the Corporation. The controversy appears to have started
with a letter from Cameron dated 6 July 1863 soliciting a fixed salary
of £250 per annum. This letter was read at the quarterly meeting of the
municipal council on 3 August 1863, and referred to Committee No. 2,
which was asked to prepare a preliminary, and then a more thorough
report into the question.[22] The date of this letter, right in the middle of
the controversy that became known as 'the sugar question' (see later
in this chapter) might reasonably be construed as an indication that
Cameron's desire to work *pro bono publico*, without remuneration, had
been strained to breaking point by the public abuse he received during
the incident.

The Committee held two meetings in response to his request, one
on 19 October 1863,[23] which was adjourned until 27 October 1863,
when the matter was finally resolved.[24] The minute books report the
proceedings of these two meetings somewhat circumspectly. They
show that the Committee made much of the fact that Cameron did
not reside in or have a laboratory within the borough—at the time, he

---

20 *The Morning News*, 8 May 1863.
21 Ibid.
22 Minutes of the Municipal Council of the City of Dublin, vol. 23, p. 422.
23 Ibid., vol 24, pp 28–33.
24 Ibid., pp 109–11.

lived in 6 Waterloo Terrace, Upper Leeson Street, which was merely a few hundred yards outside the city boundary (and it seems likely that much of his analysis was done inside the city boundary, using the facilities of the laboratory in the Royal College of Surgeons—a great financial advantage to the Corporation). They also admitted that his existence may not have been publicised sufficiently, and that the public was in all likelihood unaware of the small fee charged for his services. Their solution to this problem was to recommend that the Lord Mayor be allowed to purchase suspect food items, which would then be analysed by Cameron for a fixed fee of 10 shillings. They also pointed out, in an obvious side-swipe at Cameron, that the Corporation was entitled under the 1860 Act to appoint more than one Public Analyst, and that these posts should be offered, without salary, to chemists living within the borough, who would have 'a fixed and easily accessible place of business therein', and added the statement that 'the application of Professor Cameron for salary, be not complied with'.

A large part of Committee No. 2's argument against paying Cameron a salary was that, according to themselves, 'they had been in communication with several cities in England, and the only city there paying its public analyst was Birmingham'.[25] This was a somewhat disingenuous, not to say misleading, observation, since at the time of Cameron's appointment, only two other cities had appointed a public analyst, London and Birmingham, so 'several cities' was an exaggerated claim.

At the next meeting on the subject, which took place on 27 October 1863, the Council finally agreed, after much discussion, to pay Cameron in the same manner as Dr Hill of Birmingham, i.e. a salary of £100 per year; as well as this the Lord Mayor, or people appointed by him, would pay him ten shillings for each analysis of suspect food, with all fees from other parties availing of the service to go to the borough fund. The proposal was seconded by Mr Redmond who said that 'if such an officer never made an analysis, his office would confer more benefit on the citizens as a deterient [sic] than would be equal to fifty times the sum paid to him'.[26] It was opposed by Mr Devitt, who said that Cameron would not be satisfied with a salary of £100 per year;[27] as far as salary was concerned, Mr Devitt would appear to have been proved only partly right; Cameron's request for a fixed salary of £250

25 Ibid.
26 Ibid., pp 109–11.
27 Ibid.

appears to have been a bargaining ploy, and he accepted the offered £100. His salary did increase over the years, in increments of £50, but it did not reach the figure of £250 until 1872.

The newspapers of the day reported the proceedings in a less circumspect and more colourful way, giving a verbatim account of the exchanges between councillors on the matter, revealing clearly the divisions that existed between various factions and vested interests within the Corporation. Mr Devitt expressed doubts as to Charles Cameron's philanthropy as Public Analyst, and declared 'if he did not now ape the office which he had worked so hard and canvassed so much to get, let him throw it up'.[28] This view would no doubt have been applauded by Mr Magrath, who claimed that 'sending policemen into every trader's house was only suitable for such a country as Russia' and believed that 'there was no freer from fraud than those dealing in every description of public food'.[29] The Lord Mayor responded to this by inviting Mr Magrath to come to his office 'any day in the week where he would see that adulterated food was sold to a large extent in Dublin'.[30] Mr Magrath had a further exchange with Mr Dillon, claiming that there were no fraudulent traders in Dublin, a claim that provoked laughter in the chamber, and a reply from Mr Dillon to the effect that 'laws were made on the supposition that men sometimes were found to act fraudulently, and it could not be said that Dublin was altogether an exception to this rule'.[31]

On 31 October 1863, *The Nation* newspaper joined the fray, with some trenchant comments on the situation. It pointed out that, before the appointment of a Public Analyst, 'only the very glaring cases of offence [of adulterated food] were brought to justice . . . [and that] the active operations of a public analyst . . . would soon rectify such a state of things'.[32] The newspaper went on to claim that 'scarcely had the act become law, however, when it became manifest that the groundless and exaggerated fears of the provision-dealing class, a large, respectable, and a highly-influential class in every borough, would prevail to make the act a dead letter.'[33]

It singled out Mr Reynolds, 'that immaculate patriot', and pointed

28 This report is in an un-referenced newspaper cutting in the Cameron archives in the RCSI library. It appears to be possibly from *Saunder's News-Letter*, based on a letter addressed to the editor of that newspaper a few days later, also in the archives.

29 Ibid.

30 Ibid.

31 Ibid.

32 *The Nation*, 31 October 1863.

33 Ibid.

out that, of the 15 councillors who voted against a resolution that
the Lord Mayor be allowed to purchase suspect food for analysis,
'twelve were vendors of articles amenable to analysis'.[34] In the 1860s,
Dublin Corporation had a sizeable contingent of small traders among
its members, and representatives of poorer wards were even more
likely to fall into this category. It is likely therefore that these members
would have been less than enthusiastic about the imposition of what
amounted to a consumer watchdog in the person of Charles Cameron.
The Nation went on to report that Mr Redmond 'left the opponents of
the resolution not a shred of argument to stand on . . . [demolishing]
the idea that the protection of the poor from unwholesome food was
not worth the salary paid for carrying a "sword" or a "mace" at city
pageants.'[35]

The latter was a direct hit at the priorities of some members of
the Corporation and a direct comparison between the salary of £100
eventually offered to Charles Cameron as Public Analyst, and the
salary of £125 paid, apparently without controversy, to the Corporation
Mace Bearer.

It is true that the question of a salary was not mentioned in the
advertisement for the post, and Cameron may or may not have
discussed the question with his supporters in Dublin Corporation
when canvassing for the post—there is no way of knowing. He freely
admits in his autobiography that it was through the influence of Sir
John Gray, the driving force behind the Vartry water scheme, that he
was elected Public Analyst.[36] Cameron was almost certainly a shrewd
businessman, and had a mercenary streak; he made no secret of the
latter in his autobiography.[37]

Cameron was obviously a man of enormous energy and ambition,
so it is likely, from what we know of his character through his diaries
and through his actions, that there may have been a mixture of motives
for his desire for the post of Public Analyst. The prestige of what would
have seemed to be a high profile post would have appealed to his need
for a public profile—in which case he was no doubt disappointed that
the post was not as public as he had expected. However, an examination
of his overall career shows strong evidence that Cameron cared deeply
for the poor of Dublin and would genuinely have felt it an injustice that
they were denied a service that they were by law entitled to, simply

34 Ibid.
35 Ibid.
36 Cameron, *Autobiography* (1920), op. cit., p. 25.
37 Ibid., p. 19.

because the Corporation did not choose to publicise the service. It is also likely that he would have viewed the post as a stepping stone to other things—he stood in for Edward Mapother when he was absent, and would have been shrewd enough to see an eventual opening for himself as Medical Officer of Health; he was, after all, newly married, and would have been anxious to establish himself. He was widely respected in many areas of expertise, and was well aware of his own value; even before his appointment as Public Analyst, he was a more public figure than, for example, Edward Mapother, so would not have been overawed by the parochial infighting of Dublin Corporation. He would also have been aware that he was better suited than most to be Public Analyst; of those already appointed, and who would later be appointed, Cameron was unique in that he was a trained chemist who had later qualified as a medical doctor—most public analysts were medical doctors who learned a smattering of chemistry. Cameron was supremely qualified, therefore, both to analyse food and drink, and to prove his case in court when required to do so.

The most important fact is that Cameron gave Dublin Corporation very good value for the salary they paid him as Public Analyst. His surviving diaries exist only from 1880, so there is no record there of his early years in the post. From the commencement of his diaries, however, he constantly mentioned his work in that position. Each day's entry, almost without exception, starts with the phrase 'Went to PHO [Public Health Office] and Laboratory', and show that, regardless of any personal problems, he carried out his work as Public Analyst and as Medical Officer of Health diligently.

'The sugar question'

Shortly after his appointment as Public Analyst, Cameron was forced to defend his reputation as a chemist in a bitter feud about sugar mites, which became known as 'the sugar question', or, as one correspondent who went by the *nom de plume* 'William Scribble' termed it, 'the mitey sugar question'.[38] During the months of June and July 1863, the Dublin newspapers carried a detailed account of claim and counter-claim from prominent doctors and chemists about the existence or non-existence of *acari*, or sugar mites, in the sugar supply of the inmates of the South Dublin Union. The dispute arose after Cameron presented a report to the Board of Guardians of this establishment to the effect that he had found sugar mites in a sample of sugar delivered to his house

---

38 *The Irish Times*, 14 July 1863.

for analysis by a messenger from the workhouse. The *Dublin Medical Press* commented on Cameron's findings in what he termed an *ex parte* manner, on foot of which he issued legal proceedings against them, a fact he addressed 'To the Editor of *The News*' on 26 June 1863, after this paper reprinted the article.[39]

The *Dublin Medical Press* returned to the fray with an article on 8 July, in which it claimed that a substitution had been made in sugar samples and called for a full investigation into the matter.[40] At a meeting of the South Dublin Union held on 2 July, a report from Cameron dated 24 June was read which gave the final results of two experiments he had carried out on two sugar samples from the contractor.[41] In his report, Cameron said that 'having reported accurately on each occasion, it is, perhaps, unnecessary that I should attempt to reconcile the discrepancies'. Cameron went on to say that his findings in the first sample analysed had been confirmed by Dr Minchin of the Ledwich School of Medicine, 'a very experienced microscopist', who had pronounced the results 'equally startling' to Cameron's first report. At Cameron's request, Dr Minchin sent a portion of this sample to Dr Hassall of London, 'the most eminent authority on the subject'.[42] Dr Hassall detected 'a great number of *acari*, the majority living, but some dead' in the sugar, and said in his report that 'it is, therefore, certainly no exaggeration of language, or of the fact, to say of this sugar that it "swarms" or is "alive" with *acari*".[43] Cameron, having asked yet another chemist to analyse sugar samples, and having himself 'almost incessantly' examined sugar 'for the last fortnight', concluded that the sugar samples analysed were 'not . . . of one kind of sugar, but of a mixture of different classes'.[44]

On the following day, *The Irish Times* published a letter from Robert Galloway, Professor of Practical Chemistry, to the effect that, having found that the public appeared to believe Cameron's findings, and to believe that he, Professor Galloway, Mr Tichborne, Mr O'Leary, Mr Draper, and Dr Frazer are 'totally wrong on the sugar question',[45] Professor Galloway and his colleagues were 'ready to meet Dr.

---

39 Letter to the Editor of *The News*, dated 26 June, 1863 this appears to be a section of a newspaper, from a cutting in the Cameron archives.

40 *Dublin Medical Press*, 8 July 1863.

41 Letters read to Board of Guardians of South Dublin Union, from Charles Cameron, dated 24 June, 1863.

42 Ibid.

43 Ibid. (letter included from Arthur Hill Hassall).

44 Ibid. (letter from Charles Cameron)

45 *The Irish Times*, 9 July 1863.

Cameron and the Guardians in a court of law' on the matter. [46] The matter appears to have finally come to an end with two letters to *The Irish Times* dated 10 July 1863, in response to Professor Galloway, from Glascott R. Symes, surgeon to Dr Steevens' Hospital, and John Aldridge MD (Professor of Chemistry, who had trained the young Cameron, and had been a rival applicant for the post of Public Analyst), who confirmed that they had voluntarily examined the sugar samples in question and verified Cameron's findings. 'William Scribble' had the last word on 14 July, when he said that the final decision should be left to one of the porters at a sugar suppliers, who 'would be able to tell at a glance, without the aid of a microscopist, to say whether the sugar in question was mixed or not'.[47] The 'sugar question' gives a good insight into the petty jealousies, and possibly even the enmities that existed in the Dublin medical world at the time. It indicates that Cameron experienced some hostility from his medical and scientific peers, who possibly had personal axes to grind—perhaps as a result of the appointment to a prominent public office of a relatively young upstart, albeit one who had already achieved a considerable reputation as a chemist. The altercation also proved Cameron's willingness to do battle when his professional expertise was called into question, and shows the thoroughness with which he would defend himself and his work.

Cameron sets to work

The Adulteration of Food Act of 1860, under which Cameron was appointed Public Analyst, was generally considered to be unworkable, due to the difficulties of implementing its provisions. Cameron, however, made the Act work; in fact he is acknowledged to have been the only public analyst who did so.[48] His efficiency and determination were immediately obvious when he tackled the powerful cattle traders who, before his appointment, had been used to an unhindered existence selling diseased meat for food. Shortly after his appointment, Cameron became aware that there was little inspection of animals for human consumption. He made enquiries at the knackers' yards and discovered 'that no diseased oxen, sheep or pigs were ever sent

---

46 Ibid.
47 *The Irish Times*, 14 July 1863.
48 Wohl (1983), op. cit., p. 54; F. H. A. Aalen and Kevin Whelan (ed.) (1992), 'Health and Housing in Dublin c.1850 to 1921' in *Dublin: from prehistory to present*, (Dublin, Geography Publications), p. 291; Prunty (1998) op. cit., p. 70.

to them'.[49] He immediately requested the services of four constables as food inspectors and they quickly unearthed a thriving industry in diseased meat and fish. Figures 5.1 and 5.2 show examples of the results of their work.

Figure 5.1 *Quantity of food (in lbs) condemned 1870–1875*

1870	392,057
1871	413,151
1872	332,961
1873	224,552
1874	258,682
1875	380,679
Total	2,002,082

Source RPDCD, 1876, vol. 1 p. 235

Figure 5.2 *Total quantities (in lbs)of each kind of food condemned as unsound during 1876*

Beef	204,173
Sheep	2,788
Pork	17,042
Veal	1,690
Goats	336
Bacon	1,764
Black puddings	7
Fish	392
Butter	65
Vegetables	672
Fruit	182

Source RPDCD, 1877, vol. 1, page 351.

Under the terms of the 1860 Act, traders could not be compelled to sell food to inspectors, whom they quickly came to recognise. Cameron reported that his inspectors had to use their ingenuity to obtain samples for analysis, working round the clock, seven days a week, in an effort to suppress the traffic in diseased meat. Cameron noted, for example, of one of the inspectors, a Mr Webb, that 'on very many occasions I have known [Mr Webb] to be on duty from 6 o'clock a.m. until midnight. He calls upon me at all hours of the day and night,

---

49 Cameron (1914), op. cit., p. 29.

and there is hardly a Sunday in the year on which his services are not called into requisition'[50]

Cameron's annual report for 1870, for example, showed that he had acted as Medical Officer of Health during Mapother's absence in America; attended court on 106 occasions to give evidence in cases of adulterated food; attended 52 meetings of the Public Health Committee; condemned 392,057 lbs of food, including 609 carcases; achieved 46 convictions for adulterated food, including 4 imprisonments.

In July 1870, the monthly report of the Medical Officer of Health, Edward Mapother, claimed that the mortality from zymotic diseases was low, 'probably lessened by the precautions taken to prevent the sale of stale fish and unsound meat in the city'. In July alone, there were seized and confiscated 38,400 lbs of beef, 140 lbs of veal, 140 lbs of mutton, 5,964 lbs of bacon, and 672 lbs of fish.[51]

Speaking of the difficulties caused by being unable to compel traders to sell suspect food, Cameron claimed of another of his staff, George Edwards, that 'if he had the power of compulsorily purchasing food or drink, his services would be still more valuable; as it is, he has to adopt expedients and to exercise his ingenuity in order to obtain specimens of adulterated food.'[52]

This problem was somewhat alleviated by an Act of Parliament in 1872 (35 & 36 Vic. c. 74) which amended the 1860 Act, enabling local authorities to employ persons to purchase food with the object of prosecuting the vendors if the food were found to be adulterated. However, as Cameron pointed out in his annual report for the year 1875,[53] the Sale of Food and Drugs Act, 1875 (38 & 39 Vic. c. 63), repealed all previous Acts and was defective in several respects; whereas, under previous legislation, an inspector could 'procure' items for analysis from an institution or a street vendor, he was now obliged 'at the time of purchase notify to the vendor that he intends to have the article analysed, and he must offer to divide the article into three parts, and to give one of them, sealed up, to the vendor . . . therefore, if a private person finds that a spurious article has been palmed off upon him he is not in a position to prosecute the vendor.'[54]

Cameron recounted how, since the introduction of the new Act 'several prosecutions . . . have failed upon apparently trivial technical

---

50 RPDCD, Charles A. Cameron, Tenth Annual Report for the year 1871, no. 20 (1872).
51 RPDCD, Monthly Report of the Medical Officer of Health for July, 1870, no. 52 (1870).
52 RPDCD, Charles A. Cameron, Tenth Annual Report for the year 1871, no. 20 (1872).
53 RPDCD, Charles A. Cameron, Fourteenth Annual Report on Food, etc., vol. 1, no. 31, (1876), p. 235.
54 Ibid.

points'. With the determination that was his trademark, he immediately reverted to using the provisions of a much older Act, the Dublin Improvement Bill of 1849, recommending that 'this simple-worded section of our Local Act should be taken advantage of' and adding a determined footnote to the effect that 'a prosecution has, since this Report was read, been successfully sustained under this Act, and it will in future be frequently taken advantage of'.[55]

As well as sniping from his professional peers and faulty legislation, Cameron had to face the opposition of vested interests, such as dairy-men and cattle traders, who were angered by his determination to stamp out unhygienic practices. Cattle traders and back-street slaughter-houses posed a constant threat to public health in Dublin throughout the 19th century as a proliferation of unregulated and unhygienic slaughter-houses existed in close proximity to densely populated areas. Whitelaw gave a graphic and memorable account of how, in the course of his survey in Joseph's Lane, 'I was interrupted in my progress, by an inundation of putrid blood, alive with maggots, which had, from an adjacent slaughter-yard, burst the back-door, and filled the hall to the depth of several inches.'[56]

The inhabitants of the tenement house being surveyed, obviously inured to such occurances, simply waded through the mess. Whitelaw also told how one of his surveyors, who remonstrated with a butcher in Ormond market, had had 'flung at him a quantity of blood and offals'.[57]

As Public Analyst, Charles Cameron instigated a long and difficult campaign against the vested interest groups responsible for diseased meat. He was vilified by the groups concerned, and often unaided and hampered by those in authority; it was a campaign that he would wage throughout his long career. In 1871, for example, a deputation from the Public Health Committee, which included Cameron, called on the Lord Lieutenant, in an effort to have the law dealing with diseased meat strengthened. The deputation argued that any diseased meat should immediately be buried, rather than permission being given to salt it down for pig feed, claiming that 'under the pretence of salting down meat to be used as food for pigs, an enormous quantity of diseased food might be distributed amongst the people'.[58] Cameron cited the case of one such owner who, when brought to court, claimed that he 'might

55 Ibid.
56 Whitelaw,(1805) op. cit., p. 53.
57 Ibid., p. 5.
58 *The Irish Times*, 10 February 1871.

possibly eat some [of this meat] himself', his case was dismissed, and he was awarded costs.[59] Cameron revealed that 'we seized 400,000 lbs weight of diseased meat last year'.[60] The Lord Lieutenant's reply was that he 'would be very glad to give what assistance he could' but that 'it would be difficult to alter [one act] in order to strengthen another act',[61] adding the comment that Cameron's claim that 400,000 lbs weight of meat was seized in one year 'would lead to the impression that there was a great deal of disease existing at present amongst cattle, and which persons were disposed to conceal.'[62]

The fight continued over the years. In 1879, Cameron and his colleague Dr Edward Mapother produced a report on the prevention of disease in Dublin in which they claimed that the establishment of two official abattoirs, one on the north side of the city, and one on the south side, in which 'the detection of diseased meat would ... become much more easy than it is at present', would be 'one of the most important sanitary improvements that could be effected in Dublin'.[63] As the law stood at the time, the Corporation were unable to revoke any slaughter-house licences held since before the municipal restructuring of 1849; they could buy out the owners, but as the bargaining prices were usually inflated, the impecunious Corporation was virtually powerless to do this. When it came to detecting and prosecuting for diseased meat, the powerful Cattle Traders Association was highly organised, ceaselessly trying to find loopholes in the law, and Cameron and his staff had to exercise constant vigilance.

During one period when the food inspectors were diverted to deal with an outbreak of foot and mouth disease, there was an immediate cessation of diseased meat appearing in the knackers' yards, only reappearing when the inspectors came back on duty. On one occasion the cattle traders were aided and abetted by the Guardians of the North Dublin Union, who co-operated with the Association in calling in medical experts to question Cameron's confiscation of diseased meat. The medical experts supported Cameron, who had great satisfaction in reporting that their services were not called on again by the cattle traders, but pointed out that 'the encouragement and support of the Guardians ... will in future make it difficult to put a stop to the

59 Ibid.
60 Ibid.
61 Ibid.
62 Ibid.
63 RPDCD, Charles A. Cameron and Edward Mapother, *Report on the Means for the Prevention of Disease*, vol. 1, no. 33, (1879), pp 341–53.

traffic in unsound food'.[64] The same Guardians of the North Dublin Union objected strongly to the erection of a public abattoir in their area, claiming that it would affect property values, and 'cause and be the resort of a class of persons notorious for unruly and improper conduct',[65] a strange claim given their previous support for those who sold diseased meat. A public abattoir was eventually built on the north side of Dublin in 1882, and was used by some, but not all, cattle dealers. Despite unending work and campaigning by Cameron and his staff, private slaughter-houses remained in the centre of Dublin for many years after the abattoir was built, but Cameron never gave up his fight against unhygienic slaughter-houses; in his report on the state of public health and the sanitary work performed in Dublin in 1900, he was still urging that 'all the most objectionable [slaughter-houses] should be abolished, even if the cost were considerable',[66] while on the other side of the equation, as late as 1906, the Public Health Committee of the Corporation supported the granting of a licence for a disused slaughter-house in Carman's Hall, right in the middle of Dublin's Liberties, one of the most densely populated and unsanitary areas of the city.[67]

In his autobiography, Cameron reported how the Veterinary Department in Dublin Corporation introduced stringent measures in an effort to stamp out pleuro-pneumonia in cattle, as 'in no part of Ireland was pleuro-pneumonia so prevalent as among the dairy cows of Dublin'.[68] A deputation of dairy-men called on the Public Health Committee to relax the new measures, which they said were too severe. Cameron reported that 'at my earnest solicitation the Committee took no action in the matter' and that the disease was eventually stamped out.[69] He had been unrelenting in his efforts to stamp out the sale of pleuro-pneumonic beef for human consumption throughout his career, always pro-active in his approach. He reported that 'at my request a circular letter was addressed to the medical men and veterinarians of Dublin, and to the Medical Officers of Health of the larger towns in the United Kingdom, requesting their opinions as

---

64 RPDCD, Charles A. Cameron, Report upon the use as food of the flesh of animals affected with contagious pleuro-pneumonia, vol. 3, (1877), p. 496.
65 Minutes of the North Dublin Union, Resolution, 29 November 1879, cited Prunty,(1998) op. cit., p. 93.
66 RPDCD, Charles A. Cameron, Report upon the state of Public Health, etc., vol. 3, no. 212, (1901), p. 398.
67 RPDCD, vol. 2, No. 145, (1906), pp 503–4.
68 Cameron, *Autobiography* (1920), op. cit., p. 31.
69 Ibid.

to the use of pleuro-pneumonic beef as food for man. 290 replied that under no circumstances should it be used.[70]

The elimination of this disease was a significant health measure as, since the introduction of pleuro-pneumonia into the country, 'the prevalence of carbuncular maladies, such as boils and anthrax, had greatly increased'.[71] Ever vigilant for factors that caused risks to public health, Cameron, in 1881, having made 'a chemical and bacteriological examination of oysters taken from Clontarf', concluded that the oyster beds were a source of enteric fever. At his request, the licences were withdrawn by the Port and Docks Board. He reported in 1920 that 'this was the first statement that enteric fever might be contracted from polluted oysters, but there is now an extensive literature on the subject'.[72]

Unhygienic dairy yards were as numerous as unhygienic abattoirs: in 1886, there were more than 1,100 in Dublin.[73] Like their human counterparts in tenements, cattle were penned in deplorable conditions, usually in proximity to an ever-growing and seldom removed manure heap, one such adjacent to Mercer's Hospital consisted of 30 loads of manure.[74] These yards were a cause of several dangers to public health — from diseased meat, usually as a result of pleuro-pneumonia, and from impure milk, often carrying tuberculosis or typhoid. Used to an unhindered existence before the arrival of Cameron as Public Analyst, the milk and butter traders were now forced to answer in court against charges of selling adulterated and unhygienic produce. Cameron personally attended every court hearing to prove his charges, as the lenient court system would not accept his certificate, and traders used every loophole to escape conviction. Even when convicted, they organised clubs to pay the fines of convicted members. Cameron's diaries constantly recorded his attendance at court, for many hours at a time — his days often ran to a pattern of visiting tenements, abattoirs, dairy yards, and attending court. It was not until 1893 that the Public Health Committee appointed his son Douglas, then working as his private assistant, as an additional Public Analyst, 'so that he may have a status in court and be able to give evidence there. It is evident that the City Analyst is unable to do personally so large an amount of work

70 RPDCD, Cameron, (1877) op. cit,, p. 498.
71 *Police Intelligence*, 29 April 1871.
72 Cameron, *Autobiography* (1920), op. cit., p. 139.
73 *British Medical Journal*, 14 January 1871.
74 RPDCD, Letter of 10 July 1875 from John Morgan, surgeon to Mercer's Hospital in Reports, correspondence and resolution in relation to dairy yards, etc., no. 36, (1875).

as he has lately been called upon to perform.'[75]

The Public Health Committee had already agreed to allow Cameron an extra £10 per month 'for laboratory expenses and additional chemical assistance, in view of the greatly increased work lately imposed upon him'.[76] However, the salary of £5 for Douglas's new position had to be paid out of this £10, so no extra expense accrued to the Corporation for the provision of an assistant. The extra money had been requested by Cameron in view of the fact that 'analyses of butter, margarine, and mixtures of those articles were a tedious, delicate, and costly operation; that they involved considerable expenditure of money in chemical re-agents and apparatus.'[77]

It was pointed out by the Committee that

the chemical apparatus in the City laboratory, estimated to have cost over £1,000, has been purchased by the City Analyst, and many fixtures in it were presented by him. With the exception of the grant [of £10 per month] given recently to him, he has paid the cost of apparatus and re-agents, and the salaries of the assistants. Your Committee saw one bill for £88 7s. 10d. for mere chemicals used in analysis during six months, and were informed that this amount was but a small proportion of the laboratory expenses, exclusive of the salaries of assistants, seven in number.[78]

It is also worth noting that for twenty years the Corporation, by virtue of employing Cameron, had the advantage of using the laboratory of the Royal College of Surgeons free of charge, except for Cameron's salary as Public Analyst, and only after that length of time bowed to pressure from him to provide the city with a dedicated laboratory for his work. Cameron's skill as a chemist was a vital factor in his battle against contaminated food and drink. In 1878 67 cases of typhoid fever occurred in Fitzwilliam Square and the surrounding areas. Cameron traced the cause of the outbreak to a dairy where two cases of the disease had occurred and, using the theory of probability, proved that infected milk was the cause of the outbreak.[79] *The Lancet* stated that this would be a 'classic' case.[80]

Cameron's fight against the rogue dairy trade was recognised by the *British Medical Journal* in 1871, which proclaimed that

75 RPDCD, Report of the Public Health Committee,. vol. 1, no. 48, (1893), pp 381–7.
76 Ibid.
77 Ibid.
78 Ibid.
79 Charles A. Cameron, *The Dublin Journal of Medical Science*, 1 July 1879, Vol. LXVIII, No. 91, Third Series, pp 1–25.
80 Cameron (1914), op. cit., p. 39.

the dairymen of Dublin are in a sad predicament. They can neither sell
their diseased meat for purpose of human food . . . [as] is now largely
practiced by their happier and less oppressed brethren in London, nor
can they, like them, peaceably mix 30 or 40 per cent of water with their
milk . . . It is hopeless to expect that equally energetic means will be tak-
en to extinguish the abominable practice of adulterating milk and dress-
ing diseased cows in London.[81]

Although there were other factors involved in improving conditions
in the dairy trade, Cameron's crusade against unhygienic practices
must be credited with playing some part in the decline in the number
of dairy yards in Dublin, which decreased from 1,100 in 1886 to only
226 in 1914.[82]

Cameron falls foul of the Waterworks Committee

As well as vested private interests, Cameron also faced opposition
from those charged with public services; the board of the North Dublin
Union has already been shown to have sided with cattle traders, but
even earlier in his career, Cameron spoke out in the interests of Dublin
citizens. In 1866, *The Irish Times* reported that after a series of tests
on the Vartry water, built to supply the city with pure water, Charles
Cameron had recommended the use of pipes manufactured from a
special alloy upon which 'the Vartry water could exercise no corrosive
influence'. The newspaper claimed that Cameron had been censured by
the Waterworks Committee for revealing these facts when, according
to *The Irish Times*, the Committee would have thought it 'better far that
the people of Dublin should be poisoned . . . and that our children
should drink a concoction of lead precipitate than that the infallibility
of the Waterworks Committee should be questioned.'[83] The paper
believed that 'The citizens have actually been saved from imbibing
poison by the skill, study, patient experiments, and courage of Doctor
Cameron.'[84]

This hyperbole may have been partly induced by *The Irish Times'*
belief that the ratepayers had been 'mulcted . . . heavily in the name of

---

81 *British Medical Journal*, 14 January 1871.
82 Cameron (1914), op. cit., p. 44, in which he also notes that in 1886 when parts of the Contagious
    Diseases (Ireland) Act, 1886 and of the Contagious Diseases (Animals) Act, 1878 came under
    his remit, he 'prepared an elaborate set of regulations or by-laws relating to the cleansing of
    Dairies, Milkshops, Milk Vessels, Cowsheds, &c'.
83 *The Irish Times*, 24 January 1866.
84 Ibid.

the Vartry Waterworks';[85] however, since, as we have seen, Cameron admitted that he was appointed Public Analyst largely on the recommendation of Sir John Gray,[86] who was the prime mover behind the Vartry Waterworks, his revelation about any adverse effects did require some courage, and reveals an independence of mind outside that of his Corporation allies in carrying out his perception of his duties.

Cameron's achievements as Public Analyst

Cameron's efforts as Public Analyst for Dublin, often criticised by those nearer home, were gradually recognised by those further afield. The *London Chemical News* compared his achievements favourably with those of Dr Letheby, Public Analyst for London, and drew attention to 'the enormous amount and great diversity of labour performed by Dr. Cameron . . . in his capacity as analyst to the City of Dublin', and said that 'it appears that at Dublin they thoroughly understand, value, and carry very efficiently into effect what is very properly termed *administration de la salubrité et sureté publique* . . . the excellent example given by Dublin deserves to be imitated elsewhere; for the want of a good and efficient system exists in many English towns, and not the least so in this metropolis.'[87]

In his autobiography,[88] Cameron estimated that around eight million lbs of contaminated food had been detected, analysed and condemned during his time as public analyst. He commented on the fact that the 1860 Act was defective, and 'that it has often been stated that in Dublin this Act only was operative', a point also made by several modern commentators.[89] He also revealed that 'the considerable cost of the chemical apparatus, books and reagents used in the City Laboratory is defrayed by me', and that the fines 'several hundred pounds a year' go to the Corporation.[90] Evidence of Cameron's work as Public Analyst in Dublin compared to other towns in Britain and Ireland can be seen from the following table of convictions in 1893.

The job of Public Analyst became a more respected profession with the formation of the Society of Public Analysts in 1874, of which

85 Ibid.
86 Cameron, *Autobiography* (1920), op. cit., p. 25.
87 *London Chemical News* (Cameron archives, no date, probably 1866–7).
88 Cameron, *Autobiography* (1920), op. cit., pp 137–9.
89 Wohl (1983), op. cit., p. 54; Aalen and Whelan (ed.) (1992) op. cit., p. 291; Prunty (1998) op. cit., p. 70.
90 Cameron, *Autobiography* (1920), op. cit., p. 138.

Figure 5.3 *Convictions for breaches of Sale of Food and Drugs and Margarine Acts in 1893*

	Dublin	Other Irish[1]	Scottish[2]	London[3]	Other English[4]
Population (000s)	245	410	1,008	1,774	3,796
Food & Drugs Act					
Convictions	96	31	26	176	316
Fines	£201	£85	£38	£400	£745
Margarine Act					
Convictions	44	7	26	10	97
Fines	£200	£41	£38	£18	£125
Convictions per 100,000	57	9	10	16	11

1. Belfast, Cork, Cork, Limerick, Londonderry
2. Glasgow, Edinburgh, Dundee
3. Islington, St Pancras, Hackney, Southwark, Kensington, Holburn, Shoreditch, Paddington, Chelsea, Whitechapel, City, Croydon
4. Liverpool, Manchester, Birmingham, Leeds, Sheffield, Bristol, Bradford, Nottingham, Salford, Newcastle, Leicester, Brighton, Birkenhead, Norwich
Source: Appendix B, Report of the Public Health Committee to the Right Honourable the Lord Mayor, Aldermen and Burgesses of Dublin, RPDCD, 1893, vol. 1, p. 387 (summarised)

Cameron later became President in 1893.[91] The problem of food adulteration waned in the face of increased vigilance and improved legislation, but in the early days of the profession, where the legislation was faulty and inadequate, Charles Cameron is recognised as the only Public Analyst who successfully dealt with the dangers posed by unsound food, and Dublin was held up as an example of how it should be done.

Analyst in criminal cases

In becoming Public Analyst for Dublin, Charles Cameron had found his *métier*; when the appointment became mandatory in 1870, he was chosen by 33 counties and boroughs as their official analyst. 'From the number of his appointments he was often humourously referred to as 'The Public Analyst for Ireland'.[92] The man who, as a youth of

91 Dyer, (1932) op. cit., p. 37.
92 Bernard Dyer, 'Obituary of Charles Alexander Cameron', *Jnl. Royal Society of Chemistry*, May, 1921, Vol. XLVI, No. 542.

19, had pondered 'What was the most congenial way of making an income?'[93] had found it in the profession of chemical analyst. For the rest of his long life, it was clear that it was this scientific aspect of his work that gave him the most personal and professional satisfaction. Not only did he use his analytical skills in the fight against adulterated food and drink for the improvement of the quality of life for citizens, but for eleven years, from 1870 to 1881, he also put his skills to use in criminal trials as the government expert 'in cases where bloodstains had to be examined and human viscera analysed for the detection of poison'.[94] The Victorian era seemed to spawn an epidemic of poisoning, although what actually happened was that, while the number of cases of poisoning did not actually increase, several high profile cases raised public awareness, and the press responded with an increased interest and no doubt the hope of increased sales. Poisons such as strychnine and arsenic were readily available, and this availability coincided with the introduction of life insurance—a combination that proved fatally tempting for many. Ireland was no exception to this trend, and Cameron, who 'had considerable reputation as a toxicologist'[95] and who had become a pathologist,[96]acted as government witness during many trials. He used his analytical skills to give evidence that helped to defend or to convict the accused and, on one memorable occasion, gave evidence on both sides.[97] He was called as a witness in the trial of those accused of the murders of Lord Frederick Cavendish, the new Chief Secretary for Ireland, and the head of the Irish civil service, Thomas Henry Burke, in the Phoenix Park in Dublin on 6 May 1882.

Cameron's *Autobiography* and *Reminiscences* recount many stories of criminal cases to which he travelled during the assizes. His accounts of his experiences are largely anecdotal, but they give a good flavour of the cases he was involved in and, while some may well be apocryphal, they were undoubtedly entertaining, and no doubt contributed to his fame as an after-dinner speaker. Unfortunately for our entertainment, Cameron recounts only a few such incidents, and the Chief Secretary's Office registered papers give very limited details of trials attended by him, mainly simply recording that a payment was made to Dr Cameron for analysis.[98] Cameron resigned from his duties as a government

93 Cameron, *Autobiography* (1920) op. cit., p. 19.
94 Ibid., p. 58.
95 Dyer (1932), op. cit., p. 37.
96 No official record of this has been found, and there is no reference to it by Cameron, other than the above duties, but it is claimed by Feeney (1993), op. cit., p. 50.
97 Cameron, *Autobiography* (1920), op. cit., p. 66
98 See, for example, CSORP 7730, 13197, 17743, 17744. These files all relate to 1872, and record

analyst in 1881 when appointed Executive Sanitary Officer for Dublin at a salary of £1,000 per year. He described the post of Government Analyst in criminal cases as a 'lucrative position',[99] but is reticent on the exact remuneration he received. However, a letter from Dublin Castle to James F. Hodges, Esq. MD of Queen's College, Belfast, dated 6 September 1879, gives the following details:

> Sir,
> With reference to your letter of the 3rd instant, I am directed by the Lord Lieutenant to inform you that the fees usually paid by the Irish Government to Analysts are as follows, viz:-
> For analysis in each case £5-5-0
> Attendance to give evidence each day £5-5-0
> Personal allowance for hotel expenses per day £1-1-0
> And actual travelling expenses

The letter is signed J. N. Burke.[100]

Cameron's combined annual salary as Public Analyst and Medical Officer of Health was £450 in 1879[101] — under £9 per week. This was more than a Professor in the Royal University, and less than the Director of the National Gallery. A remuneration, therefore, of £6 6s for one day's work as a government witness, plus a fee for analysis, was certainly lucrative. When Cameron was offered overall control of the Public Health Office in 1881 on the proviso that he gave up some of his other commitments, he provided the Corporation with books detailing the income he would forego under the proposed new arrangement. This income included 'giving evidence on behalf of the government . . . private individuals in local cases, attendance as a professional expert in various parts of the United Kingdom, and private practice as Analyst'.[102] Cameron was allowed under the proposed arrangement to continue his work as analyst for 'provincial public bodies'.[103]

When considering appointing Cameron to his new post in 1881, the Corporation referred to the fact that his analytical work was performed, as it had been for the previous 20 years, in the well-

payments to Cameron only. There are similar examples from 1873, 1876, 1879, and 1881, with no references at all for the years 1870, 1871, 1873, 1875, 1877, 1878, 1880.

99 Cameron, *Autobiography* (1920), op. cit., p. 140.
100 CSORP/1881/43530.
101 Cameron (1914), op. cit., p. 39.
102 RPDCD, Future Arrangements for the Management of the Business of the Executive of the Public Health Department, vol. 3, no. 173, (1881), p. 17.
103 Ibid.

equipped laboratory of the Royal College of Surgeons, and that any change in this arrangement would result, not only in a higher financial outlay for the Corporation, but also in a less efficient service. It would seem that, almost 20 years after it half-heartedly appointed Cameron as Public Analyst, and even more unwillingly paid him a salary for the job, Dublin Corporation was finally forced to recognise his calibre and contribution.

Forty years later when Cameron died in 1921, the Corporation found itself in a dilemma regarding the post of Public Analyst. Cameron had 'defrayed the expenses of the chemicals and re-agents required in connection with analytical work carried out in the City Laboratory, and the apparatus, as distinct from the furniture and fittings there, were his property'. He also 'employed and paid private assistants, some of whom were engaged in Corporation work'.[104] The Public Health Committee revealed that it had not been able to ascertain the exact amount derived by Cameron for his outside work, but they believed it to be in the region of 'at least £2,425 per annum' from government bodies, and a variable, and unknown amount, from private companies and individuals.[105]

At the time of his death, his official salary as Public Analyst to the city of Dublin was £575. The Public Health Committee decided, in the interest of the continued efficiency of the City Laboratory and of long-serving staff, that Mr Fagan, who had been serving as an additional Public Analyst since 1918, would be employed as Public Analyst for six months, with the power to take outside work, and at the end of that period his remuneration as sole Public Analyst would be re-examined.[106] The Committee also decided to continue to employ Cameron's staff temporarily at the same rates of pay, and to make an offer to his executors for his chemicals and apparatus, for which they eventually settled at £329 13s 10d.

---

104 RPDCD, Report of the Public Health Committee as to the Position of Public Analyst, and the Future Conduct of the City Laboratory, vol. 1, no. 77, (1921), pp 561–5.
105 Ibid.
106 In fact, Bernard Fagan continued to serve as Public Analyst from 1921 to 1956.

*The scene of the collapse of tenement houses
in Church Street in September 1913, which
precipitated the Inquiry into the Housing
Conditions of the Working Class, whose* Report
*was damagingly critical of Cameron.
(Royal Society of Antiquaries)*

Chapter 6 The new Medical Officer of Health

Once launched on a public career, Cameron rapidly established himself as a significant force in the public health arena. Not content to rest on his laurels as Public Analyst for Dublin, he continued to consolidate his professional reputation, becoming analyst for other towns and cities throughout Ireland, and continuing his lectures in the smaller medical schools and in the Royal College of Surgeons. He wrote prolifically, at first on agricultural chemistry, but gradually extended his sphere of expertise, and in 1868 he published *Lectures on the Preservation of Health*. The following year he published a 'half-yearly report on public health' in the *Dublin Quarterly Journal of Medical Science*, (later the *Dublin Journal of Medical Science*)—he would continue to publish these regular reports in this journal throughout most of his career.

When he published the first report in 1869, Cameron had no responsibility for public health, other than for adulterated food and drink as Public Analyst, so why he should have taken on this responsibility is a mystery. Dublin had had a Medical Officer of Health, in the person of Edward Mapother, since 1862, and it would have seemed more appropriate for him to publish such reports. The immediate supposition is that this was a type of one-upmanship on Cameron's part, but this theory does not fit what we know of the relationship between Cameron and Mapother. They worked closely together, and remained friends, even after Mapother's retirement, when Cameron continued to visit him in London. The more likely explanation is that Cameron was more vocal than Mapother, and said what he felt needed to be said, regardless of whether it was his territory or not. He often deputised for Mapother, and was obviously a key player in public health in Dublin. While Mapother may have had the official title of Medical Officer of Health for Dublin, and Cameron may have been a willing occasional assistant and deputy, it seems obvious that he did not regard himself as playing permanent second fiddle, and believed he had or would have a significant role to play in improving the health of Dublin citizens.

A new piece of legislation enacted in 1874 gave Cameron the opportunity to formalise his position in Dublin's public health arena. The Public Health Ireland Act of 1874 (*37 & 38 Vic. c. 13*), made the

Local Government Board the overall public health authority for Ireland. Under 'a sealed order . . . dated 21st October, 1874',[1] the board instructed Dublin Corporation to appoint three new officers. Following this order, the Corporation appointed Edward Mapother as Consulting Sanitary Officer, and James Boyle as Executive Sanitary Officer, each at a salary of £300 per annum. Charles Cameron was appointed Medical Officer of Health at the existing salary of £300 which he was paid as Public Analyst[2]—both of his posts were still part-time, and it would appear that he received no extra remuneration for taking on the additional title and responsibilities of Medical Officer of Health.

Under the Public Health Ireland Act of 1878, Mapother was elected Superintendent Medical Officer of Health, but without any increase in salary. Later that year, Mapother wrote to the Corporation, stating that he was agreeable to the Superintendent position being amalgamated with that of Medical Officer and City Analyst; a letter to the same effect was read from Cameron.[3] Mapother retired from the Superintendent position, remaining as Consulting Sanitary Officer on an allowance of £150 per annum, while Cameron took on the amalgamated positions and duties for a total salary of £400 per annum. This was on the proviso that Cameron undertook:

> to devote his whole time and attention to the duties of the office, with permission to discharge his present duties at the College of Surgeons or others of a similar nature, and analyses and similar duties for local bodies and private individuals, but not to engage in other professional duties without the permission of the Committee.[4]

A further report on the issue in 1879 amended this slightly, in that Cameron's salary appears to have been set at £300 for the combined posts of Superintendent and Medical Officer of Health, together with a reduced salary of £200 as City Analyst—a total overall salary of £500.[5] Cameron agreed to all of these terms, although his own account of his salary is that he was only paid a total salary of £450.[6] Mapother agreed to act as his substitute when necessary, remaining as Consulting

1 Cameron, (1914) op. cit. p. 37.
2 Ibid.
3 Letter of 28 November 1878 from E. D. Mapother in 'Special Report: Amalgamation of Offices of the Superintendent Medical Officer and Medical Officer of Health', RPDCD, vol. 3, no. 257, (1878), p. 841.
4 Ibid.
5 Report of the Public Health Committee 'Amalgamation of Offices of Medical Officer of Health and Superintendent Medical Officer', RPCD, vol. 2, no. 88, (1879), pp 91–3.
6 Cameron (1914), op. cit., p. 39

Sanitary Officer until 1890, and receiving a pension of two-thirds of his salary in 1891.[7] When James Boyle died in 1881, Cameron took on some of his duties as well, under the title of Executive Sanitary Officer.[8] This appointment marked a distinct shift in Corporation policy, as Dublin now for the first time had a full-time Medical Officer of Health. The Corporation report of the transfer of complete power to Cameron indicates that it was not a straightforward matter. The process began with the death of James Boyle, leaving a large and varied set of duties which had been carried out by him to be allocated to another person.[9] The Public Health Committee appointed a sub-committee to consider the situation, as a result of which they decided that the most efficient and financially viable way to deal with the situation was to appoint a full-time Medical Officer of Health for Dublin. Cameron was asked what salary he would require to devote his entire time to the post, and 'to abandon all other emoluments.'[10] His reply was that he would require £1,500 per annum, and added the proviso that the Corporation should provide a new laboratory, or allow him to continue his connection with the Royal College of Surgeons, whose facilities he presently used as Public Analyst.[11] The same question was put to Mapother, who said that he 'would not be willing to enter into such an arrangement, being of the opinion that it would not work.'[12] A compromise was reached whereby Cameron was offered 'entire charge and control over the sanitary department' for a salary of £1,000.[13] Under this compromise agreement, Cameron would give up all his outside commitments, except his lectures in the Royal College of Surgeons, and his work as analyst for provincial public bodies.[14] An important advantage of this arrangement from the Corporation's point of view was that Cameron's connection with the Royal College of Surgeons would ensure that they would continue to have the benefit of the superior laboratory facilities available there for use in analytical work for the city, at no expense to the Corporation. The report states that Cameron accepted the post on these conditions; however, throughout his time as Medical Officer of Health, he constantly campaigned for a dedicated municipal

---

7 Ibid.
8 'Future Arrangements for the Management of the Business of the Executive of the Public Health Department', RPCD, vol. 3, no. 173, (1881), p. 16.
9 Ibid.
10 Ibid.
11 Ibid., p. 15.
12 Ibid.
13 Ibid., p. 11.
14 Ibid., pp 16–17.

laboratory, and regarded its eventual establishment as one of the main achievements of his career.[15]

The most important elements of the offer to Cameron, and his acceptance, was that Dublin now had its first full-time overseer of public health, and that Cameron had agreed to accept the post and try to make it work, when his colleague, Mapother, had turned it down in the belief that such a position could not work. There seems little doubt that Cameron was capable of making a good living outside the public service, so the fact that he chose to serve in the public rather than the private sphere would seem to make a definite statement about his interests and ambitions. This fact has not been emphasised in any evaluation of Cameron's career; instead, his career path has been portrayed as almost accidental, from his days with the Dublin Chemical Society, through his appointment as Public Analyst due to his connections with that society, and his shadowing Edward Mapother in the Royal College of Surgeons and as Medical Officer of Health. His decision to accept the full-time post of Superintendent Medical and Executive Sanitary Officer[16] in 1881 can perhaps be viewed as an opportunity to make his own mark on the public health problems in Dublin. From the beginning of his career, it was obvious that Cameron had strong views on what needed to be done to solve the problems of public health, and the fact that he was at last offered full control of the situation may have seemed both an opportunity and a call to duty. From the time he accepted the post of full-time Medical Officer of Health in 1881 until 1918, when he handed over active duties to Dr Russell, Cameron remained at the forefront of public health in Dublin. In trying to evaluate his contribution to Dublin in this post, it is worth taking a look at the career of his predecessor, Edward Mapother and, to a lesser extent, that of the other person whose shoes he filled in 1881, James Boyle.

Edward Dillon Mapother

Edward Dillon Mapother was appointed Medical Officer of Health in June 1864, almost two decades after similar appointments had been made in the equivalent public health black spots of Liverpool, which appointed William Henry Duncan in 1847, and London, which appointed John Simon in 1848. He was also appointed Professor of

---

15 Cameron, *Brief History* (1914), op. cit., p. 142.
16 'Future Arrangements', (1881), p. 16.

Hygiene at the Royal College of Surgeons in Dublin the same year,[17] a post in which Cameron would later succeed him. This fact is important for any evaluation of the careers of Mapother and Cameron. The Chair of Political Medicine (also known as the Professorship of Hygiene) in the College of Surgeons school was the first of its kind in the British Isles, and had been vacant for 18 years before Mapother's appointment.[18] It had been instituted in 1841, partly due to the influence of a ground-breaking speech given to the college by Henry Maunsell, a prominent Dublin doctor, who also had simultaneous careers as a politician and journalist.[19] Maunsell had been the first occupant of the chair, and his views can be gauged from his characterisation of the leading doctors of his day as 'professional traders'. He criticised them for having 'abandoned the higher and more honourable walks of their profession', i.e. preventive medicine, with 'the higher objective of protecting the public health', to become 'the servants of individuals'.[20] The fact that Mapother and Cameron, both eminent in their fields, chose to serve as public servants and promote preventive medicine, rather than follow careers as private doctors is indicative of their commitment to the cause of public health.

O'Doherty claims that Mapother is 'a much neglected figure', and this statement is borne out by the fact that references to him in the literature on public health in 19th-century Dublin are very sparse, while in some major works he is not mentioned at all. This indicates a particular viewpoint, rather than an accurate evaluation of Mapother's contribution. The omission of someone who held a post that could be regarded as a milestone in public health administration in Dublin indicates that the emphasis in the literature to date has been on the political, economic and legislative aspects of public health reform, while the key personalities involved have been relegated to a minor role. A closer examination of those concerned, however, indicates that individual character, personal networks and interconnections, together with common or conflicting beliefs and ideologies, played a significant part in shaping public health reforms.

Although, as Public Analyst, Cameron had already stamped his

---

17 Mary O'Doherty, 'Salus populi— the endeavours of Edward Dillon Mapother (1835–1908)', Jn. Irish Colleges of Physicians and Surgeons, vol. 28, No. 3, July 1999, p. 170.

18 John F. Fleetwood, The History of Medicine in Ireland (Dublin 1983), p. 77; O'Doherty, op. cit., p. 170.

19 Henry Maunsell, Political Medicine; Being the Substance of a Discourse Lately Delivered before the Royal College of Surgeons in Ireland, on Medicine, Considered in its Relations to Government and Legislation (Dublin, 1839).

20 Ibid.

personality on the issue of adulterated food, it was Mapother, on his appointment as Medical Officer of Health for Dublin in June 1864, who became the public face of health reform. He appears to have lost no time in making his views known, stating that there was a 'pressing necessity for immediate legislation' in sanitary matters.[21] In fact, even before his appointment to either of the above posts, he read a paper to the Statistical and Social Inquiry Society of Ireland (SSISI) on 10 February 1864, on 'The Sanitary State of Dublin'.[22] As this was some months before his appointment as Medical Officer of Health, it is tempting to speculate if it was a publicity exercise, or a pre-emptive strike on behalf of public health reform. Mapother's commitment to and concern for the plight of the Dublin poor, evident in this and two subsequent papers to the SSISI, indicates that it was the latter.

In his paper, Mapother said that he was certain that many deaths in Dublin 'are avoidable by improvements which may be very readily attained'. He acknowledged the debt he owed to the statistics produced by Sir William Wilde and to the investigations of Thomas Willis. He displayed a very practical turn of mind, suggesting that a simple and inexpensive solution to the problem of foetid air in tenement rooms would be to install two gratings in the outer wall of each room 'such as are now usual in club houses and public offices'. Obviously realising that this was unlikely to happen in the existing houses, he called for these to be introduced into all new houses.[23] In his 1864 paper to the SSISI, Mapother displayed a comprehensive knowledge of conditions in English cities, quoting statistics and statements from English public health reformers. This type of knowledge was common to all Irish public health campaigners, indicating the close contacts between those of similar interests in the two countries, and Mapother made a strong statement that what was required for Dublin was 'an efficient system of health-inspection, which every city in the United Kingdom of equal size to Dublin now enjoys'.[24]

The following year, 1865, Mapother read two more papers on sanitary matters to the SSISI, in February and December, and one in May of 1866 to the RDS on working-class housing.[25] In a paper read to the SSISI on 19 December 1865, he acknowledged the power of hard facts when he stated that 'any general satement [sic] as to the unhealthiness

21 Prunty, (1998) op. cit., p. 70.
22 *Jn. SSISI*, Vol. iv, Part xxvi, Jan. 1864–Part xxxiv, Jan. 1868, pp 62–76.
23 Ibid., p. 65.
24 Ibid., p. 72.
25 *Daily Express*, 29 May 1866, cited Daly, (1984) op. cit., p. 72.

of towns would be likely to meet merely with an apathetic assent'[26] and was careful to enumerate in detail the individual sanitary state of each town.

Commenting on the difference in the rate of mortality between urban and rural populations, Mapother stated: 'There is nothing in a well-regulated town to kill people faster than in the country'.[27] His statement that Dublin Corporation now had the power to deal comprehensively with unsanitary housing is interesting, [28] and can be contrasted with evidence by James Boyle, Executive Sanitary Officer, to an inquiry into conditions in Dublin in 1880, in which it is evident that dealing with such housing is not quite so straightforward. Boyle's statement to the inquiry revealed that, despite constant occurrences of fever in a house in Ardee Street, the fact that there was no evidence of structural defects in the house, which could cause disease, prevented Mapother from issuing a certificate for its closure.[29] It would appear that Mapother's optimism was misplaced, and that he was to be disillusioned by later experience. The difficulties of closing unsanitary dwellings would remain a bugbear of his successor, Cameron.

In an earlier paper in February 1865, Mapother had outlined 'The differences between the Statutes bearing on Public Health for England and Ireland'. He professed himself 'unable to account for the remarkable exclusion of Ireland from many salutary statutes which should be universal in all parts of a United Kingdom'.[30] It would appear that his appeal had an effect: in his 'Address' at the opening of the 30th session of the SSISI, Jonathan Pim claimed that Mapother's papers had been influential in the introduction of the 1866 Sanitary Act, 'in which Ireland was united with England in sanitary legislation',[31] a fact further confirmed by Norwood's paper to the SSISI in February 1873, in which he claimed that the Corporation appealed for legislation to the Irish executive in 1865, 'having been directed to the matter by a report of Edward D. Mapother . . . their officer of health'.[32]

In 1864 Edward Mapother had stated that he believed that, although the Corporation had been given the power under the Nuisances'

26   *Jn. SSISI*, vol. iv, Part xxvi (1865) p. 251.
27   Ibid., p. 263.
28   Ibid., p. 250.
29   *Report of the Royal Commissioners appointed to inquire into the Sewerage and Drainage of the City of Dublin, and other matters connected therewith, together with Minutes of Evidence, Appendix, Index,* etc., evidence of Mr. Boyle, PP 1880, xxx, Cd. 2605, Par. 1518.
30   *Jn. SSISI*, Vol. iv (1864–8) p. 210.
31   Ibid. Vol. vii, Part L. (1876) p. 1.
32   Ibid., Vol. vi, Part xliii (1873) p. 230.

Removal and Diseases' Preventions Act to appoint a Medical Officer
of Health,

> the duties could not be efficiently performed, unless there were funds
> available to secure the entire services of a physician of the highest scien-
> tific attainments, who should be recompensed by an adequate salary for
> the sacrifice of all other engagements.[33]

Although Mapother was appointed as Medical Officer of Health
some months later, this condition was not met, and he continued
to lecture at the RCSI as well as fulfil his duties as Medical Officer.
Mapother was a founding member in 1867 of the Industrial Tenements
Co., which was the first body to build working-class dwellings in
Dublin; indeed he was the only non-businessman to be a member. It was
not particularly successful in its efforts, developing only one housing
scheme of 50 small flats; the scheme itself eventually became a slum,
and the Industrial Tenements Co. wound up its activities in 1914.[34]
It was a forerunner of associations such as the Artisans' Dwellings
Co., formed in 1876, but it exemplifies the networks of collaboration
that existed among health and housing reformers at the time. In his
diary of 5 January 1891, Cameron recorded that he attended a meeting
of the City and Suburban Building Co., and on 8 May of the same
year he wrote of a meeting 'with reference to amalgamation of the
Industrial Tenements Co. with the City and Suburban Workmens
Co.'.[35] Mapother's involvement with this housing association shows
that he moved outside what could be considered his 'normal' duties
as Medical Officer of Health—a trend that would be followed by his
successor. Cameron and Mapother appear to have been friends as well
as colleagues and, although they were very different in temperament,
they worked well together. Cameron's personal respect for Mapother
is indicated by the two entries written by him in successive editions
of his *History of the Royal College of Surgeons in Ireland and of the Irish
Schools of Medicine*.[36] It is not until the 1916 edition, after Mapother's
death, that Cameron mentions that Mapother's father, a bank official,
left his office one day, never came home, and was never seen again.[37]

In his autobiography, Cameron described Mapother as '[devoting]

33 Ibid., Vol. iv, Part xxvii (1864) p. 74.
34 Daly (1984), op. cit., p. 296; Murray Fraser, *John Bull's Other Homes: State Housing and British
    Policy in Ireland, 1883–1922* (Liverpool, 1996), p. 70.
35 Cameron, Diaries, 8 May 1891.
36 Cameron (1886 and 1916) op. cit.
37 Ibid., (1916), p. 501.

himself to his duties with great earnestness and with much success',[38] and this seems an apt description for a public servant who worked efficiently, if relatively unobtrusively, at his job. Mapother, although he held the post of Consulting Sanitary Officer with Dublin Corporation until 1890, left Dublin in 1888, and returned to his original speciality of dermatology in London, where he lectured and wrote papers on the subject until his death in 1908 at the age of 72. Cameron's diaries record several visits to Mapother on trips to London,[39] so it is obvious that they maintained a personal friendship as well as a professional relationship. Mapother's obituary described his life as 'one of honourable and honest work',[40] although he may have achieved more than the sparse references to him in modern literature indicate; in speaking of the role he played in the introduction of the Sanitary Act, 1866, Norwood claims that 'from that date the history and operation of effective sanitary legislation in Ireland practically commenced'.[41]

Mapother also had some professional success outside his role as medical officer. Fleetwood claims that his paper on shock, read in 1879 'is still of considerable clinical interest,[42] and that it was Mapother, during an operation carried out at St Vincent's Hospital, who was involved in the longest ever administration of chloroform as an anaesthetic.[43]

James Boyle

James Boyle was one of the trio of public health appointments made by Dublin Corporation in 1874. He was appointed Executive Sanitary Officer at a salary of £300 per annum, the same salary as Cameron and Mapother—this indicates that the three roles were seen as equally important. However, the report of the Public Health Committee in 1881 makes it clear that James Boyle had actually been employed by the Corporation since 1866 as secretary to the committee.[44] When he was first employed, the committee was 'then the least important of all the standing committees of the Council',[45] and Boyle's job was part-time— two days a week, at a salary of 30s per week.[46] However, his duties

38 Cameron, *Autobiography* (1920), p. 138.
39 e.g. Diaries, 31 July 1895.
40 *British Medical Journal*, i, March, 1908, p. 661.
41 *Jn. SSISI* vol. vi, Part XLIII, p. 230.
42 Fleetwood (1983) op. cit., p. 294.
43 Ibid., p. 143.
44 'Future Arrangements', op. cit., p. 11.
45 Ibid., p. 12.
46 Ibid.

(and it would appear, his salary) gradually increased over the years in line with the increased duties of the committee. A trained engineer and surveyor, James Boyle not only performed secretarial duties but also fulfilled some duties of a sanitary officer and city surveyor.[47] Mr Boyle's position, in an interesting turn of phrase by the Public Health Committee, 'was exceptional, and to some extent accidental',[48] and could probably be more accurately viewed as a convenient arrangement for the Corporation, which made good use of 'his great ability and industry' and, it would seem, his friendly personality, which enabled him to work on good terms with several different areas of expertise within the Corporation. James Boyle fares even worse than Edward Mapother in modern literature; there appears to be no mention of his contribution to public health. Yet, when he passed away suddenly and the Corporation were forced to find a replacement, they realised that it was impossible to find any single individual who could competently carry out all the duties that he had undertaken.[49] He had eventually come to occupy

> a more and more important position, and to discharge functions of the most varied character, which . . . he, owing to his great ability and in-dustry, was able efficiently to carry out; but which the Committee fear it would be very difficult to have discharged by any single individual not thus trained by actual experience and practice.[50]

They were obliged to come up with a solution whereby in future, all architectural and survey work would fall to the Architect and City Surveyor,[51] and Charles Cameron would undertake 'the entire control of and responsibility for the working of the Public Health Department.'[52] James Boyle

> not only performed the secretarial duties and the duties strictly appertain-ing to an Executive Sanitary Officer, but also to a considerable extent those which would more strictly and properly fall to the Medical Sanitary Offic-er, as well as those which under ordinary circumstances, if the department were now being reconstituted, would devolve upon the City Surveyor[53]

He remains one of the many unsung heroes of the 19th-century

47 Ibid., p. 12.
48 Ibid., p. 14.
49 Ibid., p. 12.
50 Ibid.
51 Ibid., p. 9.
52 Ibid., p. 10.
53 Ibid., p. 12.

public health staff in Dublin Corporation.

Cameron takes over

Although Mapother had done his job conscientiously, and he and Cameron had worked closely together, during his first years as Medical Officer of Health Cameron was somewhat under his predecessor's shadow. But when he added Mapother's duties to his own in 1879,[54] there was an almost palpable change of tempo in Dublin's public health administration. Whereas Mapother had been reactive, Cameron was more inclined to be proactive, and seems to have been determined to put his own stamp on the position he now occupied. A measure of the results of this increased tempo can be gauged from the following statistics: from 1851 until 1877, a period of 26 years, about 200 houses in Dublin had been closed. In 1879, the year he took over as Superintendent Medical Officer, Cameron immediately prepared a handbook of instructions for sanitary inspectors, and himself 'resolved to personally inspect every tenement house in the city, and also some hundreds of small cottages occupied by very poor people'.[55] By the end of 1880, that is, in one year under his stewardship, 602 houses and 204 cellars had been closed.[56] In 1881, Cameron and his staff obtained orders to close '447 houses, 161 rooms in other houses, and 99 cellars . . .'[57] Cameron enforced the construction of several hundred water closets in tenements, and by October 1879, 743 water closets had replaced back-yard privies, with the hope expressed by him that, within a year, water closets would be in nearly every tenement dwelling in the city.[58]

The first joint report by Mapother and Cameron in 1879 is outspoken, unequivocal, and makes forceful and practical suggestions for improving public health in the city. Reading it in the light of subsequent reports by Cameron, it is obvious that it is his work, although Mapother's name is attached.[59] On housing it advised that 'decayed buildings should be pulled down, and replaced by houses specially adapted for the artisan and labouring classes'; on sewers it stressed that 'the new Public Health Act gives the sanitary authority greater power in relation to private sewers than they formerly possessed,

54 Cameron (1914), op. cit., pp 38–9.
55 Ibid., pp 66–7.
56 Ibid., p. 67.
57 Ibid., p. 68.
58 Ibid., p. 12.
59 Charles A. Cameron and E. D. Mapother, 'Report on the Means for the Prevention of Disease in Dublin', RPCD, Vol. 1, no. 63, (1879), pp 341–53.

and this power, we beg to suggest, should be vigorously exercised'; it recommended that 'there should be established two public abattoirs, one at the north, the other at the south side of the city', and considered this 'one of the most important sanitary improvements that could be effected in Dublin'; on the disinfection of houses it recommended that 'in order to afford proper shelter to the families whose tenements are being disinfected, we suggest that a small wooden house be provided . . . At present the families have to stay in the halls or on the stairs, until the disinfection of their rooms is completed. In winter this is a great hardship . . .'[60] A further suggestion was made that 'if under the provisions of the "Baths and Wash-houses Act," baths were established in which a cold bath could be procured for a penny, and a hot one for twopence, the boon would be a valuable one to the poorer citizens'.[61]

Although the concluding paragraph states that many of the measures may have been adopted for some years past by the Public Health Committee, this report, with Cameron's name given most prominence, would seem to be a clear indication of his wish to stamp his own way of doing things on the workings of the public health office. He had been waiting in the wings for a long time, and as soon as he took the stage he made his presence felt.

In 1881, at just over 50 years of age, Charles Cameron must have felt great personal satisfaction at the course his life was taking. He held two chairs in the Royal College of Surgeons, was recognised by his peers as one of the leading sanitarians of his day, and now had overall control of public health in his native city.

His personal life was also on an upwardly mobile curve. Like most middle-class Dubliners, he moved outwards from the city as his means improved, and between 1862 when he married and became Public Analyst, and 1881, when he took overall control of the city's health, he moved progressively further out of the city. By 1881, he was living at 51 Pembroke Road with his wife and six of the seven children born up to that date—Charles (Charlie), born in 1866, Edwin Douglas (known as Douglas), born in 1868, Lucie (1869), Helena Margaret (Lena), born in 1870, Ernest Stuart (1872), and Mervyn Wingfield (1875)—another son, Ewen, would be born in 1882. Many well-to-do Dubliners moved to what they hoped were the healthier surroundings of the suburbs to avoid the overcrowded and unhygienic conditions of the city. Ironically and tragically, this did not work for Cameron. An expert on

60 Ibid., p. 350.
61 Ibid., p. 352.

sanitation and the dangers of contagion, he was powerless to prevent the effects on his own family, and his second son, William, who was born in 1867, died from scarlet fever at the age of eight. There are no diaries of this period, so there are only brief details of this tragedy in Cameron's autobiography.[62]

In 1880, on 1 January, Cameron began keeping a diary that would in a sense be his most constant companion and confidante until a few years before his death. The diaries would eventually be placed in the archives of the Royal College of Surgeons, an institution dear to his heart. Apart from a break of a few years between 1883 and 1890, he conscientiously recorded every day. The journals survive in four volumes: 1880–1883; 1890–1901; 1901–1909; 1910–1916 (16 June).

The format of the first volume of diaries, from 1880 to 1883, is A5 size, a small notebook, whereas all of the later diaries are in large foolscap volumes. The entries in this first volume are shorter than in the others, mostly just a few lines giving brief details of his day, unlike the other volumes, where most of the entries, in a larger size book, are at least half a page long, and sometimes longer.

The diaries appear to have been written quite quickly, as if Cameron was determined to record something each day. There are no unguarded revelations, other than of a personal nature, when he records his feelings about his wife's and sons' deaths. It is not clear why he kept the diary, but the fact that he wrote his name and address on the first page of the first diary indicates that he had some notion that posterity might take an interest; this is also indicated by an entry on 27 February 1903, when he carefully indicated his address for future readers: 'last night one of the greatest storms of the century occurred . . . Great damage throughout the country. Some, but not much to this house 51 Pembroke Road.'

The fact that the first diary coincided with the period when Cameron took full control of public health in Dublin is perhaps significant; however, there is little of note recorded about his professional life —even at times like 1913, when he was in the public eye. Nor does he comment on political events, such as the First World War, or the 1916 Rising. In writing of the Rising, for example, he simply records events as they impinge on his own daily life, rather than any political comment. Perhaps he regarded his professional life as totally separate from his personal life, and the diaries were a means of expressing personal emotions that he could not show elsewhere; even so, the

---

62 Cameron, *Autobiography* (1920) op. cit., p. 29

diaries are remarkably devoid of any critical comment.

The diaries show a man of great determination, who worked hard at his job, even at times of great personal stress; they record the deaths of four of his sons, and the mental breakdown of another and, although his wife's death is not covered by the diaries, it is mentioned on each anniversary of her death. He also continued to work at times of political stress – his diary for Easter Week 1916 tells of him dodging a hail of bullets as he tried to get in to work – this was when he was aged 85! The diaries reveal a humane man – one instance tells how, when his driver took ill, Cameron drove him to hospital himself and later went to visit him; he did the same when his cook got scarlet fever, while another entry tells of him attending the funeral of a man he had worked with for 30 years. He comments on how few are at his funeral, remarking that 'he was a peculiar man and very reserved but interfered with no one'. There are several such incidents mentioned casually throughout the diaries, visiting and helping friends in need.

The diaries, although superficially not revelatory about his professional life, do give some indication of Cameron's attitude to his professional duties. For example, he commenced almost every entry of the diaries with the same sentence 'Went to PHO and laboratory'. If he did not go to the Public Health Office, he usually noted what other official duties he performed that day, for example housing inspections, or attendance in court; on most occasions he carefully noted that he went in to the PHO later in the day. If he did not go in at all, he was careful to state that it was a Corporation holiday.

The diaries also show evidence of Cameron's links with his peers in London and elsewhere in Britain, revealing regular visits to London on official public health business. He had a large network of friends in the public health arena in Britain, and the fact that he visited them and they in turn visited Dublin on public health matters is important for understanding the links and ideas that influenced Cameron in his work. He would have been familiar with developments, not only in sanitation and medical matters, but with social attitudes and movements for change. For example, Cameron's call for a public meeting in 1887 where he requested 'benevolent men' to build houses for the very poor, who could not afford even two shillings rent, is almost identical to the pleas of Canon Barnett in London at the meeting he called before the formation of the East End Dwelling Company a few years earlier in 1883. From Cameron's diaries it is possible to match the entries with newspaper reports of conferences, and thus gain a wider insight into his contacts outside Ireland.

The Cameron who wrote his autobiographical *Reminiscences* and *Autobiography* was very upbeat, full of jokes, puns, and stories about himself. In these books he portrayed himself as a great raconteur and bon viveur, and could be described there as self-congratulatory and a self-propagandist. The Cameron who wrote the diaries was much less self-confident, ebullient and jokey; he seemed genuinely grateful and surprised when he received praise. In later years the diary incrreasingly became a means of coping with and expressing emotions that he felt unable to reveal in public—a shoulder to cry on after the deaths of his sons, or on the anniversary of his wife's death. Writing, whether privately in his diaries, or publicly through his books, reports and papers, seemed to be, along with an unremitting workload, the medium Cameron turned to when under stress.

The diaries end abruptly, without any further comment, on 16 June 1916, exactly one month short of his 86th birthday. He had just had another serious fall, but was still upbeat, preparing his Public Health Report for 1915 at home, with 'my left eye quite closed up and round about it swollen and discoloured'. The final entry simply recorded 'at P.H.O. and Laboratory. Eye much better. Ernest dined out'; there is no indication of why, having kept a diary conscientiously through all the vicissitudes of a long life, he suddenly decided to cease the practice. Perhaps at the age of almost 86, a great age for that period, having lost his wife and five sons and suffered the ignominy of the 1914 Report, he may simply have felt he had recorded enough.

The early diaries are snapshots of the life of a happy family man, confident in himself and in his lifestyle, with no thought of what the future might bring. Cameron and his wife Lucie enjoyed a lively and busy social life, with constant visits to the theatre, together and with friends. The diary entries show a happy and close couple, devoted to each other and to their children. It was a typical middle-class Victorian lifestyle; the older boys went to boarding school, Charlie when older went to Reading in England, travelling on his own by boat, while the others stayed in Ireland, coming home for holidays. The younger children stayed at home, looked after with the help of a nurse, Annie Webber, from Bath, in England, who came to work in Cameron's household in 1880. When the children grew up, she became Cameron's housekeeper, and she would remain a part of the family, and a support to Cameron until his death. Cameron had mentioned previously visiting her, so the family obviously sought her out for the post. The Census returns show that Annie was a Roman Catholic, another indication of Cameron's non-sectarian views. She appears to have been, probably unusually for one of her station at the time, an outspoken person—which could explain why she got on so well with Cameron; there is a letter from Annie Webber in *The Irish Times* of 25 February 1897, in which she volunteers 'although I am only a poor woman', to contribute £5 towards any fund set up in support of a Father O'Malley, who was involved in a lawsuit over the proposed contents of his will with Archbishop Walsh (incidentally a friend of Cameron's). Annie died three years after Cameron, on 1 January 1924. A memoriam notice was placed in *The Irish Times* three years later on 3 January 1927: 'In loving memory of Annie Webber, for many years faithful friend and housekeeper to the Cameron family'— it would be nice to think that it could have been placed by one of Cameron's family in recognition of her long and faithful service—a likely supposition, since her own family appears to have been in England.

Cameron and Lucie frequently dined out and entertained at home, a practice that Cameron would continue all his life. Their social circle was varied, and involved much dining, both on official occasions and with friends. Their home entertaining involved mainly dinner parties for small numbers, which were not always formal occasions—Cameron's diary for 6 October 1881 records all the guests 'singing till 2 o'c in the morning'; he still put in a full day at the Royal College of Surgeons and a Social Science Congress the following day. They were equally at home with each other's company, and the theatre was a big feature of their lives, as were outings and holidays with the children. Cameron was a very hands-on father, probably unusual for his time, bringing the children to the Zoo and for walks, and on several occasions to his lectures at the Agricultural Institute in Glasnevin. The family regularly attended the Magdalen Chapel in Leeson Street. This was attached to the Magdalen Asylum, founded by Lady Arabella Denny in 1766 'for unfortunate females abandoned by their seducers, and rejected by their friends, who were willing to prefer a life of penitence and virtue to one of guilt, infamy and prostitution'.[63] The chapel, capable of holding 700 people, was described as an 'opulent and respectable congregation', whose subscriptions supported the asylum. The Magdalenes attended the service, at which the chaplain 'lectures the penitents every week . . . exhorts and reproves them when required . . . and reads, whenever

---

63   J. Warburton, Rev. J. Whitelaw and Rev. Robert Walsh, *History of the City of Dublin, from the earliest accounts to the present time . . . etc.* (Dublin, 1818), p. 771.

it has been unfortunately necessary, the form of expulsion of the irreclaimable'.[64]

The Magdalen was Low Church, with an austere decoration and ethos:

> ... no vaulted domes or gilded ceilings, no swelling columns or sculptured capitals adorn this humble roof; no crowned or mitred canopies are erected to point out wealth and title to the gazing crowd. None here can pray in state. But all must kneel without distinction as partakers of the same impartial God.[65]

Cameron attended St Patrick's Cathedral on a few occasions, availing of the Vice-Regal pew, and family ceremonies of baptism, weddings and funerals were held in the High Church milieu of St Bartholomew's, but it was to the Magdalen that he went on a weekly basis, as a private individual, so perhaps the above description of its ethos says something about his personal view of religious observance. He appears to have been an active member of the congregation—he always recorded in his diaries what he contributed to the collection, and on several occasions mentioned that he himself took the collection in the gallery.

Outside his weekly visits to the Magdalen Chapel, Cameron does not appear to have had any strong religious leanings and, in fact, would appear to have had more social contact with members of the Roman Catholic clergy than with Church of Ireland clergy. His early diaries show him as he would remain for the rest of his life—a man who enjoyed the company of others, a good sing-song with friends, not too highbrow entertainment, and a simple family life. The fact that he would retain this *joie-de-vivre* despite what would subsequently overtake him, is all the more remarkable.

---

64 Ibid., pp 771–2.
65 A. Peter, *A Brief Account of the Magdalen Chapel, Leeson Street* (Dublin, 1907), p. 70.

Three remarkable pioneers of public health (clockwise from top left): Sir John Simon (Wellcome); James Burn Russell (Wellcome); William Henry Duncan (Liverpool Records).

Chapter 7 'We have done our duty in our generation'[1]

Although he was the first full-time Medical Officer of Health in Ireland, Charles Cameron was not the first in the British Isles. That honour went to William Henry Duncan, who was appointed MOH of Liverpool in 1847 and remained in office until 1863. He was the first of a series of remarkable men pioneering this field. Other notables among them were John Simon, Medical Officer of Health for the City of London from 1848 to 1855, and James Burn Russell, Medical Officer of Health for Glasgow from 1872 to 1898. All three were, like Cameron, the first full-time Medical Officers of Health in their respective cities. They, therefore, like him experienced the difficulties and challenges of pioneering such a task, and provide useful comparators to evaluate Cameron's work in Dublin.

There is evidence of continuous links between these men; Duncan knew Simon, and corresponded with Gairdner, Russell's predecessor and mentor. Simon was prominent in public health circles during the careers of Russell and Cameron, while the Royal College of Surgeons in Ireland, under Cameron's presidency in 1885–6, awarded an honorary doctorate to John Simon. Cameron also corresponded with Gairdner and Russell[2] and, at the annual congress of the British Institute of Public Health in 1893, of which Cameron was the retiring President (having been President for the previous four years), Russell presided over the Preventive Medicine Section.[3]

William Henry Duncan, Liverpool

William Henry Duncan was appointed as Medical Officer of Health for the borough of Liverpool from 1 January 1847. His post was originally part-time, at an annual salary of £300, but was made full-time in 1848, with an increased salary of £750; some years later, Duncan would claim that he accepted this salary 'on the understanding that it would

---

1 Willliam Henry Duncan, excerpt from letter to a friend, cited in W. M. Frazer, *Duncan of Liverpool* (London, 1947), p. 102.
2 PP, 1880 xxx, c.2605, *The Royal Commission on Sewerage and Drainage in Dublin*, Par. 1379.
3 *The Times*, 31 July 1893.

be increased after a time'.[4]

Duncan was born in Seel Street, Liverpool on 27 January, 1805, the fifth of seven children of a Liverpool merchant. He was educated by an uncle, Rev. Henry Duncan, and his mother's brother, Dr James Currie, was a well known Liverpool doctor. Little is known of his early life, but he graduated as an M.D. at Edinburgh in 1829.[5] After spending some time in France, he returned to Liverpool, and to his early career of general practitioner, during which he became aware of the conditions under which the poor of Liverpool lived. During the 1832 cholera epidemic, he published an analysis of the connection between living conditions and disease and submitted evidence to the Inquiry into the Corporation of Liverpool (1833), the Commission on the Condition of the Poor in Ireland (1836 report), and the House of Commons Select Committee on the Health of Towns (1840), detailing the deplorable 'sanitary state of the labouring classes' in Liverpool.[6]

In 1843 he wrote a paper, 'On the physical causes of the high rate of mortality in Liverpool' which was published in the report of the Commission on Large Towns and Populous Districts in 1844.[7] In this paper he claimed that Liverpool was 'the most unhealthy town in England'.[8] He collaborated with Edwin Chadwick in preparing his *Reports on the Condition of the Poor*, and, as already mentioned, gave evidence before a Select Committee of the House of Commons.[9] His career before being appointed Medical Officer of Health included the post of physician to the South Dispensary Liverpool, physician to the Royal Infirmary, and lecturer in Medical Jurisprudence in the Medical School at the Royal Institution.[10]

19th-century Liverpool

The 19th century had seen the sustained expansion of Lancashires's factories, and with this expansion came an enormous increase in trade through Liverpool's docks. Between 1815 and 1835, eight new docks were built, with an increase in trade, in banking, in warehousing and

---

4 W. M. Frazer, *Duncan of Liverpool* (London, 1947), p. 47.
5 Adrian R. Allan 'Duncan, William Henry (1805–1863)' *Oxford Dictionary of National Biography*, (Oxford 2004)
6 Allan, *Oxford Dictionary of National Biography*, op. cit.
7 Paul Laxton in Sally Sheard and Helen Power (eds) *Body and City, Histories of Urban Public Health* (Aldershot, Hampshire 2000) p 61
8 W. H. Duncan, 'On the physical causes of the high rate of mortality in Liverpool' read to the Liverpool Literary and Philosophical Society in 1843.
9 Frazer, op. cit., p. 12.
10 Ibid., p. 48.

the import and export of goods. However, employment in the port was of casual, unskilled labour, with consequently low standards of living. When Duncan was appointed in 1847, the population of the Borough of Liverpool was approximately 340,000,[11] a great increase from the figures in his 1840 paper *Report on the Sanitary State of the Labouring Classes in Liverpool*. In that paper, he had estimated the population of Liverpool as about 250,000, of whom 175,000 could be classified as belonging to the labouring classes.[12] Of these, nearly one-half lived in unhygienic closed courts, while 8,000 cellars housed between 35,000 and 40,000 people. This already wretched situation was to worsen from 1847, when an estimated 300,000 destitute Irish arrived at the port of Liverpool, fleeing from the Famine, of whom 60,000 to 80,000 remained in Liverpool

> occupying every nook and cranny of the already overcrowded lodging-houses, and forcing their way into the cellars . . . which had been closed under the provisions of the Health Act, 1842 . . . in more than one instance upwards of 40 were found sleeping in a cellar.'[13]

The result was an increase in deaths from fever, probably lice-borne typhus—often simply described as 'Irish Famine Fever'. Duncan estimated that, in 1847, 'nearly 60,000 people in Liverpool suffered from fever and nearly 40,000 from diarrhoea and dysentery'.[14] As a port city, Liverpool was vulnerable to diseases brought in by sea, and the following year cholera arrived in the city, resulting in yet another epidemic, which caused over 5,000 deaths. These epidemics added to the existing illnesses, such as consumption and measles, which regularly affected the population—it is estimated that the death rate leaped from 13.5 per thousand in 1844 to 52 per thousand in 1849—a challenging start to Duncan's career as Medical Officer of Health.

Liverpool legislation

Made aware of its city's public health problems (mainly as a result of publications by William Duncan), Liverpool Town Council brought in private Acts of Parliament to deal with the situation—the Liverpool Improvement Act and the Liverpool Building Act (both 1842), and the Liverpool Sanitary Act (1846). Duncan's appointment was made under the terms of the Liverpool Sanitary Act of 1846 which changed

11 Sheard and Power, op. cit., p. 62.
12 Frazer, op. cit., p. 31.
13 William Duncan, First Report as Medical Officer of Health, cited in Frazer, op. cit., p. 57.
14 Frazer, op. cit., p. 59.

a 'chaos of conflicting and competing authorities . . . into a system which was at once simple and efficient'.[15]

The Liverpool Improvement Act aimed to improve the government and policing of the city, and dealt with the registration and licensing of slaughterhouses, the handling of meat, etc.; the Liverpool Building Act incorporated 'a complete code governing the erection of new buildings[16] giving precise regulations for 'thickness of party walls, the situation of flues and fireplaces, etc.'[17] The Liverpool Sanitary Act made private rights subservient to public welfare—cellars were forbidden to be used as dwellings, and lodging-houses strictly controlled. Under the Act, 'two important doctrines were established—owners whose property had caused harm got no compensation, and new works should be at the expense of the ratepayers "not, as was lately suggested for London and Galway, at the expense of others"'.[18]

The Act also changed the administration of the City with immediate effect—sewage, drainage, paving, all the tasks previously under the control of 'conflicting and competing authorities',[19] were now brought under the control of the Health Committee. Most importantly, the Act allowed for the appointment of a Medical Officer of Health, and greatly influenced the 1848 Public Health Act, which created a General Board of Health, and gave local authorities the power to appoint local boards of health. The title 'Medical Officer of Health' was used for the first time, and the Act had an effect on sanitary legislation throughout the British Isles, influencing the introduction and design of the Public Health Act of 1848.

As a result, William Duncan had a ready-made arsenal of legislation at his disposal when he became Medical Officer of Health, with all the administrative machinery, such as a City Surveyor and Inspector of Nuisances, in place to assist him in his work, together with a town council that was prepared and able to finance the reforms. However, there were many vested interests who opposed the appointment of a Medical Officer of Health, and Duncan also had to face the legal implications that arose with the provisions of the Nuisance Removals Act of 1848, which made the Select Vestry of the Parish responsible for preventive measures during epidemics, while the Liverpool Sanitary Act, under which Duncan had been appointed, gave responsibility to the

---

15 Ibid., p. 38.
16 Frazer, op. cit., p. 35.
17 Ibid.
18 Ibid., p. 36.
19 Ibid., p. 38.

Corporation of the Borough. Duncan claimed that he had considerable difficulty with the Select Vestry of Liverpool and that 'in the cholera epidemic of 1849 they refused to act on my recommendations until compelled by an Order of the General Board of Health, and even then they took legal advice as to whether they were bound to obey.'[20]

His experience and tireless campaigning made Duncan ideally suited for the job of Medical Officer of Health and for the duties he was expected to carry out, which included 'ascertain[ing] the existence of diseases . . . and point[ing] out the most efficacious modes for checking or preventing the spread of such diseases'.[21] The Act made private rights, such as those of landlords, subservient to the rights of the public, and 'established the Public Health Service as an essential activity of local government'.[22]

From 1842 the city promoted baths and washhouses for the poor, its improvement Acts gave it extensive sanitary powers, and from 1847 it gained control of the city's water supply. However, the overcrowding and public health problems would remain a problem throughout Duncan's term of office. As in Dublin, clearing tenants from one lot of unsanitary housing caused overcrowding and a repeat of the problem elsewhere in the city, and at one stage Duncan had to request that not more than 100 cellars a month be cleared in order to allow time for the supply of alternative housing for those displaced.[23]

As the first Medical Officer of Health, Duncan had no precedents to guide him in setting up the administration of his new duties—in fact, the duties themselves were somewhat indeterminate; he was to 'devise some method of controlling the epidemics of infectious diseases . . . which year by year ravaged the poorer quarters of the borough'.[24]

He was familiar with the zymotic diseases from his previous career, and was aware of the problems of the poor from his time as a private practitioner. Duncan did not believe contagion was the cause, however, stating 'I know of no instance which supports in any way the theory of contagion'.[25] As an adherent of the miasma theory of diease he concentrated on preventive measures—increased inspection of houses, increased scavenging and cleansing, a clean water-supply to the districts affected; he called for the provision of hospitals in the parts of the city affected, claiming that distance from medical

20 Ibid., p. 71.
21 Frazer, op. cit., p. 51.
22 Ibid., p. 37.
23 Frazer, op.cit., p. 78.
24 Frazer, op. cit., p. 50.
25 Ibid., p. 64.

treatment led to increased mortality. Unsanitary living conditions were synonymous with increased mortality rates so, despite the lack of guidance as to his duties, he knew what steps needed to be taken to alleviate the problem.

In his first progress report, produced in 1851 and covering the period 1847–50, Duncan appeared to be very clear on what his duties should be, duties which included ascertaining the existence of disease in the city, and pointing out 'the most efficacious modes for checking or preventing the spread of such diseases'.[26] The beginning of his tenure coincided with some of the worst health crises in Liverpool history. His first year in office saw the start of the mass immigration to Liverpool of sick and destitute Irish hit by the Famine; cholera struck the beleaguered city two years later, in 1849. Duncan followed the cholera epidemic on its path through the city, reporting that 'a disciplined force of medical combatants . . . followed close upon the heels of the enemy in every new position which it occupied'.[27] Duncan had only just been appointed to the position of Medical Officer of Health; he had no staff,[28] and was dependent for resources upon the Select Vestry, with whom he reported he had 'considerable difficulty' whenever he asked them to spend money.[29]

Duncan's report shows that in 1848 he commenced the inspection of schools to check the ventilation — as a believer in the miasma theory, he would have regarded this factor as vital to the health of the pupils. He reported that, up to end of 1850, he had inspected nearly 1,100 lodging-houses — a notorious breeding-ground for epidemics. He also reported that

> fully nine-tenths of the keepers are Irish [and] . . . experience has shown that few of them can be depended on for carrying-out the Bye-laws, unless closely watched.[30]

He believed that part of his duties as MOH was to visit daily

> some portion of the districts inhabited by the poorer classes, with the view of ascertaining the existence and procuring the removal of any local cause of disease which may be found to exist.[31]

26 Frazer, op. cit., p. 51.
27 Ibid., p. 70.
28 A facetious reply to a letter enquiring as to this staff read: 'The following list comprises the whole of the officers in my department paid by the Corporation: William Henry Duncan, M.D., Medical Officer of Health, Ibid., p. 113.
29 Letter from Duncan 1854, no reference, cited in Frazer, op. cit., p.71.
30 First official Report, Duncan, 1851, cited in Frazer, op. cit., p. 76.
31 First official Report, Duncan, 1851, cited in Frazer, op. cit., p. 73.

With this in mind he wrote that 'in planning the routine of my duties' he proposed to visit every house where 'a death from a zymotic disease had taken place, or where from other sources of information I had reason to believe that any zymotic disease was prevalent'.[32] As this territory covered 5,000 statute acres, he reported somewhat apologetically that he had to limit his inspections to the most badly affected areas. All these duties were carried out solely by Duncan. In 1851 he wrote that he had paid £25 out of his own pocket for office assistance, and used his own servant as a messenger; he also used his own horse, gig and groom. Duncan would eventually be allowed clerical staff and five lodging-house inspectors, but his pioneering work was carried out solely by him. Despite this lack of resources, Duncan could report that the cellar population, which had accounted for 12 per cent of the population in 1847, had been decreased by clearance, so that it only accounted for 2 per cent of the population in 1850.[33]

Duncan's legacy

Under Duncan's guidance, Liverpool became a pioneer in providing baths and wash-houses for the poor; water hydrants were fitted to provide increased water supply for the cleansing of tenement houses, public conveniences were erected, the regulation of slaughter-houses was enforced, cleansing and scavenging was improved, regulations governing minimum living space were introduced, manufacturers producing noxious fumes injurious to public health were regulated. Between 1847 and 1858, 80 miles of sewers were laid and connected to house drains. All of the above were carried out by the Corporation, whose Borough Engineer, James Newlands, observed that

> they have generally selected for execution such works as, in the opinion of the Medical Officer of Health, would most effectively contribute to re-move the causes of disease, and the results have abundantly justified this course of procedure.[34]

In 1861, Duncan wrote to William Gairdner, two years later to become MOH in Glasgow, that 'every house in Liverpool has a supply of water, with the exception of court houses, many of which have an independent supply'. He went on to report that a new water supply, together with existing wells, now provided '30 gallons a day for every man, woman and child'. With regard to sewers, he reported that since

---

32 Ibid.
33 Ibid., p. 78.
34 Frazer, op. cit., pp 107–108.

1847, about 180 miles of main sewers had been constructed, draining more than 40,000 houses, plus about 12,000 more in courts, adding the observation that 'When I first called attention to the subject, I believe that not a single court in Liverpool was drained. Very few instead are now undrained'.[35]

Duncan died in 1863, aged 58, having, as Sir John Simon put it,

> with the ungrudging confidence and support of a very public-spirited local authority . . . established methods of work, and initiated courses of improvement . . . under which the average general death-rate of Liverpool has been reduced by probably at least a fourth part of that which prevailed forty years ago.'[36]

The death rate had decreased from 39 per thousand to 27 per thousand during Duncan's tenure.[37] His pioneering work and achievements as the first Medical Officer of Health in Britain made Duncan an inspirtion to subsequent generations of public health officials.

John Simon, London

John Simon was the second Medical Officer of Health in England, appointed only a year after Duncan in 1848.

In London, he faced a completely different situation from Liverpool. Its rapid expansion had left the administration of the metropolis, which had a population of two million in 1848, under the control of a bewildering array of vestries, boards of guardians, boroughs, boards for paving, lighting, and cleansing, commissions for sewerage and drainage, together with eight different water companies. Edwin Chadwick, the great sanitary reformer, and the Health of Towns Association aimed to substitute an overall administration, responsible for all sanitary functions. The main objection to this proposal came from the Council of the powerful City of London, which administered the square mile, and which declared that 'the City of London, for health, cleanliness, effective drainage, lighting, and for supply of water to its inhabitants, cannot be surpassed'.[38]

The Council of the City held firm against efforts to subsume it into the overall administration of the metropolis, using its considerable

---

35 Cited, ibid., pp 125–126.
36 Sir John Simon on Willliam Duncan, cited in Frazer, op. cit., p. 151 (no reference).
37 Cited in Frazer, op. cit., p. 148 (no reference).
38 *Report of the Commissioners of Sewers, April 12th, 1847,* cited in Royston Lambert, *Sir John Simon 1816–1904 and English Social Administration* (London, 1963), p. 67.

influence to lobby support, despite counter attacks that denounced it as a 'nasty turtle-eating Corporation', and a claim that it was a 'city of cesspools'.[39] Eventually a compromise was reached; the City was allowed to introduce its own Bill in the House of Lords, which was passed, leaving its jurisdiction intact, while giving control of all drainage matters to the new Metropolitan Commission formed by the Public Health Act 1848.

The City's Bill—the Sewers Act of 1848[40]—was largely modelled on the Liverpool Sanitary Act of 1846. It gave the City Commissioners the powers to control sanitation and nuisance. Although the Act did not come into effect until 1 January 1849, the Commission decided to appoint a Medical Officer of Health immediately, spurred on by the incipient threat of a cholera epidemic. The Chairman of the Commission declared that a prime responsibility of the incumbent would be to 'prepare the City's defences against the impending scourge'.[41] Besides, as was pointed out, since clause 80 of the Sewers Bill required them to make such an appointment, not to do so could lead to the City being forced to join with Chadwick's wider administration network.[42] It was decided that the appointment would be part-time, with the appointee allowed to continue in private practice, and that it would cost the City no more than £150 for the interim period of the appointment. A short-list of candidates, which included John Simon, was drawn up. Some of the opposition tried to diminish Simon's chances of appointment by drawing attention to his membership of the organisation which was the City's arch-enemy—the Health of Towns Association. However, Simon, with an impressive list of references, influential family connections, and vehement assurances to the Council that his connection with the Health of Towns Association had been non-political and non-critical of the City fathers, was elected unanimously on 19 October 1848, and re-elected unanimously in February 1850, at a salary of £500, later increased, after much discussion and argument, to £800.[43]

Simon's background

John Simon was born in the City of London on 10 October 1816, to a second-generation French immigrant family. His father was a stock-

39 Lambert, op. cit., p. 68, 69.
40 Local and Private 11 & 12 Vict. cap. clxiii
41 Ibid., p. 99.
42 Ibid., p. 100.
43 Christopher Hamlin 'Simon, Sir John (1816–1904)', *Oxford Dictionary of National Biography* (Oxford University Press, 2004), and Lambert, op. cit., p. 158.

broker and prominent member of the London Stock Exchange, who became one of the most respected figures in the City.[44] John was the sixth of fourteen children from two marriages—his father married his sister-in-law on the death of his first wife. His parents were devoted, and their family life described as 'close and happy, quietly and unpretentiously cultivated'.[45] John was educated in small proprietary schools, not entirely to his satisfaction—when in his eighties he would write of his schooling, 'even to the end of my life I am conscious of great faults in myself which I think might have been cured or lessened by better guidance than my boyhood received'.[46]

In 1832, he was sent to Germany for a year, where he stayed with a German parson in Prussia—he would later describe his stay there as one of his 'most sacred recollections'.[47] He had been an avid reader of surgical books from an early age, so before he left for Germany, it was decided that he would be apprenticed to a surgeon. Accordingly in October 1833, at 17 he became a pupil of Joseph Henry Green, at a fee of 500 guineas for six years. His first reaction to a lecture by his future tutor was of hearing a 'continuous flow of lofty argumentative eloquence' and of 'the opening of a new world'.[48] His early training involved, until his parents leased a house for him in London, walking eight miles from home (his father having breakfasted with him in his dressing-gown) in time for 9 o'clock lectures, often not returning until 11 o'clock at night.

His early career is not well documented but, according to his biographer,

> he was interested enough [in sanitary issues] in the early forties to spend part of his time abroad examining the sanitary systems of towns he visited. Apart from this, however, it seems he had no direct experience of sanitary affairs.[49]

Despite this apparent lack of experience, Simon's name appeared on the central committee of the Health of Towns Association in 1844, in company with Disraeli, and well-known public health campaigners such as Southwood Smith, Toynbee, Guy and Grainger, when he was

---

44 Lambert, op. cit., p. 17.
45 Ibid., p. 18.
46 John Simon *Personal Recollections of Sir John Simon* (privately printed, London, 1898, rev. 1903), cited in Lambert, op. cit., p. 19.
47 Ibid., cited in Lambert, op. cit., p. 19.
48 Introductory memoir by J. Simon to J. H. Green, *Spiritual Philosophy* (London, 1865), cited in Lambert, op. cit., p. 21.
49 Lambert, op.cit., p. 64.

still only 28 and unknown.[50] He received the diploma of the Royal College of Surgeons, later becoming an honorary FRCS; he became Joint Demonstrator of Anatomy and later Senior Assistant Surgeon at King's College Hospital—both posts only paying a total of £25 a year. He was appointed a full surgeon at St Thomas's Hospital in 1847, which paid a salary of £200 per annum. He recalled that the four years 1838–41 'offered an infinity of spare time which could be given to non-professional pursuits'.[51] These pursuits included the study of Oriental languages, the formation of a society for the study of German metaphysics, and the continuation of a long-held interest in literature. He took great care with his writings and literary style throughout his career, winning the first Astley Cooper Prize of the Royal College of Surgeons in 1845, which led to his being elected to the Royal Society later that year. He was an enthusiastic traveller throughout Europe, meeting prominent scientists, artists, writers and musicians, including Mendelssohn; nearer home, he spent a memorable morning with Wordsworth, who read to him (twice) his sonnet on the Duke of Wellington.[52] For the rest of his life, his friends would be from the world of literature and art, rather than politics or medicine.

19th-century London

Unlike Liverpool, the population of the inner City of London was shrinking, not increasing, but those that were left were becoming poorer, as the wealthy moved out of the city to healthier suburbs—as was to happen in Dublin. More and more people crowded into the slum areas, and 'infinite degrees of subletting aggravated the problem'. Unlike Liverpool, there were few inhabited cellars, and the death rate was better than many cities—for example, between 1838 and 1844 the City of London's death-rate was 24.36 per thousand compared to Liverpool's 35 per thousand.[53] All streets within the City were paved, all were supplied with water, and by 1848 only 3¾ miles of sewers remained to be laid.[54]

However, the overall death-rate hid many problems: the city's infant mortality rate was 10–15 per 1,000 greater than the national average;[55] the increasingly overcrowded housing situation was

---

50 Ibid.
51 Simon, *Personal Recollections*, op. cit., p. 11, cited in Lambert, op. cit., p. 23.
52 Lambert, op. cit., p. 24.
53 *The Times* 30 June and 2 July 1849.
54 Lambert, op. cit, pp 80–81.
55 John Simon, *City Reports*, pp 85, 181, cited in Lambert, op. cit., p. 81.

worsened by the fact that the Corporation had no control over its water supply, which was supplied, unfiltered, by a private company, and worsening living conditions combined with overflowing city cemeteries, and with countless animals driven through the streets to the City markets. Refuse from slaughterhouses was thrown on the city streets, and blood was left to run down the centre channel of Aldgate High Street.[56] The Corporation however continued to deny that the City had a public health problem, the Lord Mayor stating that 'there could be no improvement in the sanitary condition of the City—it was perfect.'[57]

Simon quickly became an outspoken reformer, not afraid to demand change. Within two weeks of his election, he had presented a plan for the organisation of his office, and had arranged that the Registrar General give him full notification of all deaths in the City. City officials initially refused to believe the facts he brought before them. When his statistics were corroborated by the Registrar General, the City refused to allow them to be printed. Within a few months of his appointment Simon demanded that clauses be inserted into a National Nuisances Act, banning underground slaughterhouses and allowing the closure of burial grounds. His demand was not successful, but he had set himself on a course that he would continue.

In his first Annual Report in 1849, Simon outlined a six-point plan to reform the sanitation of the City of London, pointing out in strong and unambiguous terms the high mortality rate in the City, and itemising the causes, such as the bad housing and unsanitary water supply. The Commissioners were incensed, and tried to block publication of his report.

London's legislation

Legislation for reform of the City of London's sanitation began later than Liverpool, and the appointment of John Simon was greatly influenced by that of William Duncan. The City, anxious to keep its independence from the rest of the metropolis, lobbied for, and was successful in obtaining an Act independent of the Public Health Act of 1848, and a special City Sewers Act.[58] However, having used these Acts

56 Guildhall Papers, MS Mins. Sewer Comm. Lxxxiv, f. 12; lxxxvm f. 78, cited in Lambert, op. cit., p. 85.

57 Quoted in *Report of the Health of London Association on the Sanitary Condition of the Metropolis* (London, 1847), p. viii, cited in Lambert, op. cit., p. 67.

58 Anthony S. Wohl, *Endangered Lives, public health in Victorian Britain* (London, Melbourne, Toronto, 1983), p. 149.

to retain their independence and to appoint their first Medical Officer of Health, they were reluctant to take any further steps at reform. They soon found that John Simon was a force to be reckoned with.

By 1850, however, Simon, by constant analytical reporting of sanitary problems and by repeated calls to the City Commissioners to do their duty, by constructive suggestions for improvement, together with judicious use of his allies in the Press, had won more widespread support. *The Times* in particular supported Simon—he had many close friends on the paper.

In what would eventually come into effect on 24 July 1851 as the City Sewers Act[59] Simon ensured the insertion of clauses giving the City increased powers of legislation concerning 'cellar dwellings, slaughtering, nuisance trades, penalties, unfit food, cattle keeping, smoke abatement, slum clearance and tenement regulation . . . . and converted the faulty and lagging measure of 1848 into one of the most advanced pieces of health legislation of the time'.[60]

By 1851, Simon had established himself as the driving force behind sanitary activity in the City, distributing forms to the Inspectors of Nuisances, on which they recorded the results of their inspections in detail. 'Each week [Simon] went through these detailed returns, noting where the Act could be beneficially applied and making visits of verification himself'.[61] The City Sewers Act would remedy most of the faults that Simon had pointed out in his reports.

Simon's legacy

From the time of his appointment as Medical Officer of Health for the City of London, Simon's interest in public health matters developed into a passion for reforming administration, and he would become perhaps the most influential of the three MOHs examined in this chapter, the one whose name is most associated with public health reform in Britain in the 19th century. Duncan had been the pioneer in pointing out the duties of a local authority to protect the health of its citizens—a new concept, mooted by Chadwick. Simon brought this concept to a more advanced stage, pushing government involvement in public welfare into previously uncharted territory. The bulk of his career was at government, rather than local, level and this forms his lasting achievement. Simon remained as Medical Officer of

---

59 Local and Private Acts, 14 & 15 Vict. cap xci
60 Lambert op. cit., p. 173.
61 Ibid., p. 180.

Health for only seven years, moving on to a more powerful position as Chief Medical Officer of the Board of Health in 1855, and the reformed legislation would show most of its results during the reign of his successor, Henry Letheby. Simon's legacy was in pushing the Corporation 'into unexplored areas of interference with an impetus never wholly to be lost'.[62]

However it was during his seven years as Medical Officer of Health for the City of London that he consolidated the theories of public health administration that he would later bring to a wider platform. Where Duncan advised Liverpool Council as to the course of action they should take, Simon more confidently stated the duties of the Commissioners of Sewers and of the City Fathers, identifying himself as the channel through which these duties would be carried out. It was an important difference in attitude, one which would at first gain him enemies, but would eventually gain him adulation as one of the great Victorian public health visionaries.

Simon asserted his views on the rights of property owners—one of the sacred cows of Victorian legislation: 'And as for the rights of property—they are not only pecuniary. Life, too, is a great property: and your Act asserts its rights'.[63] The Commissioners agreed with him—the City Sewers Act was enforced to its full extent, even against several aldermen.[64]

The Minutes of the Sewers Committee show that in 1851, 496 orders for sanitary works were issued, rising to 1,021 in 1852, and 1,700 in 1853.[65] In 1854, William Haywood, the City Surveyor, could state that 'the owners of half the houses within the City, . . . have been compelled to do something on these premises'.[66]

Simon also campaigned in his reports for increased drainage, and by 1854 the City of London was the only part of the metropolis with a complete and workable sewerage system. Haywood boasted that 'there is not a house in the City of London which has not a daily water supply of some kind'.[67] Simon had continually pressed the City's supplier, the New River Water Company, to increase the supply, claiming that sanitation was compromised, and the poor put at risk by 'that vicious administration of the water trade against which I have so

62 Lambert, op. cit.,p. 214.
63 Simon, *City Reports*, pp 203-204, cited in Lambert, op. cit., p. 182.
64 MS Mins. Sewers Comm., lxxxvii, f.768; lxxxix, f.294, cited Lambert, op. cit., p. 186.
65 Ibid., lxxxvii, ff.192-3; lxxxviii, f.19; lxxxix, f.8, cited Lambert, op. cit., p. 186.
66 *Rep. Royal Comm. City*, PP. 1854, xxvi, Q.5981, cited Lambert, op. cit., p. 186.
67 Ibid., cited Lambert, op. cit., p. 187.

often protested'.[68]

Simon was also successful in closing cellar slaughterhouses, but was less successful in persuading the Corporation to spend money on baths and wash-houses and, although he made some effort to deal with adulterated food, the lack of facilities for chemical analysis locally made prosecution difficult The overall effect of Simon's efforts came to fruition in 1854, when another epidemic of cholera struck—this time, the mortality was 71 per cent lower than it had been in 1849,[69] although Simon refused to claim any credit, saying 'there can be no present demonstration that this happy result has been the unconditional effect of your sanitary labours'.[70] It appears that from around 1854 Simon may have decided that he needed to broaden his sphere of influence; in that year he published his *City Reports* in book form, bringing his expertise to a wider audience. He may well have been encouraged by the exhortations of his ever-ambitious father, who told him 'you cannot afford to remain *perdu*, your light under a bushel'.[71] In September, 1855, seven years after his appointment, John Simon resigned as Medical Officer of Health for the City of London to take up the position of Chief Medical Officer to the Board of Health, the role on which his lasting reputation would be based.

James Burn Russell, Glasgow

The third of Cameron's contemporary public health models had, unlike Duncan and Simon, a predecessor.

Scotland was later than England in appointing Medical Officers of Health, mainly due to the Scottish medical establishment rejecting control by an English board of health. Their first Medical Officer of Health was appointed in Edinburgh in 1863, followed by the part-time appointment of William Gairdner in Glasgow in 1863, in response to increased concern about public health, exacerbated by several cholera epidemics. Despite his part-time post and scant resources—his office was converted from two shops—Gairdner appears to have made a significant effort to establish some kind of sanitary administration. He produced fortnightly reports on the condition of the city (to the embarrassment of the Town Council), he employed chemists to analyse the water supply, employed female sanitary inspectors to give hygiene instruction, and was instrumental in establishing municipal

---

68 *The Times*, 3 December 1851.
69 Lambert, op. cit., p. 205.
70 Ibid., p. 206 (no reference given).
71 Family Papers, 9 September 1853, L.M. Simon to J. Simon, cited in Lambert, op. cit., p. 198.

fever hospitals and a City Improvement Trust to clear the slums. It was the latter, with its accompanying 'improvement tax' levied on householders, that brought an end to his tenure as Medical Officer of Health. Accusations were made of overspending in the sanitary department, and a decision was made to remove Gairdner and his assistants and appoint a full-time Medical Officer of Health. Despite uproar in the medical establishment at this decision, 45 applicants applied for the new full-time post.

James Burn Russell, then superintendent of the City of Glasgow Fever Hospital, a post he had been appointed to on the recommendation of William Gairdner, was the choice of the Glasgow medical establishment. It took some time for the sanitary committee to accept his appointment, some members being unwilling to appoint someone connected with Gairdner, but Russell was finally appointed in November 1872. William Gairdner, who refused the offer of a consultancy at £100 a year, would later say that his chief service to Glasgow was 'to have discovered Dr. Russell and placed him in the track of my succession'.[72]

James Burn Russell was born in Glasgow on 5 May 1837. His mother died of consumption, aged twenty-two, when he was aged two. When he was in his teens, his father emigrated to Australia, apparently following a disapproved-of liaison with a cousin, leaving the young Russell and his sister to be brought up by their paternal grandparents in Glasgow. Russell would later write a poem to his father, published in the *Glasgow Citizen,* in which he spoke of 'that lang-empty armchair'.[73] His upbringing with his grandparents appears to have been strict, and Russell would later tell the story of how his grandfather, a hero of the Battle of Waterloo, and the first steamboat harbourmaster for the Clyde Navigation Trust, as well as captain of the river police, 'a self-educated man who had carried a dictionary in his kit at Waterloo, had once corrected his [grandson's] pronunciation when he was reading aloud, and when his advice was rejected said: 'James, pronounce the word correctly, or I'll knock you down.' The boy still refused, and was duly knocked down.'[74]

Russell's later career would show him as stubborn, although he had a great fondness for his grandfather, who appears, despite this incident, to have been a caring substitute for his absent father.

---

72 Edna Robertson, *Glasgow's Doctor James Burn Russell 1837–1904* (East Lothian, Scotland, 1998), p. 69.

73 Ibid., op. cit., p. 17.

74 Ibid., p. 18.

When Russell was ten, in 1847, almost 143,000 refugees from the Irish Famine arrived in Glasgow, coinciding with, and probably largely the cause of, a typhus epidemic in the city, and later a cholera epidemic. Russell enrolled as an arts student at Glasgow University at the age of 17, showing a talent for composition, and an innate shyness, which he fought against, becoming one of the College's leading debaters. The College was on the doorstep of some of Glasgow's worst slums, and the students had first-hand knowledge of conditions—a Scottish Universities Commission in 1858 reporting that it was 'hardly possible to conceive a combination of circumstances less favourable to the bodily and mental well-being of the Youth attending a University'.[75] Like Simon and Cameron, Russell had a deep interest in literature and poetry. He read medieval French literature, took an interest in the connection between American slang and old English phrases, and recorded the words of Scottish ballads from his grandparents' servant. His father sent him natural history articles from the *Sydney Morning Herald,* and Russell shared nature walks near Glasgow with his lifelong school-friend James Bryce, who would later become a member of Gladstone's cabinet, British Ambassador to the United States, and be regarded as 'the most educated politician of his time'.[76]

With this wide range of interests, Russell's medical calling did not become evident for some time. Instead, his first appointment after his graduation in 1858, was as unpaid assistant to his former lecturer in Natural Philosophy, William Thompson, later Lord Kelvin, on board HMS *Agamemnon,* in which he was part of the first successful attempt to lay a cross-Atlantic cable. Russell kept a journal of the expedition for his sister Agnes and, when the *Agamemnon* put into Queenstown (Cobh) for provisions, he visited Blarney and the Lakes of Killarney. He later recalled this visit as 'a happiness so pure, that we can scarce believe it ever to have been ours'.[77] When the cable was successfully laid, and messages began to be transmitted from Valentia Island, Thompson left Russell in charge of the station and instruments. That cable would eventually fail, but Russell recalled his cable-laying experience in his journal:

> I shall never forget these six months . . . I have lived more in that time than in all the preceding years.[78]

---

75 -Ibid., p. 26.
76 Ibid., p. 28.
77 James Burn Russell, 'Atlantic Cable: Leaves from the Journal of an Amateur Telegrapher' in *The West of Scotland Magazine,* No. 59, August, 1859, pp 312–4.
78 Ibid., cited in Robertson, op. cit., p. 41.

Russell regarded the cable-laying episode as something he had done as a favour to William Thompson—he had already decided to become a doctor, and enrolled at Glasgow Medical School. In his third year of study, he joined Joseph Lister's first surgery class. Lister was impressed by Russell's 'superior abilities' and 'literary culture' and predicted that he was destined for 'a bright career of usefulness'.[79] On graduation in 1862, he began work as a houseman in Glasgow Royal Infirmary, but had set his mind on a career in public health, much influenced by William Gairdner's lectures on public health which he had attended. In 1863, during a typhus epidemic, Russell was appointed Assistant Medical Officer of the Glasgow poorhouse, with responsibility for the fever wards. He did a survey of 300 cases within the hospital, concluding that overcrowded accommodation, where washing was impossible, was the cause of the disease, and that 'dirtiness begins, therefore, as a sin of circumstance'.[80] As the epidemic continued, a loan was obtained, and the first municipal fever hospital in Scotland was opened in 1865; Russell was appointed its first Medical Superintendent and resident physician at a salary of £240—he was aged 27. He had no medical staff, and was involved in all aspects of hospital management, including the housekeeping accounts, but after a year the hospital had become such a valuable asset to the disease defences of the city that it was made a permanent hospital—the first such local authority hospital.

In 1870, he also took charge of the new Belvidere fever hospital, described as 'the largest fever hospital out of London and the finest in the three kingdoms'.[81] Between the two hospitals, Russell was now responsible for more than 4,000 patients a year, only applying for two salary increases—one in 1870, which was granted, and one the following year, which was refused; instead, he was given a £100 bonus for 'the great labour devolved upon Dr. Russell during the past nine months'.[82] In 1872, he applied for the post of Medical Officer of Health for Glasgow.

From the time he decided to study medicine, Russell decided that he would work in the area of public health—not then an established or remunerative area for a young man. His career from the beginning was one of service to the less privileged, devoted to the prevention of

79 Letter of support from Lister for Russell's application for the post of surgeon at Glasgow Royal Infirmary, cited in Robertson, op. cit., p. 45.
80 Robertson, op. cit., p. 52.
81 Ibid., p. 67.
82 Ibid., p. 68.

disease and the improvement of Glasgow's public health.

19th-century Glasgow

The Glasgow of which James Burn Russell became Medical Officer of Health in 1872, was a prosperous industrial city, with a growing population. Russell's part-time predecessor, William Gairdner, had started to tackle the slum problem in 1863, and the City Improvement Trust initiated by him had begun to demolish unsanitary dwellings and replace them with new ones. Municipal cleansing had been put in place, and water closets had begun to replace the old privies. The City Improvement Trust had begun to demolish the worst of the slums, and during the early 1870s, more than 15,000 people were moved from the worst areas.[83]

As in Dublin, many of those displaced were housed in the cast-off houses of the middle classes, who were moving to the suburbs, and significant swathes of slum areas still remained untouched in the city. In the second half of the 1870s Glasgow's economy suffered a particular setback, as the Glasgow Bank failed and the building boom came to an end. Houses that had been earmarked for demolition were instead sketchily renovated, and municipal public housing did not recommence until 1896, much later than in other cities, including Dublin. Although many of the devastating diseases, such as typhus, typhoid and cholera, had been brought under control, pulmonary diseases remained a problem, and infant mortality was still high. During Russell's first year as MOH, there was an epidemic of scarlet fever, and of those children who died, 30 per cent lived in one-room tenements.[84]

The Irish, even a generation after the Famine, remained a problem, and Russell's attitude to them and the Catholic Church was ambivalent. He had become interested in the Irish question during several stays in the cable station at Valentia, and during training at the Rotunda. He was a vigorous opponent of Home Rule. He regarded the Irish poor in Glasgow as the 'most obstinate' overcrowders who spent money on whisky instead of rent, describing them as 'people who cannot be trusted to live without supervision and guidance',[85] yet he believed that these traits were not due to national characteristics but to their living conditions. In his cable-laying journal he had blamed

---

83 Robertson, op. cit., p. 97.
84 Ibid., pp 88–9.
85 James Burn Russell, *Public Health Administration in Glasgow*, p. 189, cited in Robertson, op. cit., p. 134.

the Catholic Church for 'the spirit of intolerance' which was 'the ruin of Ireland',[86] but in the Glasgow slums he worked closely with priests, gaining their support to ban wakes to prevent the spread of disease.

In taking over the reins from Gairdner, Russell faced a different administrative structure. Gairdner had had sanitary staff at his disposal, whereas Russell, although full-time, had no authority over sanitary staff—these were under the authority of a Chief Sanitary Inspector. This post was created by the Scottish Public Health Act of 1867, ahead of the post of Medical Officer of Health, giving the impression that the former was the more senior position.

Russell's first task was to establish his own authority and to gain the trust and support of the sanitary staff, whose help was essential if he was to carry out his duties. He faced resistance to his reforms from the same sources who had objected to Gairdner—councillors who ridiculed slum clearance, with remarks such as 'if they put a dog in a palace it was still a dog'.[87]

Russell was more outspoken than his predecessor and gained even more adversaries with his outspoken condemnation of all parties who endangered public health, including industrialists, teachers, and the medical profession. However, he gained the support and lifelong friendship of a group of reforming councillors, whom he described as 'day-to-day committee men rather than fortnightly town councillors'.[88] The most influential of these was John Ure, who became Lord Provost in 1880, and was determined to use his office to reform legislation in line with Russell's plans.

When Ure found that planned national legislation was delayed, his and Russell's other supporters decided to bring in local legislation in the form of the Glasgow Police Bill, which included provision for, among other things, the enforced cleaning of unsanitary houses, the removal of patients with infectious diseases from their homes, a ban on children from infected homes attending school (and fines for teachers who ignored this ban), compulsory provision of indoor sanitation, and the closure of unsanitary houses. The bill would take a decade to come into law, but when the Glasgow Police (Amendment) Act came into force in 1890, it put Glasgow at the forefront of public health reform.[89] In the meantime, Russell often took the law into his own hands.

---

86 Robertson, op. cit., p. 134.
87 *Glasgow Herald*, 25 September 1874, p. 5, cited in Robertson, op. cit., p. 103.
88 James Burn Russell, Obituary of W. R. W. Smith, *Proceedings of the Philosophical Society of Glasgow*, 1892–3, pp 206–210, cited in Robertson, op. cit., p. 117.
89 Robertson, op. cit., p. 118.

He also had to convince the press of the seriousness of the situation; in 1879 he wrote in the *Glasgow Herald*:

> we hear constantly of improvidence and intemperance, but do not let us forget vicious buildings, houses whose surroundings debase and brutalise the soul as well as impair the body, or our unnecessarily polluted atmosphere . . .

and claimed that 'the bulk of the community stands aloof'. The paper responded by attacking Russell for trying to 'break down the self-dependence of the nation's character in order to save ourselves the pain of watching momentary suffering', and accused him of playing on the feelings of the public by describing the misery of the poor. To which Russell replied by asking rhetorically:

> What can I do save 'work upon the feelings of the public' by describing that, which, in fact and reality, has worked upon my own feelings?[90]

Glasgow's health legislation

The 1848 Public Health Act, which allowed for the appointment of Medical Officers of Health, did not apply in Scotland, because the Scottish medical establishment objected to being controlled by London. In fact, most sanitary legislation that originated in London proved unworkable in Scotland, as it was incompatible with Scotland's different legal system. The prevailing doctrine, championed by many in the Church of Scotland and by the Free Church, was that the community, not the State, should be responsible for the needs of the poor. Once again, cholera proved to be 'the great reformer' and following epidemics in 1848 and 1853–4, the need for reform became more widely accepted. In 1857 a Committee on Nuisances was set up in Glasgow, and the appointment of a Medical Officer of Health for the city was then proposed.[91]

James Burn Russell's legacy

Russell remains almost unknown in the city for which he worked with so much passion and efficiency. In the Foreword to Robertson's biography of Russell, the last full-time Medical Officer of Health for Glasgow, T. Scott Wilson, describes Russell as 'one of the truly great

90 *Glasgow Herald,* 29 December 1879, p. 3, 2 January 1890, p. 4 and 6 January 1890, p. 7, cited in Robertson, op. cit., p 105.
91 Robertson, op. cit., p.72.

figures of late Victorian Glasgow' and remarks that, although he has been long forgotten by the general public, he has not been forgotten by those working in public health in modern-day Glasgow, being 'almost venerated by successive generations'.[92] Robertson remarks that Russell's name 'which a century ago was known in Budapest and Boston, is now unknown to the majority of Glaswegians'[93] — the same could be said of Cameron.

Of all the comparators, Russell could perhaps be described as the sanitarian's sanitarian, leading his men from the front, going into vigorous battle against the enemies of public health on a daily basis. He had a fight on his hands right from the beginning, beating off a field of 45 candidates for the post of Medical Officer of Health. A close friend of his part-time predecessor, William Gairdner, who had left the post in controversial circumstances, he also had to fight the suspicion of those councillors who had been hostile to Gairdner. Moreover, under Scottish public health legislation, his position was not fully defined — he had no staff of his own, and no authority over the sanitary inspectors, who were under the control of a Chief Sanitary Inspector. This system of dual responsibility would exist for Russell's entire term of office, with the result that he had to work, not only at his new post, but at winning the respect of men over whom he had no official authority. He also had to build allies within the Corporation to offset the suspicion and hostility that still existed towards the work of the Medical Officer of Health.

Unlike Duncan and Simon, Russell did not face any immediate public health crisis when he took office, there was no epidemic looming, and mortality from infectious disease was decreasing in Glasgow. It was, however, a port city, and the threat of imported disease, as well as the many threats from the city slums themselves, was a constant danger. This increased during Russell's term of office, as recession hit Glasgow in the second half of the 1870s, and paralysed many businesses. During Glasgow's boom years in the first half of the 1870s the City Improvement Trust had displaced 15,000 people in slum clearances. When the Trust found it could no longer afford to demolish the abandoned houses, it set about re-furbishing them, becoming the city's biggest slum landlord in the process, and poverty and overcrowding became once again a threat to public health in the city.

From the beginning, Russell was determined to pinpoint the state

---

92 Ibid., Foreword.
93 Ibid., Preface, p. 5.

of health of his territory. Working through the sanitary inspectors, who visited as many as 20,000 houses each month, he built up a set of statistics on the city's health problems that were unequalled anywhere else in the British Isles.[94] His admiration for these men was obvious, as they spied on doctors and infectious households in an effort to forestall epidemics, and his relationship with them grew accordingly. He saw their inspections as vital detective work in combating disease, and described one inspector as having 'the nose of a sleuth-hound when put upon the track'.[95] Russell would often accompany the inspectors if he thought there might be difficulty in getting someone with an infectious disease to go voluntarily to hospital. When serving a warrant on such a person, he would 'go in with the fighting men of our staff' and carry the reluctant patient out to the fever van.[96] On one occasion, finding the door barred, Russell sent an inspector up a ladder and through a window, whereupon he was attacked by the patient's brother.[97] Russell believed in 'the firmness of reason and not of mere despotism',[98] and showed humanity as well as toughness. While unceremoniously removing children with scarlet fever to hospital without warrants, a measure he claimed was unique to Glasgow, he allowed mothers to stay with under-fives,[99] and, despite protests that the lower classes 'would infect respectable children with their bad habits as well as their diseases', persuaded Glasgow School Board to keep playgrounds open after hours for the use of children.[100] He called for 'a few open spaces here and there . . . where boys could spin tops and little children could sprawl about in safety'.[101] He called for public parks to have playing fields for 'lads who cannot afford to lease fields like the golden youth of the wealthy', and for cities to be designed as places where children were part of the population, and to be 'less like places laid out by some Board of Bachelors'.[102]

It was in such vivid phrases used in his public lectures that Russell stirred the conscience of Glasgow's middle class, asking well-to-do

---

94 Ibid., p. 83.
95 Ibid., p. 81.
96 Ibid.
97 Ibid.
98 Ibid., p. 87.
99 Ibid., pp 87–8.
100 Health Minutes, 2 March and 21 May 1888, GCA E1 20.11, pp 237, 311, cited in Robertson, op. cit., p. 116.
101 James Burn Russell, 'Life in One Room', Lecture delivered to the Park Parish Literacy Institute, Glasgow, 27 February, 1888.
102 James Burn Russell, *Public Health Administration in Glasgow* (Glasgow, 1905), pp 301–23, cited in Robertson, op. cit., p 130.

women with large houses and servants to imagine living in one room like the poor 'crammed in like salted fish in their barrel':[103]

> You mistresses of houses, with bed-rooms and parlours, dining-rooms and drawing-rooms, kitchens and washing-houses, pantries and sculleries, how could you put one room to the uses of all? You fathers, with your billiard-room, your libraries and parlours, your dinner parties, your evening hours undisturbed by washing-days, your children brought to you when they can amuse you, and far removed when they become troublesome, how long would you continue to be that pattern husband which you are—in one room?[104]

Russell drove home his point even further: 'Place 126,000 human beings in one-room houses . . . and no matter who or what they are, you have at once determined for them much both of their moral and physical future.'[105] Russell had never forgotten, according to himself, attending a lecture at which the audience broke into 'incredulous laughter' when told that 41 families out of every 100 in Glasgow lived in one room.[106] Although painfully shy, for the rest of his career he would fight that shyness to bring the facts to public notice in his lectures.

Although much of Russell's work involved dealing with public health problems caused in slum areas, he also found dangers to public health among the elite of Glasgow society, and tackled them when necessary. For years, he pursued Glasgow's most influential industrialist, Charles Tennant, in an effort to get him to reduce smoke emissions from his factory.[107] He also fined steamship owners for smoke offences; the Distillers Company was ordered to stop discharging waste into the public sewers, and transport companies were forbidden to allow people on board carrying bundles of old clothes.[108]

By the beginning of the 1890s, his concentrated efforts were beginning to show results. The death rate had decreased by 12 per cent from 25.6 per thousand in 1881 to 22.7 in 1891. In particular, Glasgow had made significant inroads into the fight against pulmonary tuberculosis which by the late 1890s had begun to decline faster in

---

103 Russell 'Life in One Room', op. cit.
104 Ibid.
105 Ibid.
106 Ibid.
107 Health Minutes, 5 March, 1883. GCAE120.7, pp 199, 213–14. 4 August, 1884, GCA E1 20.8, pp.231–2, cited in Robertston, op. cit., p. 115.
108 Robertson, op. cit., p. 115.

Glasgow than in any other city in Scotland or England.[109] He became an authority on the prevention of the disease, but strangely he had not been particularly enthusiastic about Koch's discovery of the tubercle bacillus in 1882, believing that 'in the enthusiasm naturally inspired by a new discovery, there is always an element of danger'.[110]

Glasgow did not have powers to seize tuberculous meat and milk until the Glasgow Police Act of 1890—much later than Dublin. It is interesting that Russell's biographer mentions several times that 'the word tuberculosis never featured in his regular reports of the time', but that 'an awareness of the disease . . . was implicit in his repeated reminders of the virtues of fresh air and good ventilation'.[111]

In the late 1890s Russell came into conflict with a new regime in the Council who had decided to make sweeping developments in fifty areas of Glasgow. Russell, who had pressed for municipal housing development for many years, believed that these plans actually conflicted with the work of the Sanitary Department, demolishing buildings that they had worked hard to have renovated. He wrote: 'I can scarcely say how much I regret to find myself an obstructive in the way of the Improvement Trust, for the past work of which I entertain the deepest gratitude'.[112]

By 1898, he had left Glasgow to take up the offer of the post of Medical Member of the Local Government Board of Scotland. In his letter of resignation, he wrote 'I can honestly say that I have served the Corporation with all my heart'.[113] He died in 1904, and was buried in Glasgow; his funeral was attended by the sanitary staff of nearly 200, which prompted the comment: 'Here were the men now an army . . . in his early days he fought single with the enemy'.[114]

Public health reform in the 19th century, facing the consequences in great cities of laissez-faire industrialisation, was largely a matter of against-the-grain choices—by councils, corporations, legislators, their officials, and in particular those at the coal-face of sanitation problems, the Medical Officers of Health. Those Medical Officers of Health, faced with insurmountable problems and intractable forces, were often forced to make those choices based on pragmatism, practicality and a humane concern for those who had no other champions. Remarkable

---

109 Ibid., p. 144.
110 Ibid., p. 145.
111 Ibid., p. 145.
112 Ibid., p. 162.
113 Health Minutes, 10 October 1898, GCD E1 20.19, pp 79–80, cited in Robertson, op. cit., p. 165.
114 Robertson, op. cit., p. 183.

improvements in the key indicator, the death rates per 1000 inhabitants, were achieved: most spectacularly in Cameron's case where the rate fell from 37.7 per 1,000 in 1880 to 18.6 in 1921.

For the last quarter of the 20th century, the conventional academic view (following McKeown[115]) was that improvements in public health were the result of improved living conditions rather than advances in medicine. Such improvements, however, did not happen by the workings of market forces. They happened because of the work of men such as those described in this chapter. It is only comparatively recently that the contribution of Victorian Medical Officers of Health has begun to be re-evaluated and re-valued.

---

115 As expounded in e.g. Thomas McKeown, *The Role of Medicine—Dream, Mirage or Nemesis?* (London, 1976), *The Rise of Modern Populations* (New York, 1976).

Chapter 8 'The Bitter Cry'

In 1882, Cameron's family was completed with the birth of his eighth child, a son named Ewen Henry, born on 13 May. Cameron was solicitous about Lucie's recovery and reported her progress in his diary — 'Lucie doing well', 'Lucie came to drawing-room today', 'Lucie came to dining-room today', and the following day 'Lucie poorly today and in bed. Caught a cold yesterday.' In September 1882 the couple travelled to England on holiday, and Cameron also attended a conference. By the following year, he and Lucie had resumed their previous round of socialising, and in March they attended a St Patrick's Day ball at Dublin Castle until four in the morning. Their family life was as close as ever, Douglas returned from school for Pancake Night, Cameron would often bring the younger children to his lectures at Glasnevin. The family regularly attended Sunday services at the Magdalen Chapel. Cameron's diaries for 1882–3 continued to combine the minutiae of his personal life with details of his professional engagements.

But on Saturday 16 June 1883 the diaries stopped abruptly — the date was written, but there is no entry for that day. We can't be sure what happened to make Cameron suddenly stop what had become a regular diary habit, but what we do know is that, on 28 November 1883, Lucie, his beloved wife and companion, died of heart disease at the age of 45. Cameron's *Reminiscences*, written for his friends in 1913, state that when his wife died 'I had the misfortune to lose one of the best and kindest wives man ever had'.[1]

In his *Autobiography*, written in a slightly more formal style in 1920, he reports that Lucie died 'after twenty-one years of unalloyed happiness . . .'[2] In a booklet, *In Memoriam Lucie Cameron*, written by her cousin, the playwright W. G. Wills, he reports that she had been aware of her heart condition for several months, but had never complained, anxious 'to conceal her sufferings from the fond ones who surrounded her'. Wills continued: 'To her husband, Mrs Cameron was most tenderly attached, and almost her last words were in his praise'.[3] The pamphlet contains tributes from a wide range of people, and Wills made the point that 'it was only during her last illness and since her

---

1 Cameron, (1913), p. 83.
2 Cameron, (1920), p. 28.
3 W. G. Wills, *In Memoriam Lucie Cameron* (Dublin, 1884).

death that anything like the extent of her private charities became known'. She was reported never to have deserted friends who had fallen on hard times, and never to have refused those who appealed to her for help. She took a particular interest in the Masonic Female Orphan School, and a memorial and portrait of her was placed in the school after her death.

At the age of 53, Charles Cameron was left a widower with seven children ranging in age from 16 to just over a year old. Lucie's death affected him deeply, and he 'did not go into society for a year, and only to a slight degree during the following two years'[4] after it occurred. His diaries did not resume for several years, until 1 January 1890. The couple had been married on Lucie's birthday, and had always kept their wedding anniversary as a holiday. After Lucie died, Cameron mentioned the date of their wedding every year in his subsequent diaries, and every year, on the anniversary of her death, he visited her grave in Mount Jerome cemetery, often with his long-serving housekeeper, Annie Webber, and placed flowers in her memory. For the rest of his long life, Cameron did not socialise on that day, and his handwriting in the diary entries physically changes, indicating great emotion, as he writes of these anniversaries in his diaries every year. The depth of his feelings are obvious more than 30 years later in 1914, as he recorded in his diary of 28 November, 'Annie Webber and I went to Mount Jerome and placed for the 31st time flowers on the dear one's grave'.

While Cameron did not socialise after Lucie's death, he did occupy himself with work, and in particular with his writing. He devoted the three years after his wife's death to compiling what became the first edition of his *History of the Royal College of Surgeons in Ireland and of the Irish Schools of Medicine*.[5] He wrote that the mammoth work of 759 large pages 'entailed great labour', but that the work fascinated him, and he recounted how 'a feeling of loneliness came over me when it was completed'.[6] A second edition of this work was published in 1916, and it is still quoted by modern medical historians. He continued to produce his detailed reports on public health for the Corporation, and to contribute half-yearly reports on public health to the *Dublin Journal of Medical Science*, to which he also contributed a variety of articles, such as 'On the hygiene of Irish national schools',[7] 'On the water

4 Cameron, (1920), op. cit., p. 80.
5 Cameron, (1886) op. cit.
6 Cameron, (1920), op. cit., p. 82.
7 *Dublin Journal of Medical Science*, Vol. LXVII, Feb. 1884, pp 120–9.

supplies to high towns',[8] 'On micro-organisms and alkaloids which render food poisonous'.[9] At the same time, he contributed articles to *The Irish Builder*, such as 'The vaults in St Michan's, Church Street'.[10] The sheer volume of work and writing can have left him little time for grief—it was as if he blotted out everything with work.

In 1882, he had a survey made of all 24,211 inhabited houses in Dublin, and discovered that 32,202 of the 54,725 families living in the city inhabited only 7,234 houses, mostly living in one room per family.[11] A crucial part of the work was the conversion of the noisome and unhygenic privies to water-based sewage removal. 'In all Dublin there were 15,531 w.c.'s and 11,269 privies'.[12] By 1892, he could report that 'very few privies now exist in Dublin—the water carriage system has been nearly completed.'[13] His report to the Corporation of work carried out in the year 1884 illustrates the volume of work carried out by his staff; it included:

Inspections of tenement rooms	351,224
Inspections of tenement houses	76,053
Sanitary defects discovered	45,990
Sanitary defects remedied	45,659
Dwellings cleansed and whitewashed	12,022
Number of articles disinfected	11,086
Dwellings repaired	8,756
Sewers and house drains repaired and cleansed	3,799
Water-closets repaired	3,187
Water-closets constructed	2,798
Inspections of dairy yards	2,262
Inspections of slaughter houses	1,794
Sewers and house drains constructed	1,406
Inspections of nightly lodging houses	1,294

Source: RPDCD, (1885), vol. 3, pp 445–6.

In 1881, the staff Cameron had at his disposal for this volume of sanitary work consisted of:

A Consulting Medical Officer, a Secretary and Assistant Secretary, 15

---

8 Ibid., Vol. LXXVIII, Nov. 1884, pp 369–90.
9 Ibid., Vol. LXXVIII, Dec. 1884, pp 473–90.
10 *The Irish Builder*, Vol. XXVI, No. 630, 1 June 1884, pp 158–9.
11 'The Homes of the Poor in Dublin', RPDCD. Vol. 3, (1885) pp 441–2.
12 'Statement of the Duties carried out by the Public Health Department of the Corporation of Dublin', RPDCD, Vol. 1, no. 26 (1892) p. 235.
13 Ibid., p. 236.

District ex-officio Medical Officers of Health, a Superintendent of Disinfection and 2 Disinfectors, with a variable number of Whitewashers,
2 Inspectors of Food (re the Adulteration Act), 3 Constables acting as
assistants to the Meat Inspector, Superintendent Acting-Inspector James
Halligan, Acting-Inspector Timothy Fay, 3 Acting-Sergeants, and 12
Constables. In 1884 the number of civilian sanitary officers was raised
to 12.[14]

Difficulties of legislation

The complexities of housing legislation were often lost on those
who were not directly involved with the situation, and many of the
criticisms aimed at the apparent lack of action in closing houses were
based on lack of knowledge of the difficulties faced by Cameron and
his staff in the Public Health Office. For example, *The Times* stated
that:

> The disproportion between the alleged activities of the Dublin Public
> Health Department and its results is almost incredible. The staff claims
> to have made 272,034 inspections of rooms in tenement houses during
> 1912; the penalties inflicted for ordinary sanitary offences (including
> workshops) amounted to £157.'[15]

Even those who claimed, like Thomas Wrigley Grimshaw,
Registrar General, and prominent member of the Dublin Sanitary
Association, to have 'a greater general knowledge of these matters
than many others'[16] did not seem to fully understand the complexities
of dealing with the Dublin slum problem. He complained of the fact
that only two out of twelve unhealthy areas condemned by Mapother
had been dealt with, and claimed that 'in Dublin, the work has been
cheap and easy'.[17] Charles Cameron had a different perspective on
the matter, pointing out that clearing the two areas—the Coombe
and Plunket Street—cost the Corporation £24,000, but they only
got £200 per annum rent for these spaces from the Dublin Artisan's
Dwellings Association (with which, incidentally, Grimshaw was
connected). Cameron believed that, while this was useful work, 'I
venture to think that £24,000 spent in building labourers' cottages
would be more beneficial to the public health and profitable to the

---

14 Cameron, (1914), op. cit., pp 42–3.
15 *The Times*, 22 October 1913.
16 Thomas Wrigley Grimshaw, *The House Accommodation of the Artisan and Labouring Classes in Ireland* (Dublin, 1885), p. 18.
17 Ibid., p. 12.

Corporation', and requested 'as a tentative measure, the Corporation might at least erect dwellings for their own labourers'.[18]

As to closing unsanitary dwellings, another complaint of Grimshaw's, Cameron and his staff had two choices: 1) to close the unhealthy houses, or 2) to prosecute the landlords and force them to improve housing conditions. The first option, to close houses, simply moved the slum problem to another area, the tenants taking up residence in equally bad accommodation elsewhere. The second option, to prosecute landlords, was cumbersome—the law was designed to protect the rights of property owners, so each prosecution took months due to complex legal procedures. Cameron itemised the process in 1892:[19]

- The inspector serves a notice pointing out the complaint, giving the time it is to be rectified.
- The premises is re-inspected to ascertain if the notice has been complied with, and if not, to get permission for a summons.
- The inspector files an information for the magistrate, and obtains his authority to issue the summons.
- The summons is made and served, and entered in the magistrate's book for hearing.
- The magistrate hears the case, and gives a decision.
- A form setting forth this decision is prepared by the officer and served on the defendant.
- If the magistrate has given the defendant time to abate the nuisance, the premises is inspected again at the end of that time to see if the work has been carried out.
- If it has not, another information must be made, and another summons authorised, entered, issued and served.
- If the magistrate then imposes a fine, a warrant has to be filed, and given to the officer of the courts for execution.
- If the officer is unable to execute it, an arrest warrant and committal order is made out.
- If the defendant still fails to remedy the complaint, all that can be done by public health officials is to again summon, and go through all the procedures de novo.

In every case where an order to close a house was made, Cameron had to attend personally in court to give evidence; it was only in the

---

18 Charles A. Cameron, 'The Dwellings of the People' in *The Irish Builder*, 1 August 1881, p. 231. In 1914, Cameron claimed that the combined Coombe and Plunket Street schemes cost £54,239, with total rents of £340 p.a. (Cameron (1914), p. 62).
19 RPDCD 'Statement of the Duties', op. cit., pp 237–8.

early years of the 20th century that his certificate for closing a house, rather than a personal appearance by him, was accepted by the courts. Added to this were literally thousands of closures of individual rooms, all of which had to be inspected and condemned. Cameron recounts how 'in every instance of appeal I have to attend before the Recorder, and I have often been waiting in his Court for days for the appeal to be called.'[20]

Fines, if and when imposed, were so derisory as to be no deterrent — the same landlords came before the courts again and again. Under these circumstances, Cameron's staff was described as being 'barely adequate', and his situation was compared to that of his peer in Edinburgh, where 'Dr Littlejohn is sole judge in all nuisance cases, refers to no magistrate, but acts in each case independently and on his own judgement — thus avoiding all the delays and quibbling of the Dublin Police Courts — and his powers extend to removal of patients to hospital on his own certificate'.[21] Moreover, there were 500 police in Edinburgh, 'and they are for all sanitary purposes under the control and have to obey Dr Littlejohn's orders, and are, in fact, so far, 500 guardians of the public health in place of twenty-one, as in Dublin'.[22]

Faced with the endless and frustrating problems of the city's tenements and their attendant sanitary problems, Cameron never ceased to call on the Corporation to provide housing for them. It was not, as he said himself, that he had not got 'every desire to see the artisan class live in healthy and roomy dwellings', but that 'unskilled workers have a greater claim on our sympathy'.[23] Cameron, unlike many of his class during that era, understood that the underlying problem in Dublin was the poverty caused by casual employment or unemployment. The wages of labourers were usually between 15s and £1 per week, the work was irregular and seasonal, and thousands of people — Cameron reckoned it was around 10,000 — simply could not afford to pay even 2s for the cheapest type of tenement room, let alone the 4s or 4s 6d for voluntary housing schemes such as the Artisans' Dwellings. Year after year in his annual reports, in evidence given to official enquiries, and in any newspaper that would print his views, he came back to this theme — that the Corporation must act *in loco parentis* to those who could not help themselves.

20 RPDCD 'Statement of the Duties', op. cit., p. 236.
21 'Report of Deputation of Public Health Committee, who were requested to visit Glasgow, Edinburgh, etc.,' RPCD, Vol. 1, no. 33, (1880), p. 212.
22 Ibid., p. 213.
23 Cameron, (1914), op. cit., p. 53.

From personal visits to the homes of Dublin's poorest he could, and did, recount in detail their poverty, their miserable diet, and their living conditions, and the effects that all of these had on mortality rates. He harangued the Corporation year after year to provide housing that even the poorest could afford, believing that if they housed the very poor many of the public health problems would disappear. He was always careful to point out to reluctant rate-payers that any such improvements in the conditions of the poor would have corresponding health benefits for the rich.

He put a great deal of effort, not only into the detail of his reports to the Corporation, but also into devising schemes that would help to make these ideas a reality, painstakingly working out the cost, not only to the Corporation but to the ever-vigilant and ever-reluctant ratepayers who would eventually foot the bill.

In 1880, he suggested that the Corporation secure powers to borrow £100,000 and erect 600 houses for the poor—this suggestion was agreed to by the Corporation, but was never acted on.[24] In his report to the Corporation in 1881, Cameron recommended that a loan of £50,000 be obtained and dwellings built on a recently acquired derelict site. The result was the first Corporation housing scheme at Benburb Street. This scheme, which was the forerunner of all subsequent Corporation housing, was a result of constant nagging on Cameron's part.[25] His constant call for state housing was a daring and innovative approach by a public servant, in an era when municipal housing was still regarded by many as a step too far.

The situation in Dublin cannot be viewed in isolation—there was a general acceptance that the poor were a race apart, and that among them some were 'deserving' and some were 'non-deserving' of help. Those in positions of authority believed that it was the natural lot of some to remain poor, and that their condition was the outcome of divine providence. This theory can be seen as late as 1869, in the annual report of the Association for the Relief of Distressed Protestants which stated that:

> It has pleased God . . . that as there are distinctions in rank and station, position and occupation, there should also be variety in the circumstances of the different classes of the human race.[26]

24 Ibid. p. 52 and Cameron, (1920), op. cit., p. 140.
25 Cameron, (1914), op. cit., p 55
26 *Thirty-Second Annual Report of the Association for the Relief of Distressed Protestants*, 24 Feb 1869, p. 1.

A sympathetic attitude to the poor was not helped by the fact that there was no political gain to be had from improving their condition; in fact, it would alienate property owners and rate-payers by more stringent laws and increasing taxation, particularly as most local authorities were composed of, or elected by, those with vested interests.

However, the poor themselves were becoming increasingly aware of and dissatisfied with their circumstances; apprehension of what was seen as an increasingly militant proletariat was expressed throughout the 19th century. In 1840, Joseph Fletcher, an English statistician, claimed that 'political riots are rapidly becoming national instead of local',[27] and in 1849, in a paper dealing with the growth of socialism among the poor, Fletcher spoke of 'evil that is marching upon us from among them with gigantic strides'.[28] This view of possible threats to social order was still in evidence towards the end of the century, and an example can be seen in relation to the situation in Ireland. The President of the Royal Sanitary Institute of Great Britain, Sir Robert Rawlinson, reported to the Institute in 1884, after a visit to the Dublin slums, that they were 'seed-beds of disease and revolution', and that 'if this state of things should continue for any length of time you may have social disturbances like the French Revolution of the past century, which upset society from top to bottom'.[29]

The subject of working-class housing had gradually been gaining public interest in the United Kingdom. In 1883 and 1884 the press began to campaign on the issue with an outpouring of articles in newspapers and journals, such as the *Daily Telegraph*, 31 October and 26 November 1883; the *Illustrated London News*, 10 November and 22 December 1883; and *The Lancet*, 1, 15 and 29 December 1883.[30] A series of article entitled 'How the poor live' by George Sims was published as a book. The campaign began, however, in October 1883 with the publication of *The Bitter Cry of Outcast London*.[31]

'The Bitter Cry'—*public outrage*

'Emotive' is perhaps the most appropriate word to use when summing up the attitudes of Victorians to the problems of public health: emotive

---

27 M. J. Cullen, *The Statistical Movement in Early Victorian Britain* (New York, 1975), p. 142.
28 Ibid., p. 144.
29 *Transactions of the Sanitary Institute of Great Britain*, VI (1884–5), pp. 79–80.
30 Wohl, (1977), op. cit., p. 200.
31 Andrew Mearns, *The Bitter Cry of Outcast London* (originally published as pamphlet in 1883; republished Anthony S. Wohl (ed.) Leicester, 1970).

speeches about the moral weaknesses of the poor, about the squalid living conditions which debased the working classes and decimated them with high mortality rates, about the possibility that this squalor could spill over to the rest of the population and threaten them with disease, emotive warnings about the growing dissatisfaction and vociferousness of the poor, and about the threat that this posed to private ownership and the status quo.

But the most emotive voice of all came from an unknown evangelical clergyman, Rev. Andrew Mearns, Secretary of the London Congregational Union. Rev. Mearns wrote what was originally an anonymous, 20-page pamphlet entitled *The Bitter Cry of Outcast London*, which appeared in London bookshops in the autumn of 1883. In October 1883, *Reynolds' Newspaper* wrote that 'The revelations concerning "Outcast London" cause a tremendous sensation and thrill of horror through the land'.[32] According to Bentley Gilbert this pamphlet was 'perhaps the most influential single piece of writing about the poor that England has ever seen', [33] while Anthony Wohl claims that 'its impact was so immediate and cataclysmic that it must be considered one of the great pieces of Victorian reform literature'.[34] The *Pall Mall Gazette*, whose editor W. T. Stead used the pamphlet to launch a campaign against the London slums, wrote that 'it was not until the *Bitter Cry* stirred the nation that the slums came to be regarded as unpleasant abodes . . .'[35]

Although a great deal had been written about conditions in the slums, much of it by dedicated medical men who selflessly served the poor, it was the emotive and graphic descriptions by Rev. Mearns which had the greatest impact. His description of miserable beings living in 'pestilential human rookeries . . . where walls and ceiling are black with the accretions of filth',[36] were couched in language that appealed to the Victorians' sense of melodrama. He described houses 'swarming with vermin', and air made foetid by the 'putrefying carcasses of dead cats or birds'; he wrote of rooms that often housed more than one family, or served more than one purpose, such as preparing dead animals for the furrier, or were used for immoral purposes at night, while the children were let out into the street.[37] Mearns did not condemn the poor, but instead declared that they were

32 Wohl (1977), op. cit., p. 206.
33 Bentley Gilbert, *The Evolution of National Insurance* (London, 1966), p. 28.
34 Wohl, (1977), op. cit., p. 206.
35 *Pall Mall Gazette*, 15 Feb 1889.
36 Mearns, (1970 ed.) op. cit., p. 58.
37 Ibid., p. 59.

'entitled to credit for not being twenty times more depraved than they are'.[38] His vivid descriptions of young children, released when well from hospital, crying because they were returning to their miserable homes, and of the public house being 'the Elysian field of the tired toiler'[39] struck a chord that more circumspect writings on the slums had not previously done. His graphic descriptions of conditions that the citizens of the British Empire were more used to hearing applied to 'the middle passage of a slave ship'[40] shook the complacency of the public and politicians. Most telling of all, he hit the prudish Victorians with the weapon that hurt them most—immorality. He spoke of 'young girls being drawn into a life of immorality', of 'the common lodging-houses . . . where both sexes are allowed to herd together without any attempt to preserve the commonest decency',[41] and by the blunt statement that 'Incest is common; and no form of vice and sensuality causes surprise or attracts attention'.[42] While Mearns later qualified the latter statement, changing 'common' to 'frequent,' it was the didactic tone of his original text that would shake the (outwardly) moral and complacent Victorians. The thought that such vices were thriving in the heart of the Empire was anathema to their sense of pride and prudery, and Mearns' tract launched an upsurge of outrage.

The contents of Mearns' pamphlet was widely disseminated by the press, and the impassioned phrases 'bitter cry' and 'outcast London' became household words, and brought home to both the ordinary public and to politicians the inadequacy of existing measures to combat the slum problem. *The Bitter Cry*, with its emphasis on the problems caused by overcrowding, forced those who had previously concentrated on the external environment—improved drainage and the demolition of slum areas—to take a more rounded view of the housing problems of the poor.

In November 1883, a public meeting was called, and a petition was sent to the Queen requesting a commission of inquiry.[43] In February 1884, Lord Salisbury moved in parliament for the appointment of a commission. A clear distinction was made between the existing policy of sanitary reform and the more basic problem of overcrowding:

It has not been noticed sufficiently that the great and peculiar evil is the

---

38 Ibid., p. 60.
39 Ibid., p. 61.
40 Ibid., p. 58.
41 Ibid., p. 60.
42 Ibid., p. 61.
43 Wohl (1977) op. cit., p. 219.

overcrowding of the poor and that all the remedies proposed for these other evils [sanitation and jerry-building], instead of diminishing over-crowding, only tend to exaggerate it . . . As long as you confine your at-tention to purely sanitary legislation, and do not bear in mind this difficulty of overcrowding, which is really the dominant one, your sanitary legislation will be in vain. People will not be turned out of unhealthy houses if there is nowhere to go. The local authorities, press them as you may, transform them as you will, will not carry out your enactments.[44]

Salisbury had made a plea the previous year for state intervention in providing housing for the poor; his remarks had been seen as 'the beginning of a new epoch' and of plunging his party 'into the turbid waters of State socialism'.[45] Cameron had made almost exactly the same pleas several years before in the 1879 Sewerage and Drainage Inquiry.

A commission of inquiry was set up, motivated by Salisbury's speech, a long debate in the House of Lords, not to mention the interest of Queen Victoria and the Prince of Wales, who appear to have been transformed into housing reformers by the zeitgeist (the Prince of Wales would later serve on the commission—a change from his usual activities). The Royal Commission on the Housing of the Working Classes, 1884–5, addressed 18,000 questions to witnesses in Britain and Ireland, among them Charles Cameron. It concentrated on accommodation, rents, overcrowding and the cost of living, as well as other topics. The Commission interviewed Cameron in Dublin on 23 May 1885; the interviewing panel included Sir Charles Dilke of the Local Government Board in London, a prime mover in the formation of the Commission, and Edmund Dwyer Gray, the Irish MP.

Sir Charles Dilke appears to have familiarised himself with the state of Dublin tenement housing, addressing the following question to Cameron:

The defects of the Dublin tenements are, I believe, that the houses are very old; that the wood-work is decayed, so that it is not easy to keep them in a cleanly state; that the floors frequently make a considerable angle with the horizon, owing to the subsidence of one of the walls; that the floors are rough and worm-eaten, and often so patched that the patches project above the general level of the floor, thereby preventing the proper cleansing of the floors; that the windows are frequently with-

44 Hansard, third series, CCLXXXIV ((1884), 1679–80, cited in Wohl (1977), op. cit., pp 237–8.
45 Wohl (1977), op. cit., p. 228.

out pulleys to the sashes, and that they are also frequently composed of ill-fitting sashes, which in stormy weather permit the wind to blow freely into the rooms; that the panes are often patched or broken; that the staircases are often dark, ill-ventilated, dilapidated, and too steep; that the approach to the yard of the house is frequently so difficult that the tenants prefer the more convenient access to the street, and empty their slops into the street during the absence of the police; that the sanitary accommodation is defective, one privy or water-closet being common to a dozen families, and being often situated in some such objectionable situation as the area or kitchen, there being no yards in which to place them; that the basement storeys, which have been cleared of their tenants, through the action of the Corporation, have become in many cases very filthy; that the yards are rarely asphalted or concreted; that their clay surfaces are often very damp, and the children who use the yards as playgrounds are liable to suffer from the dampness, especially when they are unshod, as is very often the case; that too many families inhabit the same house, and use a common staircase, and that when scarlet-fever, measles, or typhus occurs in such a house it is peculiarly liable to spread from room to room?[46]

This is quoted in full to demonstrate that there was full knowledge of the state of Dublin tenements in Westminster parliamentary circles in 1885 — particularly as a lack of official knowledge would be claimed at the subsequent 1913 Housing Inquiry, in which Cameron would be castigated for lack of action. Cameron confirmed the description given, and said that he had already sent to each member of the commission 'printed papers for the information of the Commission, showing the defective state of the tenement houses in Dublin'.[47]

Questioning then began on Cameron's work in Dublin. He confirmed that up to his appointment as Superintendent Medical Officer of Health in 1879, only 30 houses had been de-tenanted and closed, but that, following his appointment, between 31 August 1879 and 31 December 1880, 602 houses were de-tenanted and closed.[48] Cameron criticised the Torrens Act and said that he found 'a very good local Act with regard to ruinous dwellings' more effective.[49] On the chairman pointing out that the Torrens Act and its amendment 'are worked to a great extent in London', Cameron replied that

---

46   *Report of the Royal Commission on the Housing of the Working Classes*, xxx, Par. 22,058, (1884–5).
47   Ibid., Par. 22051, 22052.
48   Ibid., Par. 22094–22097.
49   Ibid., Par. 22106.

> Dublin is particularly circumstanced with regard to the great number
> of the owners of houses, and I have stated the great difficulty, almost
> amounting to an impossibility, that there is of applying it in Dublin
> where we have sometimes six owners of one house. It might take about
> three year's proceedings to get a house re-constructed.[50]

Under the terms of the local Act referred to—the Dublin
Improvement Act, 1864 (27 & 28 Vic. c. 305)—the sanitary authorities
could apply to have the tenants ejected. This ejection had to be carried
out by the Lord Mayor, who was required under the Act to attend in
person.[51]

Cameron gave witness that nearly all the privies in Dublin had now
been replaced by water closets, and that in 1882, on his orders, 'Every
house in Dublin, from Dublin Castle down to the smallest cottage was
examined' for sanitary facilities.[52] He maintained that the 'powers
existing under the Public Health Act are simply terrific. There is one
clause in that Act which provides that any place which is a nuisance or
injurious to health may be dealt with',[53] but he said that once a house
had been closed 'it becomes a difficulty how to dispose of it' and that
did require further legislation, as the Torrens Act was unworkable in
Dublin. [54]

Cameron elaborated further on the legal difficulties which beset his
work—caused by the fact that most Dublin tenements were situated in
old Georgian houses with high ceilings, and therefore had more than
the legal 300 cubic feet of space per person. He believed that the high
death rate in Dublin arose from

> there being too many families living in one house, and too many persons
> in one large room; so that the danger of communicating disease is in-
> creased.[55]

> The law does not enable us to take action as to a room, if there are five or
> six people in it, so long as each person has the minimal air-space of 300
> cubic feet.[56]

> I consider it a deplorable thing when a family consisting of four or five

---

50 Ibid., Par. 22,109.
51 Ibid., Par. 22,110–22114.
52 Ibid., Par. 22,121.
53 Ibid., Par. 22,150.
54 Ibid., Par. 22,153.
55 Ibid., Par. 22,172.
56 Ibid., Par. 22,234.

persons of different sexes and various ages are obliged to live in one room. I think it is opposed to every sentiment of decency besides being unhealthy.[57]

Asked by Mr Jesse Collings if he was in favour of the Corporation housing the poor, Cameron replied: ' I am. That is, I might say, a "fad" of mine almost'.[58] He continued:

There is no other way in which persons of the lower stratum of the population can be properly housed. Those persons who give the sanitarian the greatest amount of trouble, in whose houses I may say the fires of infectious diseases are kept smouldering, cannot pay rents which would enable ordinary landlords, who merely look to the houses as a means of making an income, to keep those houses in a proper sanitary condition. These persons pay 1s 6d or 1s per week. No ordinary landlord can supply a house with a water-closet and with proper yards and accommodation of that kind at a rent of 1s or 1s 6d per week. That is the stratum alone, I think, for whom the Corporation ought to provide dwellings. Well paid artisans and clerks and persons of that kind I would leave to the ordinary landlords or to the Artisans' Dwellings Company.[59]

On being questioned by Samuel Morley on intemperance among the Dublin poor and the implication that this was responsible for their poverty, Cameron's answers left no doubt that he was not prepared to accept this explanation, and he made a strong case for extenuating circumstances for intemperance.[60]

However, Cameron's most scathing comments were reserved for those who were abusing the township system and the tenement system. In relation to the former, he mentioned by name

a Mr. Bolton, a builder, in a very extensive way of business. His premises were just inside the canal in Richmond-street, and he moved immediately over the bridge to premises adjoining the canal outside the city, and you can see his workmen streaming into his premises every morning and passing out again in the evening. By that change of position he escapes perhaps a rate of 1s in the pound on his premises, and the same time he has all the advantages of the city; all his timber and stone are drawn through the city to his works, and all his workmen live in the city, and if they get knocked up they go to our hospitals. But the township in

57 Ibid., Par. 22, 239.
58 Ibid., Par. 22, 254.
59 Ibid., Par. 22,255.
60 The paragraphs dealing with this are from Par. 22,283 to 22,291.

which he lives pays no contribution to the hospitals, and if the child of one of his workmen goes to a reformatory or an industrial school the city has to bear the burden.[61]

On house farmers, or house jobbers, who rented houses from absentee landlords, to re-let at exorbitant rents to the poor, Cameron was even more scathing, stating that they 'live by screwing the largest amount of rent they can out of the tenants. The disproportion between the rents which the actual owner of the house gets and the rents which these house jobbers get out of the tenants is sometimes as one to three.'[62]

He described a conversation with one such house jobber, whose houses he had closed as unsanitary. When the man protested that he would have to go into the poorhouse if they were closed, Cameron replied 'I cannot help that; you ought to get some other occupation . . . you ought to have some other employment than screwing rack-rents out of your unfortunate tenants'. He made his feelings even plainer by telling the interviewer that he regarded slum middlemen 'as the curse of Dublin', and elaborated by explaining that the Corporation had no means of making these middlemen contribute to the repair of the house—this responsibility lay with the owner. Cameron's views were plain: 'I say that every one who has a beneficiary interest in the houses should be made to contribute to the expense of putting them in a proper state'.[63]

On the evening of the day he was questioned, Cameron received a note from Earl Spencer, the Lord Lieutenant, asking him to call to the Vice-Regal Lodge should he be in the vicinity around 11 o'clock the following morning. Cameron reported in his *Autobiography* that, as he had been commissioned by the Board of Works to investigate the sanitary conditions in the Lodge—houses of all classes in Dublin at the time were liable to sanitary defects—he assumed that some sanitary problem was the reason for the summons. Instead, the Lord Lieutenant revealed that Cameron's efforts to improve housing for the poor of Dublin had been brought to his attention by the Prince of Wales and Sir Charles Dilke, and that he had been offered a knighthood in the Queen's birthday honours list.

Cameron had taken advantage of the Prince's visit to Dublin and, against the wishes of his entourage who were keen to show him some

61 Ibid., Par. 22, 375.
62 Ibid., Par. 22,234.
63 Ibid., Par. 22326

model housing, insisted that he see the reality of the conditions under which most of the poor lived, and brought him on an inspection of the tenements in Golden Lane. True to form, when offered the choice of waiting to receive the knighthood at a formal ceremony, or receiving it immediately, Cameron 'after the usual self-deprecation' chose the latter and, following two taps of his Excellency's sword, left the Vice-Regal Lodge as Sir Charles Cameron. Unfortunately, the housing problems in Dublin were not so easily solved. The 1884–5 Inquiry achieved little, and Cameron would have to continue to fight and give evidence for many years and in several inquiries to come.

For the newly knighted Cameron, it was back to work as usual. Two newspaper reports of the same year show how much attention he gave to the minute details of life for the poor. In June 1885, at the Artisans' Exhibition in Dublin, he was awarded a prize of £10 'for the best model of a combined stove and oven suitable for a tenement house'.[64] A few weeks later he gave a detailed lecture at the exhibition, in which he exhibited 'several specimens of gas-cooking apparatus . . . one a cheap combination, specially designed for the working classes, could be used as a boiler, a griller and a toaster.'[65] From personal visits to tenement rooms, Cameron knew that the only means of cooking the food that made up the meagre diet of the inhabitants was the open fire, which also had to be used for heating and for drying clothes. This combination of close attention to the mundane details of his job as well as the more exalted aspects of it, would remain a distinctive feature of Cameron's *modus operandi* until the end of his long career.

---

64 *The Irish Times,* 20 June, 1885.
65 Ibid., 11 July, 1885.

Chapter 9 The captain of all these men of death: 1890–1900

> The captain of all these men of death that came against him to take him away was the Consumption, for it was that that brought him down to the grave. (*The Life and Death of Mr Badman*, by John Bunyan, 1680)

On 1 January 1890, almost seven years after the death of his wife, Cameron began to keep a daily diary again; he would continue to keep it until 1916, a few years before his death, when he would stop it as abruptly as he had in 1883. He was now almost 60 years of age, and showed no sign of slowing down. On the contrary, as his diaries show, he was working even harder, and was socialising at a frantic pace; subsequent volumes of the diaries would show that he kept up this pace for at least the next 26 years. He began the new year of 1890 by spending part of New Year's Day in the Public Health Office, and the phrase 'At PHO [Public Health Office] and Laboratory' would begin almost every day of his re-commenced diaries like a mantra. The new diaries show Cameron at the peak of his career and his social life and, although there is very little of a revelatory nature there, the diaries show the pace and variety of his daily round. He had six children still at home, ranging in age from seven to 21. None were working, so Cameron was supporting all of them. His eldest son, Charlie, aged 23, was in the army, and the diaries reveal the reality of daily life for Cameron, as he tried to balance his busy professional life, a motherless family, and a hectic social life.

He was now recognised as one of the leading sanitarians in the world, but was spending most of his time on the unending and seemingly insuperable health problems of Dublin. The duties carried out by his department included:[1]
- Enforcing the removal of the sick to hospital
- The compulsory interment of the bodies of persons who die of infectious disease
- Discretion to prevent wakes (to prevent contagion)
- The disinfection of houses and the purification of clothing

---

1 RPDCD, 'Statement of the Duties' op. cit., pp 240–1.

- The confiscation of infected mattresses and bedding
- The inspection of nightly lodging-houses
- The inspection of bake-houses and slaughter-houses
- The carrying out of the provisions of the Explosives Act of 1875
- 'Multifarious other duties which need not here be enumerated'.

Cameron described his own duties as 'multitudinous' and listed them as follows:[2]

- General supervision of the Public Health Department
- Preparing an annual report of about 100 pages on the health of Dublin
- 12 monthly reports on same and on the sanitary work performed
- Approximately 6,100 analyses of water, food and petroleum per annum for the Corporation
- The inspection of diseased meat and unsound food
- Attending the Recorder's and Police Courts on average 70 times a year in connection with sanitary and adulteration cases
- Constant visits to the Corporation baths, wash-houses, abattoir, disinfecting chamber and morgue
- Frequent inspection of tenement houses, for which any magistrates' closing orders require his signature.

It was detailed painstaking work:

each district has assigned to it an Inspector, whose duty it is to go through it regularly in the alphabetical order of the streets; he hands in every evening a return of the inspections which he has made during the day ... when I make inspections, and find serious nuisances existing, I can, by looking over the officer's return, see whether they have been noticed by him, and ascertain what action he has taken with regard to them.[3]

Despite the difficulties and lack of staff, Cameron claimed that 'there is no city or town in England or Scotland of which I have any knowledge that can show an equal amount of sanitary work accomplished by us'.[4] This work was carried out with a limited staff, and despite the difficulties of legislation, the opposition of vested interests such as landlords, cattlemen, etc., and the apathy of the general public. Fully aware that the Corporation had a constant and wary eye on the ratepayers, Cameron was vigilant for any change in the law that would

---

2 Ibid., p. 241.
3 Ibid., p. 239.
4 Ibid., p. 237.

oblige the Corporation to improve housing conditions, regardless of public opinion. The Housing of the Working Classes Act of 1890 (53 & 54 Vic. c. 70), gave increased power to sanitary authorities, such as the Corporation, to clear unhealthy areas at lower expense in terms of compensation to landlords. Cameron lost no time in pointing this out, and hammered home his point by presenting the Corporation with a list of all available sites that could be utilised under the 1890 Act.[5]

This list set out a total of 284 spaces where tenement houses had been taken down or were derelict. The list covers the whole city, from Meath Street on the south side, through centre city areas such as Temple Bar and Marlborough Street, to north-side areas such as Beresford Place. This clearly shows that Cameron's schedule of tenement inspection worked, and that he was personally aware at a very detailed level of housing conditions across Dublin.

In opposition to the commonly held belief that dwellings for the poor should be built on the outskirts of the city, Cameron always maintained that existing houses in the city should be renovated, or derelict sites used for building. In pursuing this belief, he had in mind the labourers, whose only chance of employment lay in work on the docks or in transport, claiming that 'workmen like to be near the scene of their labour'.

Cameron knew the views of the Dublin poor, and this is illustrated by several practical initiatives he took to alleviate mundane aspects of their lives. For example, when he became Superintendent Medical Officer of Health, he made disinfection in the city depot free to all who attended. In this depot were also some vehicles designed by him for conveying fever patients to hospital. Previously, those with contagious diseases had to make their own way to hospital, and could be ejected if found travelling in public transport. The vehicles were later copied by many other health authorities. When the room of an infected person was being fumigated, the family had to sit on the stairs of the tenement house, or in the street, as they were not allowed into another room for fear of infection. Cameron designed a wooden house on wheels in which they could sit while the fumigation was being carried out. He had it fitted out with a table, seats and stoves, but most people refused to use it, for fear their neighbours would laugh, despite Cameron's personal pleadings with them to do so. Undeterred, he persuaded the Corporation to refurbish two derelict houses in Nicholas Street to house 50 such people, and these were widely used.

---

5 RPDCD, (1892), vol. 1, pp. 200–8.

The summer months usually brought an increase in outbreaks of dysentery, attributed to a great extent to infection of food by numerous flies. In one year, when there was a particularly bad infestation, Cameron put a premium on the insects' heads, and paid Dublin urchins for the number of flies they caught. He took in good part the jibes of the press, who claimed that flies were being bred for the purpose, believing that he had the last laugh when the scheme was later taken up by several other cities.

With his re-commenced diaries in 1890, Cameron's varied social life is revealed—a constant round of balls, musical evenings, visits to the theatre, although until the end of his life he never socialised on the anniversary of his wife's death. His daughters Lucie and Lena took his wife's place at social functions. Lucie was by this time 21 years of age, and Lena was 19. Neither worked, not surprising for women of their social status at the time but perhaps surprising for Cameron's daughters, as he appeared to admire and encourage intelligence and independence in women.

Perhaps within his own family he retained the conventions of the Victorian paterfamilias, althouigh both Lucie and Lena are mentioned among the attendance at the meeting of the Irish Women's Progressive Union held in Cameron's house on 6 January 1899. (The Union was evidently more concerned with women's employment than the franchise.) Almost without fail, the diaries mention that every Sunday, he and the girls attended the Magdalen Chapel in Leeson Street, just as he had done with his wife; Cameron's sons had also attended the Magdalen when young, with their parents, but there is no mention of any occasion in later years when they attended church with him.

Despite being a widower for almost 40 years, Cameron does not record any female interest in his life, other than women who were apparently old social friends. There is, however, some mystery about Countess Frederica Cerossi, who was first mentioned in the diaries on 30 May 1892, when Cameron recorded that he 'took charge of Countess Frederica Cerossi as far as London'. She may well have been an old friend, because, on 4 June, Cameron recorded that he attended the wedding of the daughter of an old friend in London, and that Countess Cerossi was present. Later that year Cameron went to London with his daughters, and 'the Countess Cerossi and her friend Madame Romano of Naples came whilst at breakfast'.[6] The next day,

6 Cameron, Diaries, 13 September 1892.

Cameron attended a conference, but recorded that 'The Countess and Madame Romano came today and took lodgings close to our hotel'; they all later attended a conversazione. The Countess was next mentioned two years later in June 1894, but she was not mentioned again until 1910, when she and Cameron's son Charlie saw Cameron off for London,[7] and she was again mentioned as visiting on 18 December of that year. However, the most intriguing mention is after Cameron's death; among the floral tributes is one with the words 'To dearest Sir Charles, in loving devotion, Countess F. Cerossi'.[8] They were, perhaps, in the best sense of the phrase, simply very good friends and had been for at least 30 years, but there is no doubt that for his part Cameron remained faithful to his wife's memory all of his life. The diaries do not specify where Countess Cerossi lived, but it appears that it was probably Dublin (based on the facts that she travelled to London, and that she and her friend took lodgings there). However, she does not appear in the Dublin directories, nor is she in the English Census or the 1901 and 1911 Dublin Censuses, so the one mystery woman in Cameron's life remains a mystery.

Cameron's social life would have exhausted a man or woman half his age. He entertained regularly at home, often on a lavish scale—on 18 February 1890 he held a ball for around 170 in his house on Pembroke Road, and a month later, on 18 March, he held an 'At Home' to which about 300 people were invited. He went to bed at 3 o'clock, but was up next day to go to the Public Health Office and to lecture in the Royal College of Surgeons. He kept up the pace to the end of his life.

In 1917, a Guardian of the Balrothery Union in North Dublin, obviously aware of this hectic social life, accused Cameron of 'dining out all over the country'. In a reply to his accuser, Cameron wrote that he regretted that he was not invited to dinners all over the country, and 'advised the Guardian who made that statement that he ought never to refuse an invitation to dinner, as pleasant dinners were conducive to longevity'. Cameron's reply appeared in the British newspapers, and the editor of the *Daily Express* asked him to elaborate on this remark. Cameron duly obliged, in the process obtaining his 'last earnings as a journalist under peculiar circumstances – a cheque for two guineas by return of post'. His article, entitled 'How to live long and happily. The excellent habit of dining out', written as a light-hearted piece for

7   Ibid., 27 May 1910.
8   *The Irish Times*, 3 March 1921.

a popular newspaper, could, nevertheless, be regarded as accurately summing up Cameron's life-long attitude to friends, acquaintances, and to life itself. He wrote:

> I am satisfied that in general gloomy persons who take no amusement and avoid society do not live so long as those who are cheerful, optimistic, and enjoy themselves in a rational manner.

Recalling a serious accident that he had suffered some years previously, from which the doctors believed he would not recover, Cameron claimed that he

> on the contrary, taking a humorous, optimistic and cheerful aspect of my case, believed that I should recover. I am certain that if I had become despondent and cheerless I would have died . . . In recommending dining in company as a health preservative, it was only as one of the many means by which cheerfulness and optimism may be maintained. To suspend all social functions as some desire is to plunge the people into a gloomier and still more depressed state of mind. There is good sense in the advice, 'carry on as usual', which has so often been given to us.

Cameron went on to say that, while elaborate menus might be the reason for some people dining out, he believed that the attraction for the vast majority of diners-out was

> meetings with friends and acquaintances, the lively conversations, the music which is often a feature of dinner parties. They help to make us, at least for the time, forget our sorrows and troubles . . . What I enjoy at dinner parties (with occasional exceptions) is their gaiety and sociability. I have made many kind friends through them, and they have in many instances favourably changed my opinions of certain persons.[9]

This quotation may explain Cameron's almost frenetic social life, because, as the 1890s progressed, and his public life went from strength to strength, his private life was beginning to disintegrate. From the beginning of his marriage, Cameron was an involved father, who played a key role in his childrens' upbringing, a role that increased in responsibility after his wife's early death. Although he obviously relished and even sought public recognition and adulation, it was his family that was his bedrock. He had plenty of friends, but, other than a clergyman cousin, he had no living relatives except for his children, and his diary entries record their activities almost as much as his own. It is thanks to the diaries that we know some things that Cameron

---

9 Cameron, *Autobiography* (1920) op. cit., pp 21–2.

quite naturally did not publish in his memoirs, and that give an insight into the private pressures that he had to cope with on top of the many stresses in his public life. His diary of 18 July 1890, for example, records that Charlie, who had a commission in the Enniskillen Fusiliers, was 'in trouble about staying from his regt. Arranged that he should return the next morning'. On Tuesday 19 July, Cameron reported that 'Charlie went back this morning. I had to pay £15 for debts which he contracted'.[10]

There was further embarrassment for Cameron the following year, when the papers reported that a young man had been visiting various medical men in London masquerading as Sir Charles Cameron's son, and soliciting money. It later transpired that Charlie had met the imposter in a London hotel. There is no suggestion that Charlie was in any way culpable, other than that he obviously gave his father's name and details to a stranger during a casual encounter, but the ensuing publicity must have been uncomfortable for Cameron.

In February of 1891 Cameron's younger daughter Lena had begun to assert some independence. She appears to have been a dutiful daughter, accompanying Cameron to church and social functions. However, in 1891, at the age of 20, she fell in love with Walter Johnson, who wrote to Cameron 'desiring permission for an engagement'.[11] Cameron thought this unwise, as the young man appeared to be on his way to South Africa with no prospects of a career. Cameron suggested that he try for the RIC 'as he was rejected for the army on account of being shortsighted'. He admitted in his diary to liking the young man very much, but his concern for his daughter's future as the wife of a man with no prospects outweighed other considerations, such as Johnson's impeccable social connections as the 'son of a general, the grandson of a baronet and the nephew of several generals and colonels', together with the fact that he came from 'perhaps the most military family in the Kingdom'.[12] Obviously Cameron, although an inveterate admirer of the well-connected and the military, did not allow this to cloud his judgement of what he believed to be in his daughter's best interests. He does not record Lena's views on the matter. A possible footnote to this incident is a further entry the same year in which Cameron reported that 'Dr Little came to see Lena who has lately been getting thin and who eats but little. He does not think there is any serious

10 Cameron, Diaries, 18 and 19 July, 1890.
11 Ibid., 17 February 1891.
12 Ibid.

mischief brewing'.[13] It is not unreasonable to speculate that this may have been some kind of eating disorder connected to the forbidden suitor.

In 1893, Cameron's third son Douglas followed his father into the Corporation laboratories as a private assistant. Family tradition was important to Cameron, so the fact that one of his sons was entering the same profession would have been a matter of pride. However, Douglas's employment was short lived; in June 1894, Cameron wrote that 'Mervyn and Douglas not well,' and both sons were sent to lodgings in Dalkey, at a cost of £7 per week.[14] They had contracted one of the most dreaded and intractable diseases, a disease that Cameron would continue to fight throughout his career—phthisis (pulmonary tuberculosis). This 'white plague' was at this time almost at the height of its virulence. Although Cameron reports that the two became ill around the same time, it is probable that Mervyn, Cameron's fifth son, born in 1875, was the first to contract the disease, as Cameron reported in his diary of 11 November 1893 that the doctor had examined Mervyn and declared his lungs to be weak.[15]

Mervyn Wingfield Cameron was named after his godfather, Viscount Powerscourt. This appears to be another of the inconsistencies in Cameron's personal memoirs; he obviously knew Viscount Powerscourt—they were both members of the Royal Dublin Society, and Cameron often deputised for him as President of the Art Union. Yet Cameron, who sprinkled his memoirs liberally with the names of his aristocratic friends and acquaintances, makes very little reference to any Powerscourt connection. There are a few mentions of visits to garden parties in the diaries, but nothing of a closer friendship other than a mention of a telegram from Lord Powerscourt on his godson Mervyn's death. He appears to have remained on good terms with the family, as he attended the Viscount's funeral in 1904—but again, unusually, does not mention this in his diaries, as he usually did when attending such occasions.

On 1 July 1894, Cameron went to see Douglas and Mervyn at their lodgings in Dalkey, and found 'their state much the same'. On 3 July, Mervyn came home to dinner and reported that 'he and Douglas are better'.[16] Cameron did not comment on this, but must have suspected that all was not well, as he wrote rather tellingly in his diary 'I have

13 Ibid., 16 December 1891.
14 Cameron, Diaries, 4 and 27 June 1894.
15 Ibid., 11 November 1893.
16 Ibid., 1, 3 July 1894.

a pain in my head from overwork—12 or 13 hours a day now!'[17] Cameron's state of mind when he wrote this can only be imagined, as he worked long hours on the insurmountable health problems of Dublin city, while, as an expert on contagious diseases, he must have been fully aware that his own sons were dying.

On 20 July, the doctor called Cameron to say that the condition of Douglas and Mervyn was very serious, but 'they are to stay in Ireland for the present'.[18] By September 1894, their condition had worsened, and they left Ireland for the Grand Canaries in an effort to improve their health. Their condition fluctuated while away—Mervyn improved slightly, while Douglas deteriorated—but on 28 November, Cameron was told that 'Douglas would last through the winter and that Mervyn was much better'.[19] On Christmas Day, Cameron received a letter from Douglas 'written in bed and in poor spirits'. Douglas must have known the seriousness of his condition, and it is little wonder that he was in poor spirits, being far from home on Christmas day, aware that he was near death, with only his brother, ill with the same disease, for company. Cameron recorded bleakly in his diary for Christmas day 'We thought much of the absent ones today',[20] and on 16 January 1895, he commented sadly 'Our dinner table now has only four around it'.[21]

Throughout his sons' stay in the Canaries, Cameron regularly sent them money, and was in contact with them directly or received reports from local doctors. On 21 March 1895 he was informed that 'Douglas is fast sinking and that he could only live a few weeks more or less'.[22] He was too ill to make the journey home and he died, with his younger brother the only family member present, in the Canaries on 7 April 1895, at the age of 24. He appears to have been buried there. Cameron did not hear about Douglas's death until he received a telegram two days later—Annie Webber intercepted it until he had had some breakfast. So used to dealing with the ravages of disease among the poor and undernourished in his daily work, Cameron wrote: 'It seems strange that the biggest and strongest of my sons should be struck down with this deadly disease. His death makes a great void in our family which will never be filled up as far as it affects me.'[23]

---

17 Ibid., 3 July 1894.
18 Ibid., 20 July 1894.
19 Ibid., 28 November 1894.
20 Ibid., 25 December 1894.
21 Ibid., 16 January 1895.
22 Ibid., 21 March 1895.
23 Ibid., 9 April 1895.

On a professional basis, Cameron would also feel the loss of Douglas: 'If his life had been spared he would have been a great comfort to me, as he had just before his illness been associated with me in my work. There is now no one likely to succeed him as far as my sons are concerned.'[24]

Mervyn returned home on 23 May, having put on a stone in weight and according to Cameron 'looks very well and is much bronzed . . . and gave us full particulars about poor Douglas's last hours'. Cameron, as was his custom, went to the Public Health Office and laboratory as usual that day. A few months after Mervyn's return from the Grand Canaries, Cameron noticed 'that the disease was making way, and I sent him on a long voyage up the Mediterranean Sea'.[25] This arrested the progress of the phthisis for a few months, but when Cameron saw 'that the disease was again declaring itself I sent him in a tramp steamer on a voyage to New Zealand, which lasted five months'.[26] Cameron's diary entry for 8 November 1895 reported that his passage 'cost £90 to Cape Australia and New Zealand and back,' and expressed the hope that the voyage would restore his health. The loneliness of the young man can only be imagined, aware that he had the disease which had killed his brother; he was the only passenger on the steamer, and seemed to take some pride that 'even in the most stormy weather he never missed a meal with the captain'.[27] He would seem to have had Cameron's determination, if not his constitution. There is no further comment on Mervyn's health until February of the following year, 1896, when Cameron wrote in his diary that Dr Murray of Edinburgh had written to say that Mervyn was in Melbourne; Cameron had received no letter from him since he left.[28]

On 30 March 1897, Mervyn went on a further journey to the Mediterranean, but by 9 June he had returned home, and Cameron recorded that he had 'been coughing much lately'.[29] Cameron's worries were exacerbated on 27 June, when he wrote in his diary that Charlie had returned to Dublin from serving in India with the army. This is the first time that Cameron mentioned that Charlie was away, so he was obviously selective in what he recorded in his diaries, possibly only writing whatever was on his mind at the time. In this instance, the health of his sons was uppermost, as he wrote that Charlie, having

24 Ibid.
25 Cameron, *Autobiography* (1920), op. cit., p. 29.
26 Ibid.
27 Ibid.
28 Cameron, Diaries, 24 February 1896.
29 Ibid., 9 June 1897.

spent six years serving in India 'has returned in a very bad state having been for months ill with malaria and lately had several fits. He is much altered'.[30]

However, his main concern was for Mervyn, who was obviously becoming seriously ill with tuberculosis, and Cameron's diary around this time recorded his constant worry and concern about his gradual decline, of sitting up with him at night, and of having Mervyn's bed moved to his own room. Despite what must have been overwhelming worry, Cameron never allowed his personal troubles to interfere with his work, continuing to attend to his public duties as normal. There is no record of how the other family members coped, but there is a rather forlorn entry on Cameron's birthday, 16 July, when he wrote 'My birthday. Annie Webber seems to be the only one who remembered that it was and sent me a pair of slippers. I went to Annamoe [where he had rented a house and his family were staying] by 2.45 but was at PHO and laboratory for several hours'. [31] On 25 January 1898, he recorded 'I sat up last night with Mervyn. He passed a bad night. At Public Health Office and laboratory'.[32] On Friday 28 January, he wrote 'Mervyn very bad. Not conscious for several hours but rallied about 5 o'c p.m. I had to attend to some work at the office and laboratory'.[33] Mervyn died the following day, 29 January 1898; he was aged 23.

By 3 February, Cameron had returned to work, but was further devastated to learn on 20 February that his youngest son Ewen, then aged 17 and at school in St Columba's, was ill with pneumonia. Ewen was the youngest of Cameron's children, born on 13 May 1882; he was little over a year old when his mother died in November 1883. Cameron, the trauma of losing other sons fresh in his mind, was distraught at Ewen's illness, and although Ewen's condition improved by the 23rd, Cameron wrote 'I felt very bad . . . and could hardly sleep'—however, he still put in a full day's work the following day. Cameron's diaries for this period recorded constant concern for Ewen's health, and the health of his other son still at home, Ernest, who also became ill around this time, but he continued to fulfil his duties as Public Analyst and Medical Officer of Health, working in the laboratory, making inspections, giving evidence in court.

Ewen recovered, but Cameron's state of mind during his illness can only be imagined, as can his feelings about tuberculosis, in the

30 Ibid., 27 June 1897.
31 Ibid., 16 July 1897.
32 Ibid., 25 January 1898.
33 Ibid., 28 January 1898.

public mind usually associated with poverty and overcrowded living conditions, but which Cameron knew well could strike any social class. Did he ever wonder if his own work, with its attendant proximity to those with the disease, may have contributed to his sons' illness? Since the Famine it had been well-known that those who ministered to the poor, such as doctors and clergymen, were likely to succumb to the ailments afflicting those to whom they ministered.

The Association for Housing the Very Poor

In 1897 Cameron decided to take matters into his own hands and called a public meeting for 9 June, obviously hoping that he could call on some hitherto untapped reservoir of public benevolence. He circulated a memorandum, which shows his obvious empathy with the plight of the very poor (see Appendix 1 p. 237). At the meeting, he called on 'benevolent men' to build houses at rents of 1s 6d.

The Irish Times, reporting on Cameron's call for this meeting, made clear its own priorities when it went on to state that:

> In the interest of the general welfare it is desirable to do something sub-stantial for the improvement of these, the most dependent portion of the community . . . [but that] no Company necessarily promoted upon busi-ness principles could derive a revenue from such a class of workpeoples homes as it is contemplated to furnish . . . [34]

Instead it advocated that the rehousing must be done by the Corporation itself.

Cameron's proposition was different; if the Corporation would not, or could not, provide for the very poor, then it was the duty of those who were better off to step in. However, The Irish Times' estimation of the altruism of wealthy Dubliners appears to have been accurate. The Association for Housing the Very Poor, which was formed after the meeting, eventually provided cheap housing for approximately 790 people. It was 'a combination of philanthropy and business, it was highly economical in its running costs, the directors served without remuneration and the articles of association prevented the paying of more than a 3 per cent dividend.' [35]

Its relative lack of success appears to have been due to a lack of 'benevolent men', rather than a lack of effort by Cameron, whose diaries show that he regularly attended meetings, and put personal

---

34 The Irish Times, 7 June 1897.
35 Aalen, (1985) op. cit., p. 159.

effort into making the association a success.

Cameron and the Daily Nation

In 1898, Cameron brought the subject of tenement housing under public scrutiny once again when he accompanied a reporter from a daily newspaper on a journey through the slums.

In September, 1898, the *Daily Nation*[36] launched an exposé of Dublin tenement life, entitled 'A Visit to the Slums', in which its 'Commissioner' personally visited and reported on conditions around the city.[37] The series of articles included interviews with Charles Cameron, and a visit with him to the slums, during which he expressed very forthright opinions. This is perhaps one of the most interesting instances of Cameron as witness; free from the formal constraints of an official inquiry, he appeared, for the first time in public, to express his frustration with his work and the people he had had to deal with, having worked as Public Analyst since 1862, and Medical Officer of Health since 1874.

He declared that:

> the only manner in which the vexed question of the slums can be solved is through the provision, either by the Corporation or by some benevolent company, of proper housing accommodation at reasonable rents for those whose condition is described under the nomenclature of the 'very poor'.

Cameron claimed that, in other cities, notices served by sanitary officers requiring that nuisances be rectified were, 'as a rule, obeyed'. However, in Dublin, a large percentage of such notices were disobeyed and 'the persons responsible have to be summoned before the police magistrates, often more than once, before the insanitary evils complained of are remedied'.[38]

The core of the problem, he declared, lay in 'the carelessness and utter indifference of the owners of property in the slum districts.' These slums 'are all inhabited by persons paying from a shilling to two shillings a week in rent. The landlords generally sub-let the houses to tenants who have no capital, and are not able to put the houses into proper order . . .'

The interviewer took up the question of the deplorable state of

---

36 *Daily Nation* in circulation 5 June 1897–31 August 1900, incorporated with *Irish Daily Independent*.
37 *Daily Nation* 31 August–5 September 1898.
38 Charles A. Cameron, *Sanitary Prosecutions in Dublin and Elsewhere*, 1892–5.

the sanitary facilities in tenements, and asked who was responsible for keeping them clean. Cameron's answer returned to yet another common theme—the difficulty of getting the existing legislation to work, as he explained, one suspects for the umpteenth time, that 'where a water closet is used by the families of two or more houses, all the inhabitants of the two, or more houses can be proceeded against if the really responsible tenant cannot be found'.

He went on to say that the cleansing department sent men around the tenement houses every day to clean the yards of tenement houses, and that his department received about 40 notices of faulty water closets each day. Legal action had to be taken against the owner of the property, and much time was lost when summonses were ignored, while the conditions of the water closets continued to deteriorate. Cameron suggested that the way around this was to make the tenants themselves responsible 'because it is the tenants themselves who put these closets out of order . . . the tenants generally are very much to blame for the filthy condition of their closets'.

The interviewer moved on to the more general question of what the Corporation could do to improve the slum situation, and Cameron replied that:

> The only position they can assume is this. Let them provide proper dwellings for the inhabitants of these unsanitary houses and then shut the houses up. We cannot get the landlords to put them in proper order, and if you close them without providing others in their stead, where are the people to go?

In no instance, Cameron went on to claim, had the condition of the former residents been improved when slums had been cleared; the displaced tenants found themselves unable to afford the rent of the improved accommodation to which they moved, and soon moved out, back to affordable rooms and similar conditions to those they had left, at the same time worsening the overcrowding in another area. In one of his most publicly impassioned pleas for the poor, Cameron went on:

> Supposing we closed all the slums, where would the people go? . . .
> What are we to do unless some benevolent company or some philan-
> thropic individual, or the Corporation, provides some places for them?
> Cheap and good accommodation, with good sanitary arrangements, at
> rents of from one shilling to two shillings per week, would be required
> for certainly as many as ten thousand people.

The *Daily Nation* later showed its true public spirit when it declared:

> We do not care in the least if the proceedings [for closing the slums] . . . leads to the eviction of the tenants or to the closing of the habitations referred to. This is not a matter which should concern either Sir Charles Cameron or the Public Health Committee. If the tenants of the houses described move elsewhere and continue to live in similar squalor to that which prevails in their present abodes, the law should again be rigor-ously enforced, and in the end it may be hoped that the tenants, as well as their landlords, would learn that neither can be permitted to imperil the health of their fellow citizens.[39]

The *Daily Nation*, with only its circulation figures to consider, could make such sweeping statements, dismissive of the suffering caused by eviction and overcrowding; this was not a luxury available to Cameron and his staff.

Cameron went on to compare slum conditions in Dublin and London, and to point out that conditions every bit as bad existed in London; he returned to the problem of legal difficulties. Out of 10,956 notices to abate nuisances in 1896, many were ignored—1,417 people had to be brought to court, and most were convicted. He contrasted this with the city of Birmingham where, around the same time, in a city of half a million people 'there were only two summonses for disobeying notice of unsanitary dwellings'.

On 3 September 1898, Cameron took the fight into his opponents' corner, by inviting a *Daily Nation* representative to accompany him and Mr John O'Sullivan, Secretary of the Public Health Department, on a visit to some improved tenements in Dublin. They also discussed the several new developments of dwellings at moderate rents provided by the Corporation, and Cameron admitted to the representative that these were 'a mere drop in the ocean'; when the representative asked if the slums could not be demolished and replaced by similar developments, Cameron 'was doubtful that it could be done, the main objection which he foresaw being on the score of cost'.

On a more practical level, the representative described how, in many of the houses visited, 'hardly a pane of glass was to be found' in the rere windows; Cameron explained that the Corporation 'had ceased giving notice to parties to put in window panes in their rooms, as the practice of the juveniles of the locality was to break the windows

---

39 *Daily Nation* 3 September 1898.

with stones as fast as they were put in'. They visited houses in Jervis Street; the journalist's description is one of the few instances where the unending and thankless task of Cameron's workforce, so often criticised for not attending to the needs of the poor, is described.

> The sanitary arrangements generally were good. The dustbin had recently been emptied, and was quite ready for the reception of its usual contents; but the tenants, or some of them, preferred, it would seem, to utilise the yard, which was paved with cobblestones, for the purpose of a slops receptacle, and, accordingly, the ground was plentifully strewn with matter of this description. In the yard of the house 63 Jervis Street, we found excellent closet accommodation, but both the floor and seat of the closet were in a filthy condition.

Cameron's frustration was obvious as he asked, 'What more can the Corporation do than they have done here . . . and now, does it not remain for the tenants themselves to keep their places clean?' He outlined the difficulties of keeping a close watch on tenement conditions and said that he had a staff of 30 Corporation sanitary inspectors to inspect the homes of 32,000 families, or about 1,200–1,400 houses to each inspector. His view was that 'No inspector could, under such circumstances, visit the same house more than once in two months—in the meantime what may not happen between one and the other!' In Lurgan Street, where, in a house 'on which the Corporation had issued a closing order on the grounds of unsanitariness, we were informed that the landlord, who had himself only just left the workhouse, was too poor to do anything towards putting the house in a sanitary condition.' Ultimately, the *Daily Nation* agreed 'with Sir Charles Cameron in regarding it as doubtful if the civic exchequer would be equal to meeting any large further demand for the erection of model lodging'. The newspaper accepted that the unsanitary state of the slums was 'the result of physical incapacity to cope with the volume of work, and not of any treacherous neglect on the part of responsible officers'.

In 1899, Cameron must have felt vindicated in his comments to the *Daily Nation* when he was made a Companion of the Bath in recognition of his work, but the following year he and his staff would be interviewed again, this time in an official inquiry into public health in Dublin.

1900 Public Health Inquiry[40]

Following a letter from the Local Government Board to the Public Health Committee of Dublin Corporation on 18 November 1899, Cameron, as Medical Officer of Health for Dublin, was asked to report on a sharp rise in the death rate in the city for that year. His report was that the most likely specific cause was an outbreak of influenza, which developed into, and was recorded as, other maladies, such as bronchitis and pneumonia. Once again he gave a litany of the well-known and well-publicised causes—unsanitary housing, overcrowding, prevalence of slaughter-houses and dairy-yards, etc.—all of the reasons he had been bringing to municipal and public inquiries for decades. He concluded with the statement that 'Dublin is, in truth, a poor city, and no street or square in it is distant 500 yards from a purlieu'.[41] Despite, or perhaps because of, Cameron's report, the Local Government Board instigated an inquiry into the high death-rate, which began on 13 February 1900. The Corporation appeared concerned about this inquiry, and requested that their witnesses be allowed to appear with counsel. This request was refused on the grounds that counsel did not appear on their behalf before the Royal Commission on Sewerage and Drainage in Dublin in 1879. Answering this refusal, Mr Seymour Bushe QC for the Corporation, pointed out that 'the inquiry of 1879 could never have led to the preferment of charges of neglect, or of misfeasance on the part of the Sanitary Authority'—the implication being that it was feared that this inquiry would lead to such charges, as he continued, 'if your ruling is that we are not to have the ordinary protection and advantage on the part of people who may be, nay, who are certain to be made the objects of allegations and charges, we will be placed in a position of great disadvantage'.[42]

Cameron was questioned on the second day, and it is obvious that he shared Mr Seymour's fears, and believed that 'the Sanitary Authority, and, to a certain extent, myself, are really and truly, though not nominally, on trial'. He launched straight into a defence of the state of public health in Dublin, with a stated aim to refute 'a general impression that we have a high death rate, because statements to that effect have appeared in the Dublin newspapers—by persons who have not made themselves thoroughly acquainted with the facts, or

---

40 PP 1900, Volume 39 *Minutes of evidence taken before the Committee appointed to inquire into the public health of the city of Dublin, with appendices.*
41 *The Irish Times*, 10 February 1900.
42 PP 1900 Public Health Inquiry, op. cit., p. 16.

Figure 9.1 *Return of sanitary operations in Dublin and large English towns of over 90,000 inhabitants, during 1897, 1898, and 1899*

Towns	Population (1899)	No. of notices	Prosecutions	Convictions	Fines
Dublin	245,001	36,637	5,849	5,845	£598 6s 6d
Oldham	150,772	12,002	65	60	£35 0s 0d
Halifax	97,721	3,035	9	5	£1 14s 0d
Liverpool	634,212	136,687	3,437	810	£860 17s 5d
Sunderland	145,613	17,992	429	351	£71 4s 0d
Plymouth	100,637	5,760	nil	nil	nil
Huddersfield	103,464	2,492	18	11	£5 10s 0d
Leicester	213,851	13,542	1	1	£0 5s 0d
Gateshead	106,552	4,374	59	27	£30 11s 6d
Manchester	543,902	38,462	1,486	843	£776 11s 6d
Derby	106,401	3,679	1	1	£0 17s 6d
Newcastle	228,625	15,349	43	25	£10 9s 0d
Birmingham	514,956	54,822	12	12	£11 13s 6d
Croydon	127,759	4,804	8	8	£2 4s 0d
Brighton	123,226	25,833	9	8	nil
Preston	117,622	8,878	8	8	£35 0s 0d

Source PP 1900 Housing Inquiry, Par. 284

with the actual statistics.'[43]

He presented a chart which showed 'the mean death rate, up to last year, in the thirty-three great English towns, including London, and the zymotic and infantile death rate', taken from the reports of the registrars-general of England and Ireland.[44] Since improving the zymotic death rate was the responsibility of sanitary authorities, these figures were an indicator of their efficiency in carrying out their duties. Cameron pointed out that, for the five years ended 1898, the zymotic death rate in Dublin was 2.66 per 1,000, while in London, 'the city acknowledged to be one of the healthiest in the world,' the death rate was 2.76.[45]

The infantile death rate was another accepted indicator of the state of a city's health. Cameron handed to the committee the returns of death rates per 1,000 registered births of infants under one year of age in 33 towns, for instance:

Burnley	269	Birmingham	269
Nottingham	210	Dublin	210

---

43 Ibid., Par. 281.
44 Ibid.
45 Ibid.

Manchester	206	Birkenhead	206
Liverpool	198	Cardiff	198
Portsmouth	197	Norwich	197
Newcastle	193	Brighton	193

He elaborated on these figures by pointing out that there had been an epidemic of measles and scarlatina in 1897, and of measles and influenza in 1899, with the statement that 'Now it is clear that though, of course, we might be better, we are not as bad as we are represented, or as some English towns are'.[46]

He continued:

Of the death rate that still prevails, I venture to say that the diminution of it is largely not within the power of the Corporation, because I believe the high death rate results from poverty, insufficiency of food, and from the bad environment which the lower classes live in—their being crowded into very small areas . . . We exceed all other towns in the number of families in one house. We have only about 25,000 houses in Dublin, as against 80,000 or 90,000 in Belfast—with a population not very much larger. But here we have ten persons to each house, instead of about four and a-half in other towns. I attribute the high death rate . . . to the adult rate amongst the lower classes in Dublin largely to the insufficiency of food, for I do not think there is a more underfed population than the poor of Dublin. Then they are not well clothed.[47]

He repeated that 'the public should have it made clear to them what the Corporation had done',[48] revealing that the officers 'have very often, in the self-same premises, to serve notices [against nuisances] monthly in as many as ten months out of the twelve'. He pointed out that in most English towns, when a notice was served, it was, as a rule, obeyed. In Dublin, 10 per cent of nuisance notices were disregarded, and time-wasting law proceedings had to be instigated.

On the question of nuisances, Cameron was once again obliged to give evidence on the state of water closets in tenement houses, and the difficulties of prosecuting those who abused them. This subject would form a major point of questioning in the 1913 Housing Inquiry, with a lasting detrimental effect on Cameron's professional reputation, so it is worth noting his vehement comments thirteen years earlier.

He had commenced

46 Ibid.
47 Ibid., Par. 284.
48 Ibid.

a crusade against privies, and succeeded in the course of twelve or four-teen years of getting rid of nearly every one. Almost 10,000 have been abolished . . . and replaced by water-closets. Unfortunately, the latter are often abused; no sooner is an expensive water-closet put up than most improper use is made of it . . . We get notice from the scavenging depart-ment of about 100 a week of these water-closets being blocked up.[49]

Cameron demanded an urgent change in section 21 of the 1890 Public Health Act, as he believed it had a bearing on the death rate. He explained 'if two families occupy each of them one house with a yard in common they come under the provisions of the 21st section of the Public Health Amendment Act of 1890; but if there are sixteen families living in one house and having sanitary accommodation in common they do not come under it.'[50]

Cameron had once brought a case against a large number of persons which ended up in the Court of Queen's Bench, which decided that the law did not apply to one house occupied by several families. 'In the vast majority of tenement houses in Dublin each house has its sanitary accommodation, and there the tenants cannot be got at. We want an amendment of the law'.[51] He also revealed another anomaly: 'nuisances in individual rooms cannot be dealt with in the existing state of the law'.[52] He described how, having gone to court to give evidence against a filthy room that was a health hazard to the rest of a tenement house, the magistrate judged the case 'No rule', but did not dismiss it, 'out of a compliment to me personally',[53] telling Cameron 'Provide for it in your bye-laws',[54] 'and the way the matter stands is that no matter what state of filth we see in a room we cannot deal with it'.[55]

The Report of the 1913 Inquiry was to find that Cameron had favoured members of the Corporation, so it is worth noting that Cameron brought the Chairman of the public health committee to court to force him to put in sanitary accommodation—'he was convicted, and had to spend £30 or £40 or £50 on his own house'.[56] While critical of the difficulties of having houses repaired and made sanitary, Cameron revealed that Dublin had a better record than many places in actually

49 Ibid., Par. 289.
50 Ibid., Par. 292.
51 Ibid., Par. 293.
52 Ibid., Par. 295.
53 Ibid.
54 Ibid., Par. 595.
55 Ibid., Par. 295.
56 Ibid., Par. 304.

closing houses, but that this in itself caused problems, and that 'I have the greatest hesitation now to give a closing order, because where are the people to go to?'[57]

Returning once again to housing the very poor, Cameron said that he was pleased that the term 'housing of the working classes' was now giving way to the term 'housing of the very poor'. He recalled taking part in a discussion of the subject in the London *Times*, when he was attacked by 'political economists of the old school of political economy, who think that nothing should be given for nothing under any circumstances'.[58] Despite this, Cameron re-iterated his belief that:

> It is the duty of the municipality to provide for that class of persons when they have cleared the areas that were occupied by that class of persons. The areas cleared in Dublin have been occupied by persons who paid only 2s a week, and not one of these persons has ever gone back to the cleared places. We have improved the ground—not the people. Things have come to such a pass that something must be done for those 10,000 of the very lowest class of the population, whose dwellings, I think, no sanitary inspector could ever have kept in order.[59]

He continued: 'I say now what I have said over and over again in reports that something must be done for the very poor'. He referred to various meetings on this subject in the Mansion House and the Public Health Office, as a result of which an organisation had been formed which would build dwellings for 48 families. Describing this as 'a mere bagatelle', Cameron said: 'That company should be reinforced by a substantial number of the citizens of Dublin . . . a company like that can do good if largely supported.[60]

Cameron's evidence resumed the following day, and he referred to another charitable housing company, run by the Alexandra Guild, who refurbished five houses and let them in single rooms. Cameron commented that he had visited the houses and found 'the most exceptional sanitary accommodation of the most modern description in such a state that no one could make use of it', and said that he mentioned this

> to show that when it is so difficult for a company of ladies, who have tenants in five houses, to make them keep their places in proper order how much more difficult must it not be in the case of a sanitary officer

57 Ibid., Par. 311.
58 Ibid., Par. 312.
59 Ibid.
60 Ibid., Par. 313.

who has to inspect several hundred of this kind of houses.[61]

Showing the practical side of his nature, Cameron said that he had recently devised a new kind of water-closet, that had been approved by the Society of Architects, that he hoped would improve the situation and that 'we expect a large consignment of them to be on sale in Dublin very soon'. [62]

Report of the committee[63]

The committee gave its report to the Local Government Board for Ireland on 14 May 1900. On page 2 of this report, the committee conceded that there had been significant improvements in Dublin since the 1879 Inquiry, some of the main points of which were:
- The number of tenement houses (which they defined as 'a house let to two or more families') had decreased from 9,760 to 6,585.
- There was now a regular system of scavenging, carried out by a large staff of men and horses.
- All the major, and many of the minor streets had been paved.
- There were now two large swimming baths and a wash-house.
- In 1879 there were 104 private slaughter-houses—this had been reduced to 56.

Commenting on the 'drainage and removal of filth' they remarked that 'to those who remember the little that was done in regard of such cleansing twenty years ago in Dublin, the improvement since effected must be apparent.'[64]

They admitted, as Cameron had pointed out in his evidence, that

it has to be borne in mind that the proportional amount of poverty in Dublin is very large, so that these unfavourable conditions associated with the houses of the poor are widely spread throughout the city. The poverty of much of the population of Dublin is in itself, apart from the insanitary conditions referred to, a serious factor in the high death rate of the city. The concomitants of poverty, more especially insufficient and unsuitable food and scanty clothing, both directly and indirectly exert a marked influence upon the death rate.[65]

The report contained many recommendations, but from the point

---

61 Ibid., Par. 387.
62 Ibid., Par. 403.
63 PP 1900, Volume 39, *Report of the Committee Appointed to Inquire into the Public Health of the City of Dublin, 1900.*
64 Ibid., p. 7.
65 Ibid., p. 10.

of view of Cameron's evidence, one recommendation worth noting is 'that the legal procedure in cases of prosecution for sanitary defects and nuisances should be materially shortened, and that there should be no appeal from the magistrate's decision on matters of fact'.[66] Cameron's work had been vindicated by the committee's report, but in the event, once again, no material improvements were to take place.

Later in the year he faced an increased workload and further worry with the threat of an incursion of bubonic plague. He took immediate precautions, visiting possible premises for use as isolation hospitals, recording that he, the Lord Mayor and some of the Corporation visited the Beneaven convalescent home of Cork Street fever hospital 'and took it for a hospital for bubonic plague should it appear'.[67]

A few days later he moved quickly when a woman and two children, who had just arrived from Glasgow, where there was an outbreak of the plague, were suspected of carrying it. Cameron had them put in the Corporation refuge and visited them the following day, going back to work in the laboratory until 7 o'clock, as most of his assistants were on leave. He records working late most of the following week, while carrying out numerous inspections during the day. On 29 September he wrote that he visited Cork regarding a sewage problem at a creamery, and that 'it was a long day's work and I had a good deal of jumping over ditches and I felt rather tired'. [68]

The Christmas holiday of 1900 brought no let-up; his diaries record that, on both Christmas Eve and St Stephen's Day, Cameron went to the laboratory and Public Health Office. He still made time to make his usual visit with his family to the North William Street orphanage. Obviously Cameron, now 70 years of age, a widower, with three of his sons dead from contagious diseases, had lost none of his energy or enthusiasm for his work.

---

66 Ibid., p. 17.
67 Cameron, Diaries, 8 September 1900.
68 Ibid., 29 September 1900.

Cameron at 76, in 1906. He was still 'in harness' and was to remain in office for a further 15 years (Dublin City Library and Archive).

Chapter 10 Still in harness

In 1901, Charles Cameron must have felt that, at last, his family life was beginning to assume some semblance of normality, as his remaining sons appeared to be settling into careers. In January of that year, Dublin Corporation approved his son Ernest's appointment as co-analyst.[1] Ernest had first entered the Corporation 'for a short time' on 31 August 1892, but his work is not mentioned again until five years later, when on 18 January 1895 Cameron reported that 'Ernest went into laboratory to work today'. However, it was not until October 1900 that the committee 'arranging the reconstruction of Committees and Departments . . . agreed to Ernest being made assistant analyst at a salary of £100 per annum'. In October 1901, Cameron wrote that his youngest son Ewen 'today entered the service of the Great Northern Railway Company and was located in the manager's (Mr Henry Reeves) office',[2] and in March 1902, Charlie left for South Africa with the army, as a captain in the 4th Battalion of the Dublin Fusiliers.

A wedding in the family

The year 1901 also brought romance for Cameron's younger daughter Lena, for whom no romantic attachment had been mentioned since the unsuitable Walter Johnson had been banished twelve years previously. Rupert Stanley became a regular visitor to the Cameron household, attending the theatre with Lena, and taking part in the family's annual charitable visit to the North William Street orphanage. He appears again in the diaries on 27 August 1903 when Cameron records that 'Rupert Stanley . . . was unanimously elected Teacher of Physics and Electrical Engineering in the Belfast Technical School. Salary £350 a year'.[3] An engagement was announced between Lena and Rupert in *The Irish Times* on 5 September 1903 and, on 9 September, Cameron wrote in his diary that he 'began tonight to send out invitations for Lena's wedding with Rupert Stanley'.[4]

Cameron took a hands-on interest in preparing for this, the first wedding in his family, writing that on the eve of the wedding he

---

1 Cameron, Diaries.
2 Cameron, Diaries, 28 October 1901.
3 Ibid., 27 August 1903.
4 Ibid., 9 September 1903.

and Ewen 'worked hard all day getting the house ready for Lena's wedding'.[5] Lena was married at St Bartholomew's Church on 7 October, only a month after the engagement, which could be explained by the fact that their first child, Rupert, was born just over six months later, on 27 April 1904.

The wedding was followed by a reception for 170 people—a much smaller affair than her sister Lucie's would be some years later. Cameron, unusually, as he was an inveterate socialiser, wrote that 'After dinner all went to the theatre except myself',[6] so the occasion was obviously more stressful than he admitted. The couple went to live in Belfast, and had three sons, Rupert, Vivian and Mervyn, who gave Cameron a great deal of happiness in his later years. His diaries mention regular visits to Lena's home in Belfast and by Lena's family to Dublin. Their visits followed the same pattern as Cameron's own children, with visits to the pantomime in Dublin and Belfast. Cameron was a devoted grandfather, reporting proudly on each of his grandsons, and making comments such as the 'baby is fine child' and that the 'baby took quite to me'.[7] On Christmas Day, 1905, Cameron wrote: 'Lena's little son aged 20 months is strong, big for his age, good tempered and most interesting. He and I have great dancing and he uses his feet with great vigour.'[8]

Some measure of Cameron's personality (and stamina) can be gauged from his diary of 28 January 1911 when, aged 80, he reported 'this morning whilst playing with Vivian in the hall I slipped and I fell on my back with much force. The oil cloth on the hall floor had been waxed and was very slippery. I felt very sore and could hardly breathe. I went to bed. The girls would insist on sending for Surgeon W. Taylor although I knew no bones were broken.'[9]

Rupert Stanley

Although Cameron was obviously close to all his remaining family, it was Lena's husband, Rupert Stanley, who provided a great deal of companionship to him in his later years. The original formal references in the diaries to 'Mr Stanley', soon became 'Rupert Stanley', and eventually he became simply 'Rupert', regularly visiting Cameron with Lena and the children and frequently accompanying Cameron

5   Ibid., 6 October 1903.
6   Ibid., 7 October 1903.
7   Ibid., 25 and 26 March 1910.
8   Ibid., 25 December, 1905.
9   Ibid., 28 January 1911.

to Masonic functions. Rupert Stanley appears to have been a man in the same mould as Cameron, and was probably closer to him in personality than his own sons. Cameron records him as being 'the nephew and adopted son of Sir John Stanley, K.C.I.E.'[10] A native of Armagh, he was appointed Professor of Electrical Engineering at the Municipal Technical Institute, now known as Belfast College of Technology. He joined the 36th Ulster Division at the outbreak of the First World War, specialising in electrical and wireless engineering; he later became Chief Wireless Instructor of the British Expeditionary Forces, and was promoted to Staff Officer to the Commander in Chief (Signals), the highest appointment attainable in France in that branch of the service. He was mentioned twice in dispatches and received the Legion of Honour from the Commander in Chief of the French army. After the war, Rupert Stanley, now Major, returned to the College of Education in Belfast and was made Principal in 1919. He became Consultant Electrical Engineer to the Belfast Asylums Board, and was responsible for the electric lighting at various churches and other buildings in Belfast and the surrounding districts. In 1924 he was appointed the first Director of Education for Belfast, a post which he held until he resigned in July 1941. His last service to his father-in-law was to act as a joint executor with his brother-in-law, Denny Gerrard, to Cameron's will. He died at the age of 89 on 26 December 1965. He was survived by two of his sons, Rupert and Vivian. His son Mervyn was lost on operations with the Royal Air Force in the Second World War. His wife Lena had died in 1951.

How the Poor Live

In 1904 Charles Cameron published a small booklet entitled *How the Poor Live*.[11] The flyleaf states 'printed for the author', so it would appear to have been at his own expense. It is not clear why he wrote it—it is only a pamphlet of 23 pages, so would not have been written for commercial gain or as a literary effort. The most likely reason for its publication is that he wrote it to bring the plight of Dublin's poor to an audience that he believed could do something to help them—the middle classes. This assumption is given credence by the content of the final two paragraphs of the booklet, in which Cameron enumerates some of the charitable societies helping the Dublin poor,

---

10 Cameron, *Autobiography* (1920) op. cit., p. 30.
11 Charles A. Cameron, *How the Poor Live* (Dublin, 1904). A note on the first page of the copy in the National Library, in what appears to be Cameron's writing, states 'Presented to National Library of Ireland May 8, 1905'.

and adds, 'they deserve the most liberal support from all who can spare the money', and 'were they more liberally supported they could accomplish greater benefits to the very poor'.[12] The booklet could be said to fit into a genre of such writings—all *exposés* of life in Victorian slums, designed to bridge the gap that existed between the 'two worlds'—'who', as Disraeli put it, 'are as ignorant of each other's habits, thoughts and feelings, as if they were dwellers in different zones or inhabitants of different planets.'[13] Cameron would undoubtedly have read the pamphlets associated with *The Bitter Cry of Outcast London* of the early 1880s and remembered them when he wished to highlight the plight of the Dublin poor. In *How the Poor Live* Cameron shows that his understanding of the privations of their lives was sympathetic and non-judgemental, and he does not let his frustration with the fact that some of the poor were neglectful of the facilities provided show.

His opening sentence announces bluntly: 'There are probably no cities in the United Kingdom in which so large a proportion of the population belong to the poorest classes as is the case in Dublin'.[14] He compared the housing statistics of Dublin with those of Belfast, Lancashire, Glasgow, Edinburgh and London, showing that Dublin had by far the highest proportion of dwellers in single rooms, and claiming: 'surely that is proof of the poverty of a large proportion of the population'.[15] He described again how, unlike other cities where slums were in a limited number of areas, the slums in Dublin 'are to be met with everywhere'.[16] Cameron described what he referred to as 'the banker of the poor'—the pawnbroker. He spared no detail of this facet of slum living, showing an intimate knowledge of it:

> No inconsiderable number of the poor get out of their beds, or substitutes for them, without knowing when they are to get their breakfast, for the simple reason that they have neither money nor credit. They must starve if they have got nothing which would be taken in pawn . . . articles of very small value will be accepted by the pawnbroker, and some items of a slender wardrobe are exchanged for the price of one or more meals—so small a sum as sixpence may be obtained in this way'.[17]

Some years previously he had 'ascertained that in a single year

---

12 Ibid., p. 23.
13 Benjamin Disraeli, *Sybil, or The Two Nations* (originally published 1845) republished (Penguin, 1980), p. 96.
14 Cameron, (1904), op. cit., p. 1.
15 Ibid., p. 1.
16 Ibid., p. 2.
17 Ibid., p. 3.

2,866,084 [pawn] tickets were issued in the City of Dublin . . . [and that] by far the larger proportion of the borrowers belonged to the working classes'—although he did concede that the practice also extended to 'many persons belonging to the artisans' and better classes'.[18] Cameron elaborated further by detailing the difference in interest rates between pawnbrokers and money-lenders:

> The general state of things is the following: The artisan or labourer is out of employment, perhaps for a week or a few weeks. How is he and his family to live until he regains employment? He may not be able to get credit with the food purveyors, and if he does he will, as a rule, be charged more on credit than he would for ready money. To persons so situated the pawnbroker is often the only 'friend in need', failing whose assistance the resource might be the workhouse.[19]

The next pages of the booklet were devoted to analysing the earnings of the poor, illustrated with specific cases. He described a tailor who lived with his wife in Dame-court, whose wages were only 10s per week, 'owing to irregular employment and the poor payment for the making of the cheaper kind of clothes'.[20] They paid 2s 6d rent, leaving 7s 6d 'for food, fuel, light, clothes, bedding, &c', so it was not surprising to hear that they had only two meals a day, a breakfast of dry bread and tea, and one other 'dinner and supper combined: it consists of dry bread and tea and herrings, occasionally porridge'.[21] Shoemakers were in the same poorly paid position, and 'on the whole, they are no better off than the labourers and vanmen'.[22] There were, according to Cameron, '4,854 persons engaged in the boot and shoe and tailoring business; 2,087 of them are females, and the vast majority of them are working tailors and shoemakers'.

A special feature fo the Dublin situation was:

> less work for females in [Dublin] than is the case of English towns. In 1901 there were 92,956 women, twenty years of age and upwards in the City of Dublin. Of these 56,827 were not following any remunerative oc-cupation. On the other hand, there were 82,756 males, twenty years old and upwards, of whom 6,938 had no occupation.[23]

The advantage of this lack of female employment, according to

---

18   Ibid.
19   Ibid., p. 4.
20   Ibid., pp 4—5.
21   Ibid.
22   Ibid., p. 5.
23   Ibid.

Cameron, was that a high proportion of Dublin women breastfed rather than bottlefed their infants, as happened in England, where a higher number of females went to work. This, he claimed, reduced the infant mortality rate, as there was less risk of infection from dirty bottles.[24] The big disadvantage was the 'smaller average earnings of families, with consequent lower standard of diet, lodging and clothing'.[25]

Cameron then returned to his constant concern—housing the poor of Dublin—outlining the contribution over the previous 30 years of 'the Corporation, the Dublin Artisans' Dwellings Company, the City and Suburban Artisans' Dwellings Company, the Housing of the Poor Company, the Industrial Tenement Company, and by railway companies and private firms and persons (notably Lord Iveagh's and the 'Guinness Trust' dwellings)', but claiming, as so often before, that 'the great majority of the lower classes are still unprovided with proper dwellings'.[26] Dubliners had to swallow the unpalatable fact that they averaged nearly two families per house, while in Belfast nearly every family possessed a separate house. The reality in Dublin was, of course, that often many more than two families shared a house, a fact which Cameron illustrated with a case study of 74 tenements in Church Street, where the number of families per house ranged from 2 to 14.[27]

Under the heading 'Clothing and Bedding', Cameron returned to what was always his first concern—children. Their clothes, he wrote, were frequently 'the worn-out garments of their parents', roughly cut down, and 'ill-adjusted to the size of their new wearers'. Thousands of these children also 'go with naked feet, even in winter'.[28] Cameron praised 'a most useful society—the Police-Aided Society—for providing clothes for destitute children' and wrote that it 'deserves more support than it receives from the public'.[29] Two accompanying photos show the clothes market in Patrick Street in Dublin's Liberties, where the poor bought second-hand clothes. Cameron also mentioned that Lord Iveagh planned to provide new premises for this market, in which all articles for sale would be disinfected—this plan would later come to fruition as the Iveagh Market in Francis Street. The disinfection of second-hand clothes was important—in a smallpox outbreak just before the booklet was written, two pawnbroker's assistants had

24 Ibid.
25 Ibid.
26 Ibid., p. 6.
27 Ibid., pp 8–9.
28 Ibid., p. 10.
29 Ibid.

contracted the disease from handling infected clothing.[30]

Under the heading 'The Diet of the Labouring Classes', Cameron gave detailed descriptions of the diet of the poor, obviously culled from personal interviews with the persons concerned. He commented that there was a 'large consumption of whisky and porter among the labouring classes', and that there was a 'consequent deprivation of home comforts and even necessaries'.[31]

> The workman is blamed for visiting the public-house, but it is to him what the club is to the rich man. His home is rarely a comfortable one, and in winter the bright light, the warm fire, and the gaiety of the public-house are attractions which he finds it difficult to resist. If he spends a reasonable proportion of his earnings in the public-house is he more to be condemned that the prosperous shopkeeper or professional man who drinks expensive wines at the club or the restaurant, spends hours playing billiards or cards, and amuses himself in other expensive ways?

Nonetheless, Cameron believed that 'there is too much intemperance amongst the working classes, and that the women, who formerly were rarely seen intoxicated, are now frequently to be observed in that state'.[32] Despite his tolerance he knew that something should be done. He admired the work of Father Mathew, the temperance campaigner, and was an honorary secretary of the fund set up to erect a statue to the priest, attending the unveiling ceremony in Sackville Street in 1893 (with a typically ironic comment that 'It was remarked that unusually large numbers of inebriates were seen that day in Dublin').[33]

How the Poor Live contains three full pages of the 'Table of Diet' of 52 families from all areas of Dublin—southside, northside, and central—and the portrayal of a population of hardworking people on the verge of starvation must have made an impact on anyone who read it (see Appendix 2 pp 240–1). Only three of these described their employment as 'constant', the rest described it as 'irregular'. One person in this sample, a charwoman in constant employment, albeit at only 9s per week, appeared to have a regular weekly menu worked out—perhaps an indication of what could be done if work was constant. Cameron would return to this theme in his *Reminiscences* a few years later.[34]

In his concluding section 'Betterment of the Poor' Cameron claimed

---

30 Ibid., p. 11.
31 Ibid., pp 13–14.
32 Ibid., p. 14.
33 Cameron, *Reminiscences*,(1913) op. cit., p. 102.
34 Ibid. pp 172–3.

that 'it is not in the power of the Sanitary Authorities to remove all the evils from which the poor suffer . . . They could, however, soften the hard conditions under which the poor, and still more the *very* poor, exist'. 'Let us,' he continued, 'consider what is practicable'.[35] This included the following[36] (abbreviated, but in Cameron's own words):

> To provide them with homes superior to those they now have, without increasing their rents . . . I have always maintained that it is only the poorest and most dependent classes of the community that municipalities should provide with cheap and healthy dwellings . . .
>
> The washing of clothes and bedding in the tenement rooms is undesirable . . . small and plain wash-houses in convenient centres of the population would be a great boon to the poor.
>
> The working of the last Factories and Workshops Act, as regards sanitation, is now vested in the Corporation, and if carefully attended to cannot fail to benefit the health of the workers.
>
> Open spaces and play-grounds for children are important agencies in promoting health and vigour . . . but more are required, especially in the congested districts.
>
> The teaching of cookery in the primary schools for girls is but slightly carried out in Dublin: it should be more extensively adopted.
>
> If it were possible to provide the very poor children, who are now obliged to go to school, with a meal, much good would result. There is little doubt that many of the school-children have to learn their lessons on empty stomachs.

He concluded by appealing to 'all who can spare the money' to support the various charitable organisations helping the poor. Nothing came of this plea—the poor would remain poor for the foreseeable future, their frustration coming to a head in the great Lockout of 1913.

Freedom of the City of Dublin

In February 1911 Cameron received the Freedom of his native Dublin. He maintained that, of all the honours he received throughout his long life, this was the one he valued most. The proposal to make the award was put forward on Friday, 30 September 1910, at a meeting of Dublin Corporation held in the Council Chamber, City Hall, Cork Hill, in the following words:[37]

---

35 Cameron (1904), op. cit., p. 22.
36 Ibid., pp 22-23.
37 Minutes of the Municipal Council of the City of Dublin, 1910, pp 439–40.

That this Council, recognising the distinguished services given to the City of Dublin by Sir Charles Cameron, C.B., M.D., and the fact that these services have conferred lasting benefit upon the citizens:
That almost half a century of devoted exertion on his part to the extermination of disease and everything inimical to public health within the city has resulted in a courageous and efficient public health organisation:
That, owing to his ceaseless efforts, Dublin, which at one time had, from the sanitary point of view, an unsavoury name, can now boast of comparative freedom from almost all of the malignant diseases which assail mankind:
Therefore, Sir Charles Cameron be, and he is, hereby, constituted an Honorary Freeman of the City of Dublin; and that he be, and he is, hereby elected and admitted an Honorary Burgess of this County Borough, pursuant to the provisions of the Municipal Privileges (Ireland) Act, 1875.

The motion was declared carried unamimously.

The Freedom was formally conferred at a ceremony a few months later, when the Lord Mayor Michael Doyle (an old Labourite) proposed that Charles Cameron's name 'be placed on the roll of honour which contained the names of so many famous men'. Demonstrating that this was not a Unionist occasion, the motion was seconded by Alderman Tom Kelly of Sinn Féin who made use of the occasion to score a political point, and in the process give an insight into the difficulties faced by Cameron in carrying out his work. Alderman Kelly said that:

From personal experience he would say that Sir Charles had one single purpose in his mind, and that was to rid Dublin of preventable diseases. Had he been given a free hand in the past, or were he to be given a free hand in the future, the sanitary work of Dublin would be done better. Unfortunately, however, he had not had that free hand. His reading of certain laws did not agree with the views of the lawyers, it did not agree always with the Municipal Council, with the Local Government Board, and the other Boards that they were plagued with.[38]

A few weeks later, Cameron was honoured again, this time by his colleagues. On 4 March 1911, the chief officers and staff of the Public Health Department of Dublin Corporation presented him with a replica of the Speaker's Chair of the Irish House of Commons, abolished by the Act of Union, on the occasion of his 'jubilee year in the service

---

38 Ibid.

of the citizens'.[39] It is intriguing to speculate whether his colleagues perceived in Sir Charles a political affinity with the resistance to the Act of Union.

It looked as though Cameron's eighth decade was to be a happy one. In April 1911 the Duke of Abercorn resigned as Deputy Grand Master of the Grand Lodge of Freemasons in Ireland, and nominated Cameron as his successor. Later that year, he had further cause for celebration when, on 8 November, his eldest daughter Lucie married John Dennison Gerrard (Denny), an old childhood friend. Denny's late father was the Crown Solicitor, the Gerrards were longstanding friends of the Camerons, and Denny and his brother Maitland were regular visitors to the household from an early age. Lucie was by then aged 42, and photographs of her in a report of her wedding[40] and at a presentation to Cameron[41] show a rather plain but elegant woman. Before her marriage she had the usual lifestyle of an unmarried daughter of a well-to-do family, travelling with female companions, attending the theatre, involved in charity bazaars, always present at family gatherings. She appears throughout the diaries, a continuous but unobtrusive presence, playing her part as a companion to her father. Although both Cameron's daughters were regular companions, it was Lucie who appears to have taken his wife's place at official functions; there are frequent accounts of her attendance with Cameron at balls, for example with the Iveaghs, the Lord Lieutenant and dinner with the Lord Mayor of Dublin.[42]

She played a part in Cameron's daily life, and he in hers, and it is clear that despite his exalted and busy public position, Cameron tried to lead a normal family life: 'Lucie and I did Grafton St. and made purchases,' while he showed a typical father's concern when, despite being very tired, he spent a long time at a bazaar 'as I did not wish that [Lucie's] "wheel of fortune" should be a failure.'[43] Lucie, along with other members of the family, accompanied her father also on less formal occasions, such as his yearly visits to the North William Street orphanage. Despite a full social life, Lucie does not appear to have had any romantic attachments until her marriage to Denny. The marriage was conducted by the Lord Primate of All Ireland in St Bartholomew's Church, with a reception for 400 guests at Cameron's

---

39 *Saturday Herald*, 4 March 1911.
40 *Lady's Pictorial*, 2 December 1911.
41 Group photograph in restaurant at presentation to Cameron of replica of Speaker's Chair.
42 Cameron, Diaries, 13 April 1896, 19 August 1898, 3 March 1899.
43 Cameron, Diaries 31 March 1894.

'beautiful residence' at 51 Pembroke Road.[44] The cake was made by Annie Webber, who also gave them a present of a tea table.

'So large and fashionable a wedding' had not been seen in Dublin for some time, according to the *Lady's Pictorial*; the presents received 'ran to several hundreds' and included gifts from Lady Aberdeen, Lord and Lady Ardilaun, and 'a very lengthy list of titled and distinguished donors'.[45] It appears to have been a much larger and socially important affair than her sister Lena's wedding some years previously. Two of Lena's sons, Rupert and Vivian, were pageboys.

The couple went to live in Belmullet, Co. Mayo, where Denny had been appointed Resident Magistrate. Denny's appointment appears to have been either obtained or expedited by Cameron who, in a rare example of nepotism, used his influence with Lord Aberdeen in the matter. Cameron's diaries for 1911 recorded that he had two communications with the Lord Lieutenant, eventually receiving 'a long letter' from Lord Aberdeen from his home in Haddo House in Scotland 'stating that he had arranged that without delay Denny Gerrard would be appointed a Resident Magistrate.'[46] Lucie left Dublin for her new life in Mayo on 1 December; Cameron recorded that 'poor Lucie gave way to tears and I felt very much affected'.[47] Lucie appears to have settled into what must have been a completely different and less glamorous lifestyle, returning fairly regularly to visit Cameron, and on one occasion he mentions visiting them in Belmullet.[48] Denny served as a Lieutenant, Army Service Corps, for two years during the First World War, being retired due to ill health, and eventually became a Resident Magistrate in Cavan.

Cameron's appetite for work had not decreased. In June 1911 he started to organise a large sanitary conference of the Royal Institute of Public Health to be held in August in Dublin, personally visiting city shops asking for subscriptions. Lady Aberdeen, who was involved in a campaign to eliminate tuberculosis, was asked to be President of the Congress, and Cameron wrote an address for her to deliver. His diary for one day in July gives some idea of his daily workload

> At PHO and Laboratory. Condemned several cows and pigs at the abat-
> toir. Went to the opening of a dispensary for consumptives in Charles St.
> by the King . . . Saw a sick sailor on board a Greek vessel lying at the end

44 *Lady's Pictorial,* 2 December 1911.
45 Ibid.
46 Cameron, Diaries, 5 July and 11 September 1911.
47 Ibid., 1 December 1911.
48 Ibid., 7 September 1912.

of the North Wall. Found it was not a case of plague or cholera, but fever and arranged to have him removed to hospital.[49]

At the age of 81, he obviously had as heavy and varied a workload as ever, and this daily round as Public Analyst and Medical Officer of Health continued, even when he was ill, as he was in December 1911, when he had abscesses removed, refusing the use of chloroform. On 27 December he wrote that he was still weak, but on 28 December he went into the office for a short time. He also paid his usual visit to the North William Street orphanage—it was obviously an important ritual for him, as he mentioned in his diaries that he was afraid he would have had to miss it due to his illness.

Lucie's marriage and departure to Mayo had further depleted Cameron's ever-decreasing family circle. His diary for the Easter holiday of 1912 reported that he went to the laboratory, and that he was the only one at home. Charlie was away with the army, and in May left to join the 3rd Cameron Highlanders at Fort George in Invernesshire. Ewen was still in Ceylon. Lena lived in Belfast, while Ernest, pursuing a singing career, lived with his father when in Dublin.

In June 1912 Cameron decided to start his reminiscences, writing them in spare snatches of time at weekends, completing them by December, and publishing them in 1913. Perhaps this task and his increasingly solitary status made him more reflective, because he makes particularly poignant remarks about his late wife in October 1912—'this is the fiftieth anniversary of my wedding day', and in November 1912—'Annie Webber and I laid a wreath on dear Lucie's grave this morning. This was the 28th annual visit to her grave but I see it every funeral I attend at Mount Jerome, which is very often.'[50]

The death of his good friend the Duke of Abercorn on 3 January 1913 shocked him, but he received even more devastating news on 16 February. At 10 pm a telegram arrived to say that his eldest son Charlie had drowned while staying with friends in Athlone. He had been fishing on a lake when he tried to grab a fish that was trying to get away. The boat overturned, and Charlie drowned. He was 47 years of age. The gamekeeper with him clung on to the boat for three quarters of an hour before being rescued. Cameron's *Autobiography* reports the incident briefly, stating that Charlie was popular in all the battalions in which he served—the Enniskillen Fusiliers, the 3rd Battalion of the Royal Dublin Fusiliers and the 3rd Battalion of the

49 Ibid., 11 July 1911
50 Cameron, Diaries, 16 October and 28 November, 1912.

Cameron Highlanders. Cameron presented memorial cups to the latter two battalions on Charlie's death.

It is, however, the diaries that give the true picture of the devastation caused to Cameron by the death of a fourth son. In one of the most poignant entries, Cameron wrote that Annie Webber found him lying sobbing on the sofa after he heard the news. Lucie's brother-in-law, Maitland Gerrard, was telephoned and arrived at 11 o'clock. Typically, Cameron's first thought was of not inconveniencing others—he had been planning the table arrangements for a Masonic dinner, and asked Maitland to telephone *The Irish Times* to postpone it. An interesting note is that Cameron mentions that Ernest and Ewen were upstairs in the billiard room, and only seem to have been told of Charlie's death after Maitland Gerrard had arrived. Ewen would have been around 30, and Ernest around 40 at the time, so the fact that Cameron's first instinct was to telephone someone else before he told his sons upstairs says something about his relationship with them. Was he overprotective? Did he consider them too immature to have the news broken to them immediately? Subsequent events would suggest so.

Cameron's sorrow must have been exacerbated by the discovery that Charlie appeared once again to have been in debt. On 18 February Cameron wrote that he went once again to Mount Jerome. The grave that held his mother, his wife, and his sons William and Mervyn (Douglas was buried in the Canaries), held just one more space. Cameron kept this for what he no doubt thought would be his own imminent demise, and bought a new grave for Charlie just opposite.

Notwithstanding what must have been devastating grief, Cameron persuaded the Public Health Committee to hold a planned meeting on 25 February, despite the fact that they wished to postpone it on account of Charlie's death. They insisted, however, on dealing only with a few items, and Cameron recounted how 'I nearly broke down' on receiving their sympathy.[51]

A sense of his desolation and loneliness can be gauged from his diary entry on 22 March 1913:

> I have been so distracted that I have not made any entries since the 28th ... The Corporation holidays are Good Friday and following days up to and including Wednesday. I did some hours work in the laboratory. No one else there.

The tragedy obviously affected his health, physical and mental, as

---

51 Ibid., 25 March 1913.

more than a year later on 19 August 1914, while on holiday in Belmullet with his daughter Lucie, he recorded in his diary:

> My health was improved by my sojourn at Belmullet and I increased one pound in weight, namely to 10 stone 8 lbs. The leisure, however, gave me time for fretting about poor Charlie, whose image came into my mind dozens of times daily.

Cameron's wider medical connections

Cameron's connection with the Royal College of Surgeons was one of the most important factors of his professional and personal life. In a letter to the College from Ernest, after his father's death, he wrote:

> my Father was so long connected with the College and had such a deep and strong interest in its work that the very building itself would have a sentiment almost akin to an old friend. You can have no idea of the bitter disappointment he felt last Summer at not being able to give the full number of his lectures – I think that his heart was greatly bound up in the old College.[52]

Cameron was associated with the College from the time he was first appointed Professor of Political Medicine and Hygiene on 9 April 1868 until his death. He was President of the College in 1885–6, was elected Secretary to the College in 1892, and was always vigilant in the College's interests. Perhaps his greatest contribution to the College was his history of the institution, of which two editions were published, the first in 1886 and the second in 1916.[53] Cameron wrote the first edition while in mourning after the death of his wife, when

> I did not go into society for a year, and only to a slight extent during the following two years. In those years I devoted all my time, free from professional work, in writing the *History of the Royal College of Surgeons in Ireland and of the Irish Schools of Medicine*.[54]

The College honoured Cameron with a dinner when he was 90, at which over a hundred guests were present. In his speech, the President of the College, describing Cameron as 'a colleague who for so many years has filled a prominent position in the professional, social and official life of Dublin', said that 'Dubliners were extremely proud of

---

52 Letter from Ernest Cameron to the Registrar of the Royal College of Surgeons, 24 March 1921.
53 Charles A. Cameron, *History of the Royal College of Surgeons in Ireland, and of the Irish Schools of Medicine* (Dublin, London, Edinburgh, 1886; second edition 1916).
54 Cameron (1920), op. cit., p. 80.

Sir Charles Cameron. They were moved by their affection for their guest and by their appreciation of his lovable character. Not one of them could say . . . that he had made so few enemies as Sir Charles had during his long life of ninety years'.[55]

From his time as a student in Germany in the 1850s, Cameron was aware that he was part of a wider movement of concerned professionals, and his life was devoted to becoming an authoritative and outspoken campaigner for progress in the field of public health. His diaries record very few holidays, but include accounts of attendance at public health conferences, mainly in England.

His autobiography gives an idea of the extent of his connections — during the course of his career he was President of the Royal College of Surgeons in Ireland, the Irish Medical Association, the Irish Medical Graduates and Schools' Association, the Leinster Branch of the British Medical Association, the Surgical Society, the Medical and Hygienic Sections of the Academy of Medicine of Ireland, the Royal Institute of Public Health (four years), the Society of Metropolitan Medical Officers of Health, the Public Analysts' Society of Great Britain and Ireland, the Engineering and Scientific Society of Ireland, and the Art Union of Ireland. He was Vice-President of the Royal Dublin Society, the Royal Veterinary College of Ireland, and the Institute of Chemistry of Great Britain and Ireland (six years).[56]

Conferences, public meetings, and the publication of the proceedings of these events, together with books and journals, were the means of mass communication in the 19th and early 20th century, and Cameron was a frequent and adroit user of these media; an excellent public speaker, who could move and influence his audience, he promulgated his views on public health to his peers and to the public, and most importantly, to the relevant authorities. He augmented these more public connections by private visits to and from his medical connections in other cities.

His diaries, and newspapers like *The Times*, show the extent of his involvement. This is evident even from the earlier diaries, between 1880 and 1883, which show, for example, how Cameron travelled to Chester for the conference of British Medical Association, where, on 12 August 1880, he made a speech on sewage in oysters—a common cause of enteric fever in Dublin; how he attended the Social Science Congress in Nottingham and took part in debates in September 1882; how in April 1883 he went to Bolton, where he 'spent the day with

---

55 Ibid., p. 83.
56 Ibid., pp 37–8.

the Mayor and Medical Officer of Health inspecting their means of disposing of scavenge', and then to Manchester, where he inspected baths and wash-houses. He had called for the provision of baths and wash-houses in Dublin from as early as 1879.

His later diaries, from 1890 to 1916 show similar meetings, both public and private—all aimed at improving public health, and at making contacts with his peers. Thus, in August 1891 he attended the seventh International Congress on Hygiene and Demography in London. *The Times* reported on the occasion:

> every important country in the civilised world [was] represented, but, of course, by far the largest number of delegates came from European countries, particularly from France, Germany, Italy, and Austria. There was also a remarkably influential representation of India, and nearly all the British colonies also sent delegates.[57]

This report in *The Times* also shows that Cameron was a member of the Permanent International Committees of Hygiene and Demography, appointed at the Congress held in Vienna in 1887. As well as being a member of this committee, Cameron, as President, took part in the Council of Medical Officers of Health at the Congress. As part of the Congress, he attended the first council meeting of the new Institute of Preventive Medicine. This had been mooted at a meeting in London on 1 July 1889, and it was reported as recognising 'the immense value of bacteriology to preventive medicine' and how it was determined 'to establish in the United Kingdom a central institute of similar constitution to those in Paris, Berlin, St. Petersburg, Bucharest, and elsewhere'[58] *The Times* went on to comment that

> Bacteriology in this country is pursued in many institutions [in] the special laboratories of London, Edinburgh, Manchester and Dublin . . . The great and quickly increasing breadth of the subject has induced foreign Governments . . . to found and maintain hygienic institutes devoted to bacteriological research. The British Institute of Preventive Medicine is designed to fulfil the same want in Great Britain and Ireland, and to afford special opportunities both for original research and for technical education.

Several gentlemen had already agreed to serve on the Council, including Sir Joseph Lister and Sir Charles Cameron.[59]

---

57 *The Times*, 11 August 1891.
58 Ibid., 1 June 1891.
59 Ibid., 6 June and 31 July 1891.

In August 1892, under the auspices of the British Institute of Public Health, Cameron hosted a Hygiene Congress at the Royal College of Surgeons in Dublin.[60] Cameron was President of the Institute for four years, retiring in 1893.[61] At its Annual Congress in Edinburgh in 1893, a female delegate, Miss Charlotte Smith, read a paper entitled 'A Plea for Female Sanitary Inspectors', suggesting that every large town 'should employ certain specially trained women as inspectors able to speak to mothers and to give them advice.'[62]

This suggestion evidently made an impression on Cameron; he later campaigned for several years for the appointment of female sanitary officers, using the arguments put forward by Miss Smith, a campaign that resulted in the appointment of the first four female sanitary officers in Dublin in 1899. These women would play an important part in the education of tenement dwellers, women in particular, in matters of hygiene, a practical example of the changes that could flow from the exchange of ideas at health conferences.

In 1892, Cameron was elected President of the Sanitary Institute, an organisation of 1,200 members, including 'medical officers of health, sanitary inspectors, borough engineers, surgeons from the Army and Navy, and other scientific men, as well as a number of ladies'.[63] It was Cameron who suggested that the appointment of sanitary sub-officers, previously entrusted to him as Medical Officer of Health, should instead be decided by examination, the vacant position going to those who scored the highest marks; from 1897, candidates were required to pass examinations held by the Royal Institute of Public Health or the Royal Sanitary Institute.[64] In 1893, Cameron became President of the Society of Public Analysts, and his diaries show that he continued to attend and take an active part in medical conferences until at least 1904.

On 8 December 1884, Cameron, as Vice-President of the Royal College of Surgeons, brought a motion before the Council:[65] 'That the question as to the eligibility of women to be examined as candidates for the Letters Testimonial, be reconsidered with the view of declaring them to be eligible, and that a provision to accomplish this be made'.

At the meeting on 16 December, the Council resolved by 7 votes to 4, 'That a new clause be inserted to provide that all provisions of the

60 Ibid., 18 August 1892.
61 Ibid., 31 July 1893.
62 Ibid.
63 Ibid., 13 September 1892.
64 Charles Cameron, *A Brief History of Municipal Public Health Administration in Dublin* (Dublin and London, 1914), p. 43.
65 RCSI, Minutes of Council, Volume 7, 1882–4.

Charters, By-Laws and Ordinances as to education, examination and granting of diplomas to Fellows or Licentiates shall extend to include women'.[66] Eventually, 'A clause in the second supplemental charter (1885) granted women access to education and examinations. Later in the year it was agreed to make appropriate arrangements for "the accommodation of Female Students within the School"'.[67]

In his capacity as Public Analyst and Medical Officer of Health, Cameron was a champion of the right of women to work as professionals. The records of staff in the City Laboratory show that Cameron employed female assistants—from 1895, a Mary Robertson (MA Royal University) and Miss S. A. Jacob appear, while Mrs Louie Gallagher appears as an Inspector under the Shops Act.[68] His diary of 29 August 1899 reported that 'Mrs. Cecil Thompson, née Miss Robertson, my assistant, returned to the laboratory today after her honeymoon', indicating that he did not operate any prejudice against married women in his laboratory, and that they appeared to be employed on an equal status with male assistants. There is also the simple, but perhaps significant comment while visiting friends on 30 August 1891, that 'Miss Young is a learned and scientific young lady'.[69] To these instances should be added the appointment of female sanitary officers, a position for which Cameron campaigned for many years.

Cameron did not restrict his concern for the improvement of women's rights to middle-class women. In an address to the Society of Metropolitan Officers of Health, he called for outdoor relief to be given to certain classes of persons:

> widows with young children, earning a little, but not sufficient to sustain life adequately should be so assisted; so also should women deserted by their husbands . . . [and calling for crèches to be provided, as many infants were looked after by older siblings] I constantly see very small children left at home by their mothers while the latter are out at work . . . amongst the poor, infants are the nurses of infants.[70]

The Freemasons and the aristocracy

---

66 Ibid.
67 J. B. Lyons, *A Pride of Professors: The Professors of Medicine at the Royal College of Surgeons in Ireland, 1813–1985* (Dublin, 1999), p. 5.
68 RPDCD, *Report upon the state of Public Health and the sanitary work performed in Dublin during the year 1895*, vol. 3, no. 114, (1896), p. 94.
69 Cameron, Diaries, 30 August 1891.
70 Charles Cameron, 'Address to the Society of Metropolitan Officers of Health' in *The Irish Builder*, 15 January 1881, pp 29–30.

Significant sections of Cameron's *Reminiscences* and *Autobiography*, and a constant constituent of his diaries is his membership of the Freemasons. To this day, a large portrait of Cameron is given a prominent position on the walls of the Grand Lodge Room in the Freemason's Hall in Dublin's Molesworth Street, and a lodge in Belfast, No. 353, bears his name, the name having been chosen 'out of respect . . . for one of the most prominent and popular figures in masonic circles in this country'.[71]

Like most very keen Masons, Cameron was a member of all branches of Freemasonry, including the Royal Arch Chapter, the Knights Templar Preceptory and the Prince Masons Chapter. He was a 33rd Degree Freemason, and held the position of Sovereign Grand Commander, the highest office in this branch of the Order.

Initiated into Freemasonry in 1858, as a member of Lodge 125, Cameron personally revived in January 1866 the 'nearly moribund' Lodge XXV, later named the Duke of York Lodge, bringing several members with him. It was members of Lodge XXV who, in 1886 presented the portrait referred to above.[72] Lodge dinners were one of his most frequent 'dining-out' occasions.

In some ways, his Masonic associations acted as a surrogate family, giving him encouragement and support, a forum to express his witticisms and be praised for them, a place where his talents were recognised and rewarded, and an inexhaustible source of occasions for congenial gathering. There is no doubt that his membership of the Freemasons filled a real need in his personal life, and while there is little doubt that he would have had a successful career regardless of any connections; the fact that many with whom he worked were fellow Masons must have contributed to a smoothing of his path.

Cameron records meeting prominent Freemasons frequently. These meetings were mainly dining occasions, and there is only one mention of a connection with his work, when he went for a walk with the Duke of Abercorn 'to inspect alterations being made with the old houses opposite St. James Church'.[73] Other members of the medical profession were Masons; Rawdon McNamara, President of the Royal College of Surgeons in 1831 and 1869[74] was one of the members who went with Cameron to revive Lodge XXV,[75] and Thomas Wrigley Grimshaw, the

71 Archives of Grand Lodge of Antient Free & Accepted Masons of Ireland.
72 Charles Cameron, 'A History of Lodge No. XXV' in *Irish Masonry Illustrated*, October 1901.
73 Cameron, Diaries, 21 January 1891.
74 J. D. H. Widdess, *The Royal College of Surgeons in Ireland and its Medical School, 1784–1984* (Dublin, 1967), pp 165–6.
75 Cameron, 'History of Lodge No. XXV' op. cit.

Registrar General, was a member of Lodge 53. Cameron was elected to the Professorship of Hygiene at the Royal College of Surgeons in 1868, the year before Rawdon McNamara became President. Several Lord Mayors were also Freemasons—Edward Purdon, Lord Mayor in 1870, and Sir George Moyers, Lord Mayor in 1881.

In one case the bonds of Freemasonry friendship had an adverse effect; Cameron, with three others, 'became securities for Sir. G. Moyers in the Royal Bank for £350. He had lodged a policy for £1,000 but he neither paid the interest on the loan or the premiums on the policy'.[76] Moyers, who, as already mentioned, had been Lord Mayor of Dublin, was a member of Lodge XXV, as was Lord Blyth, another guarantor. They were obliged to pay the Royal Bank £180 each, Cameron having fought against paying the premiums. This incident came shortly after the death of Cameron's son Charlie, who had also left large debts, and Cameron wrote: 'It is a very foolish thing to go security for people, I had several times to suffer for having done so'.[77]

Cameron's diaries indicate that he was a loyal friend, always ready to visit and help, prepared to take time out of a very busy schedule to assist a friend, and it seems likely that it is this aspect of the Freemasons that he valued most. He looked on his advancement through the ranks of the organisation as an appreciation of him as a person, and his appointment as Deputy Grand Master of the Grand Lodge of Ireland in 1911 was of great importance to him. In 1913 he revealed that he had refused to accept the position some years previously because 'I had always felt that perhaps I have not sufficient time to attend thoroughly to the duties', and that 'it was only at his [the Duke of Abercorn's] urgent request, at his own bedside, that I consented to accept the office'.[78]

The position was a difficult one, particularly at the time of Charlie's death, and in 1913 the newly installed Grand Master thanked Cameron for 'agreeing to stay on as Deputy Grand Master . . . in the unhappy circumstances through which he has recently passed . . . [and] his claim that he has done enough service and that he has earned retirement'.[79] He would remain until 1920, when his successor, Colonel Claude Cane, said that 'his memory is absolutely perfect, but his more physical disabilities have induced him to resign'.[80]

---

76 Cameron, Diaries, 22 March 1913.
77 Ibid., 22 August 1913.
78 Grand Lodge, Freemasons, Annual Report, 1913, p. 8.
79 Appendix to Grand Lodge Reports, 1908–13, p. 64.
80 Grand Lodge, Freemasons, Annual Report, 1920, p. 4.

As the country moved towards Home Rule, Cameron was aware that, as a member of the Church of Ireland, he was in a minority. Some measure of his apprehensions in this regard can be gauged from his address as Deputy Grand Master of the Freemasons in December 1912.[81] His main focus was the efforts being made 'to exempt the Grand Lodge of Ireland and the Masonic Order from any injurious legislation that might be imposed on them in the event of a Home Rule Parliament being established in Ireland'. He reminded his readers that 'we must remember that three-fourths of the population of Dublin are hostile rather than favourable to us'. These fears, which were no doubt shared by many, resulted in section 65 of the Government of Ireland Act 1920 which exempted Masonry from any future legislation (North or South) against unlawful oaths and unlawful assemblies.[82]

In 1921 Col. Cane's address revealed that 'a very few weeks after I spoke here of his resignation, [Sir Charles] was called to the Grand Lodge above.'[83] Reading Cameron's private diaries, as opposed to his more public autobiographical writings, there is often an impression that he was essentially a lonely and somewhat vulnerable man, who needed reassurance that he was needed and appreciated. His lifelong membership of the Freemasons provided that sense of appreciation, as well as support in times of personal distress; he died with a framed and illuminated address from his fellow Masons by his side, having requested that his family read it 'over and over again to him'.[84]

Cameron's friendships within the Freemasons included several of the aristocracy, including the second Duke of Abercorn, who had nominated Cameron as his successor as Deputy Grand Master, and Lord Wolseley, Commander of the Forces in Ireland from 1890 to 1895.[85] He was particularly friendly with the Duke of Abercorn; on one occasion, having met the Duke on board ship while travelling to London, they shared a sleeping compartment,[86] and speaking on his death, Cameron revealed that he 'had experienced so much kindness and hospitality from him'.[87]

One incident, noted in the diaries, shows that Cameron, despite a

---

81 Grand Lodge, Freemasons, Annual Report, 1912.
82 Government of Ireland Act 1920 s. 65. This section remains a fruitful source of conspiracy theories.
83 Address by Col. Claude Kane, Deputy Grand Master, Annual Report, Freemasons, 1921, p. 5
84 Ibid.
85 Ian F. W. Beckett, 'Wolseley, Garnet Joseph, first Viscount Wolseley (1833–1913), *Oxford Dictionary of National Biography*, (Oxford University Press, 2004).
86 Cameron, Diaries, 2 January 1893.
87 Grand Lodge, Freemasons, Annual Report, 1913, p. 8.

certain obsequiousness towards members of the aristocracy, remained his own man. In October 1895, the Duchess of Abercorn invited Cameron to the Abercorn's Irish home, Baronscourt in Co. Tyrone. Cameron wrote in his diary that he attended a dance at which he 'danced every dance. On leaving, the Duke was cheered as was also myself as I had made myself pleasant to the rustics by jokes, etc.'[88] The cheerfulness was somewhat diminished by the news that the Duchess was required to leave for Waterford to assist Lady Waterford 'whose husband blew his brains out on Wednesday last'.[89] Cameron recorded that 'the Duke came to my room at 3 o' clock this morning and said that he felt nervous and depressed. I went with him to his room and stayed chatting for nearly an hour and then returned to my room, but did not sleep much afterwards. The Duke pressed me very much to stay till Monday but I determined to return home.'[90]

Aristocrats of varying degrees of nobility appear in Cameron's *Reminiscences, Autobiography,* and diaries, and two guest lists in the latter give some indication of his social circle. He appears to have been sufficiently close to many titled personages to invite them to dinner and 'At Homes', and they appear to have been willing to accept his invitation. He was also invited to most of the significant social occasions in Dublin, in particular at Dublin Castle, although this may have been *ex officio.*

Some of Cameron's private remarks in his diaries give the impression that he was not fully at ease in exalted company, and was very conscious of any gracious gesture they might bestow on him, and of the impression he might be making: for example, in describing a ball at Lady Iveagh's on St Stephen's Green on 1 March 1899, Cameron wrote: 'It was a very grand affair. Any number of the nobility and other 'swells' present. Lord Lieutenant and Lady Cadogan present and she came out of a set of quadrilles to shake hands with me'. On 19 May the same year he once again wrote that he attended a dinner at which 'Prince Edward of Saxe Weimar, Prince Adolphus of Teck and other "swells" present'. No doubt something of the little boy from Magee's Court remained.

Other connections

Although Cameron was a member of the Church of Ireland and a

---

88 Cameron, Diaries, 25 October 1895.
89 Ibid.
90 Cameron, Diaries, 26 October 1895

regular churchgoer, his writings mention little connection with clergy of his own communion, other than attendance at the weekly service in the Magdalen Church in Lower Leeson Street. By contrast, his writings mention several associations with the Roman Catholic clergy and with Catholic nuns. The majority of the poor of Dublin were members of the Catholic faith, although not exclusively so—there were many poor Protestants. However, simply by force of numbers, Catholics would have been a large factor in Cameron's professional life, so this may account for what was probably an unusually high level of ecumenical involvement on his part. While there is no mention of visits to Protestant clergymen, who must have had tenement dwellers among their flock, there are several mentions in Cameron's diaries of visits to Catholic clergy.

The entry for Cameron in the *Oxford Dictionary of National Biography*, enthusiastically describes him as 'a Renaissance figure, interested alike in the scientific and the literary'.[91] While his scientific interests may have had some connection with his working life, his many literary and cultural contacts appear to have been purely for pleasure, although in his younger days, as editor and part-proprietor of *The Weekly Agricultural Review and Irish Country Gentleman's Newspaper*, and as theatre critic for *The Irish Times*, he 'wrote critical notices of dramatic performances'. His cultural tastes were middle-brow rather than high-brow, and he enjoyed the occasional low-brow entertainment, such as pantomimes and 'The Christy Minstrels'. His *Reminiscences* and *Autobiography* reveal that 'from early youth I was a playgoer and there were few, if any, actors and actresses of celebrity who performed in Dublin from the year 1838 whom I have not seen. The same remark applies to the celebrities of the lyric drama'.[92]

While his wife was alive, they were regular theatre-goers, mainly to the Gaiety theatre; his early diaries record attendance at *A Midsummer's Night Dream, Much Ado about Nothing*, and several now forgotten plays, including an un-named performance of a play by W. G. Wills, his wife's cousin. The later diaries recount an undiminished interest in the theatre, and Cameron usually fitted in a visit when in a British city, occasionally being disappointed, as at a pantomime in Manchester, which he described as 'very noisy, but with little real fun in it'. Cameron's was rather a robust sense of humour.

He was particularly interested in the performers, and seemed

91 Laurence Geary, 'Cameron, Sir Charles Alexander (1830–1921), *Oxford Dictionary of National Biography* (Oxford University Press, 2004).
92 Cameron (1920), op. cit., pp 38–9.

pleased to record any acquaintance, however fleeting, with them, as on 13 April 1899, when he attended the opera at the Gaiety, the company gave him a box and he 'had a glass of champagne with one of the principal performers'.[93] He often dined with Michael Gunn, one of the founders of the Gaiety, and through him met many actors and actresses 'when they appeared as themselves and not as some other persons'.[94] He also for many years enjoyed free entry to the Theatre Royal, and often dined with the manager.

He was a member of the Savage Club in London, whose entertainment was mainly provided by the members in amateur dramatics and roisterous sing-songs, while they had special dinners to which guests of honour were invited. If the club had an ethos, it would seem to have been not to take itself too seriously, and to be a place where men who were prominent in many different walks of life could relax and 'hang their haloes in the hall'.[95] This description would fit the type of rather boyish entertainment relished by Cameron, a type of club that he obviously believed was lacking in Dublin, and the result was the formation of the Corinthian Club in 1899. Cameron recorded that, 'by the end of the year 289 members were enrolled, and by 18 May the number had risen to 382, including 197 whom I had proposed.'[96]

The club entertained a wide variety of guests, including three Lord Lieutenants, Lady Aberdeen 'in recognition of the great efforts she made to combat disease', Field-Marshal Earl Roberts, Winston Churchill, Sir Ernest Shackleton, Chief Secretary Gerald Balfour, Madame Melba 'for whom the largest dinner ever held by the club took place', Signor Caruso (who sketched a caricature of Cameron) and John McCormack.[97] In 1910, the Club held 'a well-attended dinner in honour of Irishwomen who had achieved distinction in the domain of literature'. Shrewdly Cameron noted that on the nights when 'no particular guest' was invited attendance was low; 'members [desired] to have some celebrity at every dinner.'[98]

---

93 Cameron, Diaries, 13 April 1899.
94 Cameron (1920), op. cit., p. 44.
95 Percy V. Bradshaw *Brother Savages and Guests: A History of the Savage Club 1857–1957* (London 1958) p 1
96 Cameron (1920), op. cit., p. 119.
97 Ibid., p. 123
98 Ibid.

Chapter 11 The Inquiry into the Housing Conditions of the Working Classes, 1913[1]

The year 1913 saw great industrial unrest in Dublin, with around thirty major industrial disputes between January and July. The militancy of trade unions in Dublin had been growing apace, in particular that of the union run by Jim Larkin, the Irish Transport and General Workers' Union—the ITGWU. Larkin's weapon of choice was the classic syndicalist sympathetic strike, whereby workers in firms not on strike would refuse to handle the goods of any firm where there was a strike. The main antagonist on the employers' side was William Martin Murphy, the Chairman of the Dublin United Tramways Company, owner of the *Irish Independent*, and President of the Dublin Chamber of Commerce.

In July, Lorcan Sherlock, Dublin's Lord Mayor, after much difficult and protracted negotiation, managed to get both sides, the Trades Council for the workers, and the Dublin Chamber of Commerce for the employers, to agree to conciliation talks. William Martin Murphy, who had been unable to attend the meeting of the Chamber of Commerce that agreed to Sherlock's suggestion, was enraged at what he saw as conciliation towards Larkin, and when Larkin brought 200 of his tram workers out on strike on 26 August, the battle that would become known as the Lockout began.

Murphy immediately sought and was given the support of not only the Dublin Metropolitan Police, but also the armed Royal Irish Constabulary. Two meetings of workers, on Saturday 30 August at Beresford Place, and on Sunday 31 August in Sackville Street, were baton charged by police. Between 600 and 800 civilians were injured, and two men were killed. Many of the injured were simply bystanders, and would later give evidence of indiscriminate violence and drunkenness among the police. As well as the baton charges, on Sunday night, the police ransacked flats in the Corporation Street area, where some of the strikers had sought refuge the night before, breaking up furniture and terrorising the residents.

---

1 PP.1914, xix, *Report of the Departmental Committee appointed by the Local Government Board for Ireland to inquire into the Housing Conditions of the Working Classes in Dublin* cd. 7273 (Evidence of Inquiry) and cd. 7317 (Report of Committee). This will hereafter be referred to as Evidence 1913, and Report 1914, with relevant paragraph numbers.

As the dispute worsened, more employers supported Murphy and locked out any ITGWU supporters. Within weeks, 400 firms had joined the lockout, with 15,000 union workers locked out, and many thousands more non-union workers laid off. The labouring poor of Dublin found themselves reliant on handouts of bread and food parcels simply to stay alive.

The poor of Dublin had been on the verge of starvation for a long time, as Cameron had pointed out many times—for example in his evidence to the 1900 Public Health Inquiry[2] and in his booklet *How the Poor Live.*[3] This was corroborated by the report on reformatories and industrial schools in 1913, which reported that Dublin had a larger proportion of committals than any other part of Ireland, and that 80 per cent of the offences for which children were committed were for stealing bread and other food stuffs.[4] Now, with no work and little food, the poor were at breaking point, and were stunned when, just a few days after the riots of 30 and 31 August, with the brutality of the police fresh in peoples' minds, a further disaster struck.

On 2 September two tenement houses collapsed in Church Street, killing seven people. It was not the first such tragedy, but this one had a particular resonance, occurring right in the middle of the turmoil and anger engendered by the Lockout. There was the added poignancy that one of those killed was a 17-year-old youth, Edward Salmon, who had been locked out by Jacobs Biscuit Factory the week before—he was killed while trying to save his young sister.

Cameron noted the fall of the Church Street houses in his diary, simply writing that he 'went to the scene of the tragedy'.[5] Precarious houses in an imminent state of collapse were a routine part of Dublin life, and there was always an accident waiting to happen. This situation could apply to buildings other than tenements; in fact, a few weeks later, on 6 October, Cameron and his staff had to evacuate the City Laboratory, as it was declared unsafe and might fall at any time. They had to move to new premises in the old Fire Brigade Station in Chatham Row. Cameron described it as 'a terrible inconvenience',[6] but otherwise seemed to accept it as part and parcel of Dublin housing conditions—citizens simply moved house and got on with their daily lives. Taken in conjunction with the heightened tension occasioned

2   Evidence 1913 Par. 284.
3   Cameron, (1904) op. cit.
4   *Weekly Irish Times*, 11 October 1913.
5   Cameron, Diaries, 3 and 4 September 1913.
6   Cameron, Diaries, 6 October, 1913.

by the Lockout, however, the seven deaths in Church Street acted as a catalyst in persuading the government to hold a far-reaching inquiry into the housing conditions of the poor of Dublin, making the Church Street victims what has been described as 'the posthumous pioneers of reform'.[7]

At the insistence of a deputation from the Irish Association of Municipal Authorities, Augustine Birrell, the Chief Secretary, established an inquiry to explore the housing issue. His first response was to announce that he would 'appoint a small Departmental committee to inquire into the character and extent of the slum problem in Dublin',[8] but the nationalist Lord Mayor Lorcan Sherlock insisted that the inquiry must take place in public, as 'the citizens . . . do not believe that a private inquiry will throw the necessary amount of light on the ownership of the slums'.[9] The Lord Mayor went on to say that it was known that some members of Dublin Corporation were tenement owners, that it was the Corporation who must be 'the chief administrative authority in connexion with any large scheme of housing reform' and that 'nothing short of a public inquiry . . . can elicit the facts and enlist the support of private munificence'.[10] A further dimension to this was a short piece in *The Times*[11], written by 'Our own correspondent', in which it was implied that Lord Aberdeen also disagreed with Mr Birrell on the nature of the inquiry, although Lord Aberdeen denied that there was any disagreement.

The eventual decision was that a local inquiry would be conducted by a Commission consisting of members of the Local Government Board—so the Corporation got its public inquiry as demanded, but not from a body of inquiry that they would have chosen. The Local Government Board had been formed in 1872 to replace the old Poor Law Commission. As well as taking on the responsibilities held by the Commission, the new Board now also had responsibilities in areas such as disease eradication, sanitary services and housing, and was the official arbiter on such matters throughout the country. It had a fraught relationship with most councils, seeing it as its principal remit to keep them in order and investigate any suspicion of wrongdoing. It had the authority to curb their rating powers, and could refuse requests for borrowing powers; over the years it gathered a wide

---

7 O'Brien, (1982) op. cit., p. 150.
8 *The Times*, 22 October 1913.
9 Ibid.
10 Ibid.
11 *The Times*, 8 November 1913.

range of information on local authorities.

The Board was often accused of putting British government interests above the needs of Irish citizens, and from 1918 on, Sinn Féin gradually eroded the power of the Board, encouraging many local councils to resist its authority. The Irish headquarters of the Board was in the Custom House, and it is widely accepted that one of the main reasons for the burning of the Custom House in 1921 during the War of Independence, was to destroy the records they held on the various councils throughout the country.

Since its inception, it had had a particularly antagonistic relationship with Dublin Corporation, and had moved against them on several occasions; for example in 1897 they had forced the resignation of three sanitary officers, and as recently as 1906 Surgeon David Edgar Flinn, on behalf of the Board, had published a highly critical *Report on the Sanitary Circumstances and Administration of the City of Dublin, with special reference to the causes of the high death-rate.*

Much of the antagonism between the two bodies arose from the (probably justified) belief of the Corporation that the Board, while criticising its efforts to improve housing, frequently stymied its reform efforts by its own actions and decisions. For example, the Corporation was criticised for allowing an influx of rural labourers into the city, which exacerbated the unemployment crisis. In fact, in 1906, the Corporation had tried to make two years' residency in the city a condition of employment, only to have this condition disallowed by the Local Government Board.

In the 1870s and 1880s, a Corporation scheme to clear and redevelop the Coombe and Plunket Street areas of the city with housing for the poor had been abandoned due to the high costs involved. Most of the costs stemmed from the exorbitant compensation awarded to the owners of dilapidated property in the area—compensation levels set by the Local Government Board. The Corporation was obliged simply to clear the area and rent the sites at a loss to the Dublin Artisans' Dwellings Company, who built houses at rents the poor were unable to afford.

It seemed inevitable therefore that any inquiry conducted into housing by the Local Government Board was likely to be adversarial, and so it proved.

The first public sitting took place on 18 November 1913, at the Council Chamber, City Hall. There were four members on the committee: C. H. O'Conor (presiding), J. F. MacCabe, A. P. Delany, all Local Government Board inspectors, and S. Watt, a member of the Local Government Board's internal staff. The Housing Committee of the Corporation had objected to the composition of the committee on the grounds that the situation in Dublin was complex, and that the committee should include experts who were used to 'dealing with social problems or eminent sanitarians'.[12] The inquiry called 76 witnesses, including, among others, aldermen, councillors, and officials of Dublin Corporation, clergymen, trade union officials, and private individuals with an interest in housing matters (but not including anyone who actually lived in the ubiquitous one-room tenements). One of the most closely questioned witnesses was Cameron, whose title was given as Executive Sanitary Officer and Medical Superintendent Officer of Health for Dublin.

The published record of the 1913 Inquiry and its subsequent Report published in 1914 has been described as 'one of the most important social documents in the history of modern Dublin, delineating in great detail the living conditions, housing, rents, and wages of the working classes in the closing years of direct British rule of the country'.[13] Surprisingly, given its importance, no in-depth examination has been made of the evidence given to the Inquiry or of the veracity and accuracy of the findings of the Report.

The Report re-stated what Cameron had been urging in his annual reports for the previous 35 years, However, rather than acknowledging this, the Report blamed Cameron for inaction. The Chairman of the Inquiry later distanced himself completely from its findings, stating that he believed that what had been left undone was, in his opinion, beyond the powers of the Corporation. His memorandum to this effect was, for unexplained reasons, not published until several days after the damning report.

The Report itself is selective in its findings. For example, it records in elaborate detail a minor and legitimate refund of £6 to several councillors who owned tenement houses, while devoting a mere five lines to the signifcant decline in the death rate during Cameron's tenure. Put in the most simple terms, it would appear that the 84-year-old Charles Cameron, at the end of his career, was a convenient scapegoat for the generations of neglect of the poor of Dublin by those in authority, and also a focus for those who, with Home Rule pending, did not want to see the largest Irish-run institution embarrassed.

---

12 RPDCD, vol. 2, no. 120, (1914), p. 156.
13 O'Brien, (1982) op. cit, p. 151.

The Report's charges against Cameron

Two main charges were made against Cameron in the Report.

1) That Sir Charles Cameron has taken on himself a dispensing power in relation to the closet accommodation stated to be necessary under the Bye-laws relating to tenement houses[14]

2) Sir Charles Cameron [has] taken on his own shoulders the responsibility of dispensing in certain cases with the Bye-laws governing tenement houses and with the conditions laid down by the Corporation in regard to rebates[15]

The Committee also cast a shadow over Cameron's entire career by stating:

We cannot help coming to the conclusion that had a judicious but firm administration of the powers given been exercised during the last 35 years . . . it should have been possible without undue hardship being inflicted to have produced a better state of affairs than exists at present,[16]

They supported this condemnation by claiming that there had only been 'a slight reduction in the death-rate in Dublin from all causes in recent years'.[17]

The first charge resulted from questions that began with the President of the Committee, Mr O'Conor, asking Cameron 'how many water closets do you consider necessary for so many people?'[18] Cameron replied: 'I have a very strong opinion that every family should have one water closet, and if that is not possible—if a water closet is common to two or more families—it is never in a sanitary state',[19] led to further questions about the number of water closets required by the bye-laws (answer: one water closet for every 12 families), and to Cameron's admission that even such requirements were not enforced when, 'in the exercise of my own judgement, I do not think it wise to'.[20]

He qualified this statement following further questioning, by giving his reasons for dispensing with the requirements of the bye-laws in respect of water closets: 'In many cases we find it more desirable to

14 Report 1914 Par. 28.
15 Report 1914, Par. 30.
16 Report 1914, Par. 31.
17 Ibid., Par. 13.
18 Evidence 1913, qs.1082.
19 Ibid.
20 Ibid., qs. 1086, 1087.

have only one closet—if we have two they both get into a bad state no matter how many notices are served'. He went on to say that his officials served about 20,000 notices on unsanitary water closets each year.

To O'Conor's question: 'Is the Sanitary Staff not failing in its duty if the water closets are not properly kept?' Cameron replied: 'It is not, because sometimes it is impossible to have them properly kept. We can only serve notice and the magistrate fines them 1s, but the people never pay the fine'.[21] In a later question session Cameron further explained his reasons for using discretion in implementing the bye-laws, when he claimed that one half of the tenement population could in practical terms be discounted when calculating the number of water closets, as 'I can positively state, on the authority of the leading sanitary officers and my own observation, that the women never use these waterclosets put up in the yards . . . secondly the children don't use them; they use the floors or the yards.'[22]

This claim was later verified by members of the Inquiry Committee, who reported that

> having visited a large number of these [tenement] houses in all parts of the city . . . in nearly every case human excreta is to be found scattered about the yards and on the floors of the closet and in some cases even in the passages of the house itself . . . We are quite prepared to accept Sir Charles Cameron's evidence, that the female inhabitants of the tenement houses seldom use the closets.[23]

This point was made in the early pages of the Report, but was not used to qualify the criticism in later pages of Cameron's 'dispensing powers' regarding water closets.

In conjunction with the details of slum ownership by members of the Corporation, this 'dispensing power' seemed to a casual reader potentially collusive. *The Irish Times*, which gave a summary of the Report 'From our London Correspondent', stressed the point without mitigation with a large headline 'SIR CHARLES CAMERON'S DISPENSING POWERS', and repeated the criticism without any reference to Cameron's reasons for exercising discretion.[24] Modern comments on the 1913 Inquiry have taken the same line, for example: 'the seeming connivance of officials such as Sir Charles Cameron with breaches of

---

21 Ibid., qs. 1090–5.
22 Ibid., qs 6032.
23 Report 1914 Par.11.
24 *The Irish Times*, 18 February 1914.

the sanitary regulations give rise to a feeling of disquiet'.[25] And another writer notes 'Cameron's instructions to his sanitary officers to be lax about the enforcement of the laws regarding water closets.'[26] These give no weight to Cameron's own explanation for his pragmatism, or indeed to the modern observation that 'many other houses . . . were so structurally unsound that efforts to install water would probably have led to their collapse'.[27]

It was the opinion of the Public Health Committee in 1869 that of 1,648 tenements without sanitary accommodation, 761 had no space where this could be supplied.[28]

Cameron answered questions as to the possibility of forcing owners to improve conditions, or doing the work themselves, and then charging the owners for the work done. He outlined the difficulty of (a) bringing summonses against owners, and (b) retrieving such costs in Dublin, where tenement houses had several layers of ownership, resulting from sub-letting, and citing cases 'where men [who were said to be owners of tenement houses] were taken out of the work-houses and brought into the Law Courts to give evidence in a case where we brought summonses'.[29] He further cited the instance several years previously where, at his suggestion, 'we got . . . a loan of £2,000 [to improve sanitary accommodation], and we lost a good deal of money over it when we tried to recover from the owners'.[30] Later, he cited a case whereby, when they tried to get a conviction against ten or twelve families for abusing sanitary facilities in a tenement house, 'it was dismissed in the Police Courts', and when they brought it further to the Queen's Bench, a legal technicality squashed the case.

He reiterated his commitment to one water closet per family, and cited the example of the Montgomery Street scheme, originally designed to have one water closet for every four families, but which was re-designed at Cameron's insistence to give each family a water closet. He claimed that two years previously, during a 'notorious invasion of flies', that he had inspected these dwellings and found 'in only two instances water-closets not perfectly clean', and claimed that if he went into an ordinary set of tenements 'I would hardly find a single water-closet clean'.[31]

---

25 Mary E. Daly *Dublin—the Deposed Capital* (Cork 1985) p. 318.
26 J. O'Brien op. cit. p 135
27 Daly, in Bannon, op. cit., p. 86.
28 Minutes of the Municipal Council of the City of Dublin, December 1869.
29 Evidence 1913, qs.1129.
30 Evidence 1913, qs 1181.
31 Evidence 1913 qs. 6032.

In his response to the criticisms of his 'dispensing' with the official requirements for sanitary facilities, in a letter to *The Irish Times* Cameron took exception to the way his evidence was reported:

With respect to the censure in reference to not having a sufficient number of closets, I have sufficient explanation in my evidence, but no reference is made to it in the report. The whole sanitary staff are unanimous that, under existing circumstances, there is adequate sanitary accommodation in the tenement houses, and that an increase is undesirable. The report does not refer to the fact that, on my suggestions, the dustbin system and the cleansing of the yards of tenement houses were adopted.[32]

The second charge brought against Cameron was that he had taken on himself to grant rebates to landlords. In its Report the Committee claimed that several cottages owned by three members of the Corporation had received tax rebates on property that was classed as third class property, and as such was unfit for human habitation. They further claimed that in two of these instances 'the property was certified by the Sanitary Sub-Officer as not fit for a rebate, but was subsequently passed as fit on the authority of Sir Charles Cameron'.[33]

Here again, the question of Cameron's 'discretion' in the strict application of legislation became an issue. Tax rebates for landlords of houses with a rateable valuation of under £8 had been introduced by the Dublin Corporation Act 1890 in an effort to encourage landlords to improve sub-standard tenements. Cameron had identified the conditions under which the rebates would be granted; a facsimile of the conditions, and the form which he was required to sign as 'Fit' or 'Unfit' after inspection by his sanitary officers are included in his book *A Brief History of Municipal Public Health Administration in Dublin*.[34] In it Cameron stated:

A great many applications for rebates were made, and a large proportion of them refused. In a *very small* proportion of the houses granted rebates all the conditions for them were not present. In the case of the Building By-laws they are not always strictly complied with if there is a sufficient reason for not insisting on all of them being observed.[35]

This book was obviously written after the publication of the 1914 Report, as Cameron commented on the Committee's criticism and his

32 *The Irish Times*, 21 February 1914.
33 Report 1914, Par. 29 and 30.
34 Charles A. Cameron, (Dublin, 1914), pp 78–9.
35 Ibid., p. 79

rationale for allowing the disputed rebate, claiming that

> it was a solitary instance of its kind. I was asked to visit the houses just
> before the last day that a claim could be entertained. They had been
> improved by cleaning since the Inspector's inspection, and I gave the
> recommendation for a rebate. It is not unusual, when the Inspector re-
> ports a house being 'unfit,' for the owner to request a re-inspection on
> the assurance that the defects mentioned in the Inspector's Report will be
> rectified.[36]

During the Inquiry, the President of the Committee asked Cameron
if the two disputed rebates given were exceptional 'because the two
owners are members of the Corporation?' to which Cameron replied:
'No; I don't think so. They form after all a very small fraction of the
owners of these places'.[37] In fact there were, according to the Inquiry's
own Report, 5,322 tenement houses in Dublin, of which just 102 were
owned by members of Dublin Corporation.[38] Despite nationalist
rhetoric, it was found that of the 60 members of the Corporation, only
4 owned 8 or more properties whether tenements or small houses. A
further 10 owed between 1 and 3 tenements.[39] Most of those owned by
Corporation members were in a satisfactory condition, which legally
entitled them to a tax rebate under the conditions set out in the Dublin
Corporation Act 1890.

Later in this session of questions, Cameron stated:

> I would certainly like to say that neither the officers of the Corporation,
> as far as my knowledge goes, nor myself, have ever been influenced in
> any way to act in regard to the property of members of the Corporation
> other than we would with regard to others.

This would seem to be borne out by the evidence of some landlord
members of the Corporation who also gave evidence to the Inquiry:
one, on being asked about his tenement property, 'Have you found
Corporation officials paying attention to it?' replied 'Yes, every week'.[40]
Alderman W. O'Connor, another landlord, unwittingly corroborated
this in his evidence. On being asked 'Do you think [the sanitary staff
of the Corporation] exercise proper supervision over your property?'
he replied:[41]

---

36 Ibid.
37 Evidence 1913, qs. 7343.
38 Report 1914, Par. 9 and Par. 29.
39 *The Irish Times* 14 February 1914
40 Evidence 1913, qs. 7731.
41 Ibid., qs. 7228.

I think they are very diligent in their duties, so far as I am concerned at all events. I think they are only looking for something to do in many cases'.

The Corporation Law Agent, Mr. Rice, questioned him further on this point:

When you say that you think the operations of the sanitary officers are such as to leave you under the impression they are looking for something to do, do you not base that on the fact that they are always making you do something?

To which Alderman O'Connor replied:

They are. I suggest that the sanitary office should be abolished altogether, and request the Local Government Board to do this class of duty.[42]

Mr Rice continued: 'You think it would be better if the Local Government Board did it? to which O'Connor replied:

I dare say it would. We would be under less expense. The citizens of Dublin are ground down under taxation at the present time.[43]

With regard to rebates, Cameron admitted:

I will always take a liberal view, even though I may not be strictly in accordance with the bye-laws. I want to give the reason. Well, I say I had two objects in view: first, the improvement of places that never would have been improved so much except for the rebate of rates, and secondly, also that these places would be let at lower rates to these people who find it very difficult to pay this 2s or 2s 6d a week. Now, I may have been wrong, but that was the view that I took, and I would like to say this: on no single occasion, with regard to rebate of rates, has any member of the Corporation ever called on me personally, or sent a message to me, with one solitary exception; that is the case of Councillor Crozier.

Cameron explained further that he re-examined Crozier's house, which had been refused a rebate, made a suggestion for an improvement that would allow a rebate to be made, and when this improvement had been made, he certified the house as fit for rebate.[44] He would later contend that, while 'there may be a trifling laxity in not strictly enforcing the conditions justifying rebates',

the laxity is not due to favouritism but to the desire to see the dwellings

---

42 Ibid., qs. 7239.
43 Ibid., qs. 7240.
44 Ibid., Par. 7317.

of the poor being kept in a better state than they otherwise would be . . . if the Corporation discontinue rebates many dwellings now in good condition would become more or less insanitary.[45]

The President of the Committee, in response, took a high line:

Remember you are dealing here with putting money into the pockets of the owners of these houses; in other words, you are depriving the Corporation of rates that they are entitled to get.[46]

Cameron's protestation that the houses given rebates in which he deviated from the Corporation's guidelines were 'infinitesimal' in number were countered by the President with the statement: 'So much the worse because if the number is infinitesimal we have it stated that one of them belongs to a member of the Corporation.'[47]

However, in the case of property belonging to Councillor Crozier, the Committee considered it fit for human habitation but in such bad repair as to not fulfil the 'express conditions required by the Corporation', while in the case of 12 dwellings belonging to Alderman Corrigan, they believed that Cameron had illegally dispensed with the necessary conditions.[48]

In the section of the Report dealing with tax rebates on tenements, the Committee misleadingly noted that the amount remitted was £3,819. In a response to the Report the Housing Committee of the Corporation revealed that of the total amount of £3,819 given in rebates, a mere £6 0s 6d was given to landlords where discretion in the strict appliance of the regulations was exercised. The Housing Committee stated that

the introduction of the larger sum of £3,819 immediately preceding the mention of the names of the three members of the Corporation and the omission of all mention of the actual amount alleged to have been improperly received leaves much to be desired in the way of impartial reporting, or safeguarding against the false impression on the public mind as to the actual facts, which the peculiar construction of the paragraph in the report was undoubtedly bound to create.[49]

The Housing Committee of the Corporation took further issue with the Report of the Inquiry Committee regarding comments on Charles Cameron's 'discretion' in strictly implementing the regulations

---

45 Cameron (1914), op. cit., p. 80.
46 Evidence 1913, qs. 7350.
47 Ibid., qs. 7350–2.
48 Ibid., Par. 30
49 RPDCD, 1914, vol. II, p. 165.

regarding tax rebates, claiming that 'there was an attempt in its conduct to put the Corporation on its trial, and to enlarge on any of its actions which could be criticised'.[50] They (accurately) stated that the Report took over a page to give their comments on the rebate which amounted to £6 0s 6d, and 'about five lines . . . to say as little as they possibly could on the subject of the Dublin death rate and its decline during Sir Charles Cameron's period of service'.[51]

During the Inquiry, MacCabe asked Cameron if, 'during that time, since that time, 1879 [the year Cameron became Superintendent Medical Officer of Health] the death rate in Dublin has diminished very considerably?'[52] However, in the Report, the Committee contradicted this, claiming that 'there has been a slight reduction in the death-rate in Dublin from all causes in recent years'.[53] The cyclical nature of infectious disease ensured that this was true, if statistically unsophisticated, over the short term. Taking a longer view, the death rate in Dublin in 1880 was 37.7 per thousand, in 1900 it was 30.3, and this had been reduced to 21.6 in 1913, the year of the Inquiry. During the same period the number of tenements had been almost halved, from 9,760 in 1880[54] to 5,322 in 1913.[55] The Report did not stress this reduction, which would have perhaps vindicated Cameron's work, but rather emphasised the fact that more people were now living in tenements, and that the density per house was greater than in 1880. This was, of course, a demographic rather than a sanitary problem.

The facts 'revealed' in the 1913 Inquiry had been known for decades, so it is perhaps unsurprising that the main thrust of the Committee's complaints against Cameron were of relatively minor infringements of bye-laws, infringements which he consciously and pragmatically undertook, not as 'connivance' with landlords, Corporation members or otherwise, but in the belief that they would improve the lot of tenement dwellers.

Cameron's reaction to the findings of the Report was to do what he did best, setting out the facts clearly in a book entitled *A Brief History of Municipal Public Health Administration in Dublin*,[56] outlining the work done by the Corporation, his staff and himself over the years 'in reply to a report of a Departmental Commission of the Local Government

50 Ibid., p. 166.
51 Ibid., p. 166.
52 Evidence 1913, qs. 1405.
53 Report 1914, Par. 13.
54 Report 1914, Par. 14.
55 Report 1914, Par. 9.
56 Cameron, 1914 op cit.

Board on the housing question which I considered did not do justice to the work of the Corporation'.[57] The Report was issued in February, and Cameron had completed his book for publication by May. It was published in June by Hodges, Figgis, price 1s.

It is a fair and accurate record of public health administration in Dublin, and is still a valuable source of reference to researchers. Ever equitable, even when obviously angry at what he felt was the injustice of the Commission's Report, Cameron's Foreword to the book stated that:

> Whilst taking exception to some of the statements in the Report, I admit that it contains a large amount of useful information—most of it supplied by the Corporation. I believe that no Municipal Authority in the United Kingdom has done more to improve the state of the public health than the Corporation, when due allowance is made for the peculiar conditions under which Dublin is placed.[58]

The content and style of the book shows that the octogenarian Cameron was no cipher, but was still fully competent mentally and physically.

---

57 Cameron, Diaries, 30 March 1914.
58 Cameron (1914), op. cit., Foreword.

Chapter 12 The final years

The 1913 Inquiry and its Report, although damaging to Cameron's reputation, was not the end of his career. The fact that his first reaction after the publication of the Report was to write *A Brief History of Municipal Public Health Administration in Dublin,* indicates that he was still in command of his duties. Early in 1914 he tried once again to awaken interest in the Association for Housing the Very Poor, and he still travelled on sanitary business. He continued to combine a busy life of official duties with family and other commitments; it was obvious that his grandchildren gave him enormous pleasure, in particular the one that he always referred to in his diaries as 'The Pogue', who seemed to visit him more often than the others. Although still sprightly, at the age of 83 the strain of the previous few years were beginning to take their toll; on 5 May 1914 he confessed to his diary that he had forgotten to attend a meeting of his Masonic Lodge 'the first time I ever forgot a meeting of that kind. Lately I have become forgetful'.[1]

Another son dies

The coming of the First World War in 1914 brought changes to Cameron's family as it did to so many others. His two sons-in-law, Denny and Rupert, joined up, as did his youngest son Ewen, who got a commission in the Royal Dublin Fusiliers, and was stationed at Gough Barracks.[2] Ewen had had a varied career. On 28 October 1901, Cameron reported in his diary that 'Ewen today entered the service of the Great Northern Railway Company and was located in the manager's (Mr. Henry Reeves) office'.[3] Nine years later, at the age of 28, Ewen went to Ceylon to train as a tea planter. En route, he telegraphed Cameron from London, and sent him a postcard and a letter. Cameron placed the letter in a drawer 'as it is not likely that I shall ever see him again'.[4] Cameron paid £100 to a Dr Richard Oulton to be paid by him to 'whoever may take [Ewen] as a pupil', and would later need to send money for his board. As with his brothers before

---

1 Cameron, Diaries, 5 May 1914.
2 Ibid., 27 September, 1914.
3 Ibid., 28 October 1901.
4 Ibid., 26 February 1910.

him, Ewen set off on a lonely journey; Cameron recounted that 'he felt acutely leaving home and I felt not less acutely. He was a quiet willing boy'.[5] Ewen was as unfortunate as his brothers—the climate disagreed with him and in August 1912 'he came home a wreck'.[6] He is also described as having 'a heart affection'. Cameron recorded an interesting fact on 12 August, 1912, when he wrote that 'Kelly Duggan dined with us. Her engagement with Ewen now off'. It is unclear if this is an engagement to Cameron's son—there had been no mention of this in the diaries. Cameron does occasionally mention another Ewan Cameron, although the spelling is always different. If the statement did apply to his son Ewen, this is the only mention of a female relationship for any of Cameron's sons—although in the diaries for 20 August 1914, the same Kelly Duggan is reported as being engaged to a Mr Hugo, and the next day she was reported by Cameron to be 'in a very excited state as Mr. Hugo has shamefully broken off his engagement with her'. By December of 1912, Ewen had improved in health, and put on a stone and a half in weight. He appears to have been close to his father—at one point he is described as spending some hours at the National Library with Cameron during his research for the second edition of the *History of the Royal College of Surgeons in Ireland and of the Irish Schools of Medicine*,[7] and he always spent his leave from the army at home with Cameron.

In June 1915 Ewen was on a recruiting mission in Bray, Co. Wicklow, and Cameron visited him at his camp on Bray Head. Ewen visited Cameron at home on 26 August, and Cameron reported that he was upset by the 'news from the Dardanelles',[8] where many of his friends had been killed at Suvla Bay. On 27 August, while travelling on a train between Bray and Greystones during a recruitment drive, Ewen 'went to the lavatory and shot his dear head with his revolver'.[9] Maitland Gerrard, who was with him in Bray, gave evidence at the inquest of what seems to have been Ewen's mental breakdown over the few days before his suicide. At dinner in Cameron's house, Ewen had asked 'Am I going mad? Everybody seems to be talking queerly'.[10] He was worried that all his friends had gone to the Front, and that he was afraid that they would think he was not going. He spoke of some of his 'pals' in the 7th Battalion of the Royal Dublin Fusiliers

5 Ibid.
6 Ibid., 4 August 1912.
7 Ibid., 4 September 1913.
8 Ibid., 26 August 1915.
9 Ibid., 27 August 1915.
10 *Weekly Irish Times*, 4 September, 1915.

who had died, and wanted to send a wire to his Colonel saying that he wished to go to the Front.[11] Gerrard reported how, the next day, on the train journey between Bray and Greystones, Ewen had gone to the lavatory. When he didn't return, Gerrard became uneasy, went to the lavatory, and 'saw something like blood coming under the door'.[12] When the door was broken down, Ewen was found huddled up, lying in a pool of blood, his automatic pistol underneath. Gerrard said that Ewen was physically exhausted and run down, that there were no financial difficulties and no intrigue. The verdict was death by a bullet wound, self-inflicted while temporarily insane. Cameron would later claim that the insanity was caused by sunstroke, but it would seem that it had been some kind of ongoing mental state for at least a few days. Although Maitland Gerrard said at the inquest that he had not mentioned Ewen's odd behaviour to his father, Cameron must have had some apprehension about Ewen's state of mind, because when he got a telephone call saying that something serious had happened to Ewen 'I knew at once what had happened'.[13]

It appears to have been almost the last straw for Cameron, who was then 85 years of age, and who had already lost four sons, as he wrote 'this terrible blow will leave the little of life left to me joyless'.[14] Cameron was moved that the first letter of sympathy which came that afternoon was from a Father Wall, a Roman Catholic priest in Haddington Road, an indication of the wide regard in which Cameron was held in Dublin. The inquest appears to have been held immediately and recorded death from temporary insanity, probably brought on by sunstroke.[15] Ewen's body was brought to Westland Row by special train, and then 'to that home he loved so well'. He was given a military funeral in Mount Jerome—he was 33 years of age. On 5 October, Cameron reported that 'Since Ewen's death am suffering much from insomnia'.[16]

Ernest Cameron

Of Cameron's six sons, the only one to survive him was the fourth, Ernest Stuart, born on 29 September 1872. He is first mentioned in Cameron's diaries as coming to work with Cameron 'for a short time

11 Ibid.
12 Ibid.
13 Cameron, Diaries, 27 August 1915.
14 Ibid.
15 *Weekly Irish Times* 4 September 1915.
16 Cameron, Diaries, 5 October 1915.

today' on 31 August 1892, and Cameron reported on 18 January 1895 that 'Ernest went into laboratory to work today'. However, it was not until five years later, in October 1900, that the Committee 'arranging the reconstruction of Committees and Departments . . . agreed to Ernest being made assistant analyst at a salary of £100 per annum'. The Corporation approved Ernest's appointment as co-analyst on 28 January 1901.[17] They also approved the provision of a brougham for Cameron—up until then he appears to have used public transport to carry out his many duties around the city, although his early diaries mention his private ownership of a brougham.

Ernest was still working in the Corporation in 1909, where he was described as 'Water Analyst' with the letters FCSL after his name.[18] The letters FCS usually describe 'Fellow of the Chemical Society' and it is possible that the letter 'L' denotes London. A contemporary biography of Cameron described Ernest as a 'scientist',[19] while the Census returns for Cameron's household in 1901 and 1911[20] described Ernest as 'Analytical Chemist' and 'Chemical Analyst' respectively; however, no mention is made by Cameron of his qualifications.

Ernest's real ambition, however, appears to have been to perform as a singer, being, according to Cameron 'devoted to music . . . [and having] a good baritone voice'.[21]

Entries throughout Cameron's diaries show that Ernest performed variously as Prince Brilliant in an amateur pantomime, that he sang in opera at the Gaiety Theatre and other venues, and seemed to be always willing to give a song or two at social events. There is an account that he 'sang admirably' in a production of *The Flying Dutchman* in the Abbey Theatre in 1911.[22] By 1913 he appears to have left his job in Dublin Corporation and was in Paris where he stayed for six months; his financial situation was apparently precarious, as he wrote to Cameron looking for £30. Some measure of the contrast between his approach to life and Cameron's is indicated by an entry in the diaries for 2 November 1914, in which Cameron reported that he 'brought to Ernest about (£75) (£73) [two amounts written] in nine cheques from the Corporation which he did not take the trouble of calling for during nine months'. There is a report of him, as one

17 Ibid., 28 January 1901.
18 Charles A. Cameron, *Report upon the State of Public Health in Dublin for the year 1909*, p. 9.
19 E. MacDowell Cosgrave, *Dublin and County Dublin in the Twentieth Century, Contemporary Biographies* (Brighton and London, 1908), p. 189 described Ernest as 'scientist'.
20 1901 and 1911 Census returns for 51 Pembroke Road.
21 Cameron *Autobiography* (1920) op. cit, p. 29.
22 *The Irish Times*, 2 February, 1911.

of a number of 'well-known singers', taking part in a concert for Dalkey Red Cross in Dalkey Town Hall in 1914.[23] In 1915, aged 43, he appeared to be still pursuing a singing career, and the real extent of his talent can perhaps be best gauged from a diary entry on 4 October 1915, in which Cameron reported that 'in order to get an engagement for Ernest with the O'Mara Opera Co. I had with much reluctance to invite Mr. and Mrs. O'Mara to luncheon'.[24] Ernest was to meet the O'Maras in London with a view to performing in one of their productions.

A few months later, however, on 14 February 1916, Ernest was committed to a mental asylum in Dublin, as he was 'disturbed and sleepless and had delusions'.[25] An interesting aside to this episode is Cameron's decision to choose to have him admitted to Stewarts Hospital, as it had the same level of care as Swift's, but was a guinea cheaper per week. No hint of mental instability in the family had been mentioned until this time, although his brother Ewen had committed suicide the previous year, apparently while he was 'temporarily insane'. It is possible, however, that at the age of 44, with a professional singing career apparently unsuccessful, and living with the knowledge that all of his brothers had predeceased him in tragic circumstances, Ernest simply had a nervous breakdown. He recovered, as there are several advertisements at Cameron's Raglan Road address (to which he moved in 1916) that state 'Mr. Ernest Cameron receives pupils for voice production.'

Cameron's will, dated 18 June 1920, appeared to corroborate the lack of any fixed income for Ernest; Cameron left him a lump sum of £500, and instructed his executors, his two sons-in-law, to allow Ernest an annuity of £200 per annum by quarterly payments out of his residuary estate.[26] The house on Raglan Road was sold after Cameron's death in 1921, and there is mention of Ernest Cameron appearing in mostly amateur concerts over the next few years. He died on 13 May 1949 from cardiac failure at the age of 79. He was still a bachelor, and there is no occupation or former occupation given on the death certificate. His address is given as 113 Upper Leeson Street, but the certificate shows that he died in Grangegorman Mental Hospital, so obviously his old mental problems had recurred. The

23   Ibid., 17 December, 1914.
24   Cameron, Diaries, 4 October 1915.
25   Ibid., 14 February 1916.
26   Charles A. Cameron, Last Will and Testament, 1920.

Leeson Street address was set in flats in 1949.[27] This rather depressing end to Cameron's last son is alleviated somewhat by the knowledge that he was obviously part of a close and loving family circle, as the following *In Memoriam* notice inserted by his sister Lena Stanley in *The Irish Times* two years later, indicates:

> In most loving memory of my darling brother, Ernest Stuart, on this his birthday, who went from this to a happier world on May 13th 1949—Lena Stanley[28]

Frongoch

In 1916 Cameron was requested by the Home Secretary to inspect the prison camp at Frongoch in Wales, where members of Sinn Féin were interned after the Easter Rising. On 16 December Cameron travelled to Frongoch, despite having influenza. He 'spent two days in examining the camp and buildings . . I examined the disused distillery [where some prisoners were confined], the prison cells and the sanitary accommodation. I also enquired into the health of the prisoners'.[29] Cameron wrote in his *Autobiography* that 'My report to the Home Secretary, being confidential, cannot be described here'; however, Brennan-Whitmore wrote that 'nothing seemed to escape the eagle eye of the old gentleman' (Cameron would have been 86 years of age at the time). Brennan-Whitmore describes the scene:

> Entering the dormitory he went straight over to the two latrines in the corner. Although his voice was sharp and strong we could not distinguish what it was he was saying; but we gathered that he was not quite satisfied with the arrangement. He also made down one of the beds and got into it. He looked a most comical sight in the bed, with his tall silk hat still on his head; and the whiteness of his beard accentuated by the dark-coloured tweed blankets.[30]

Brennan-Whitmore wrote that Cameron 'was certainly very shrewd'; when the Adjutant pointed out that the men had three blankets each, Cameron replied that 'in reality they only had two, as having no bed sheets they would have to use one of them as an under blanket'.[31] He also wrote that the Adjutant of the camp tried to deter

27 *Thom's Directory*, 1949, p.1264.
28 *The Irish Times*, 29 September 1951.
29 Cameron (1920), op. cit., pp 158-159.
30 Brennan-Whitmore, op. cit., p. 191.
31 Ibid.

the men from meeting Cameron while he was inspecting the premises. 'Whilst he was thus engaged, the prisoners deputed four of their officers to wait upon him and lay a series of complaints before him'.[32] As they advanced towards Cameron, the Adjutant tried to get them to return to their cells, but they refused. Cameron heard the commotion, and asked the prisoners if they wished to see him; on being told that they had complaints, he said that he would see them the following morning. The Adjutant also presented himself at this meeting, and the ensuing conversation is worth repeating in full from Brennan-Whitmore's report:

> 'Do you think I am quite safe with them?' asked Sir Charles, looking at the prisoners with a humorous twinkle in his eyes.
> 'Oh, yes,' replied 'Buckshot' [the prisoners' nickname for the Adjutant] pompously, 'they are not so blood-thirsty as that.'
> 'Then I shall not want your protection,' replied Sir Charles suavely; and bowed the Colonel out.

The prisoners then laid a detailed series of complaints before Sir Charles.[33]

Brennan-Whitmore reported:

> We did not see Sir Charles Cameron's report, but were told on very good authority that it was almost wholly in favour of the prisoners. And there is no doubt but that a report of such a nature coming from so eminent an authority, and following hot-foot upon the effects of our publicity campaign, was one of the chief factors which decided the authorities to liberate us.[34]

The fact that Cameron recorded the happenings in his *Autobiography* indicates that this incident was important to him; it certainly indicates that his mind and faculties had lost none of their sharpness.

Spanish 'flu

In 1918, at the age of 88, Cameron as Medical Officer of Health faced one of his biggest challenges—the Spanish Influenza Pandemic, later estimated to have caused between 40 and 100 million deaths worldwide. In Dublin, the epidemic appears to have peaked between October 1918 and March 1919, as shown in Figure 13.1.

---

32 Ibid., p. 193.
33 Ibid., pp 193–4.
34 Ibid., p. 194.

Figure 13.1 *Death rates in Dublin City during the Spanish Influenza Pandemic 1918-1919*

Period 13 weeks to	Deaths Number	Death Rate Per 1000 living	Rate 12 months before
End Jun 1918	1,554	20.4	21.4
End Sep 1918	1,662	21.8	16.0
End Dec 1918	2,756	36.1	16.9
End Mar 1918	2,923	37.7	21.7
End Jun 1919	1,496	19.3	20.4

Cameron took immediate steps to minimise the loss of life, disinfecting public places such as cinemas after use, disinfecting streets every day, and public trams every night. As the pandemic spread, he gave orders to close schools, theatres and cinemas, and requested the military to remove their personnel from public hospitals. The *Irish Independent* reported that

the military authorities have informed Sir Charles Cameron that they are quite willing to remove all soldiers from the military hospitals. They had acceded to his original request not to send any more wounded men to civilian hospitals, and they were now . . . willing to remove a large number of wounded in these institutions.[35]

As many as possible were nursed in their own homes by the nurses of St Patrick's and St Laurence's Homes, and public posters and notices in the press alerted the public to precautions. Cameron, still advanced in his thinking, stated that he 'was very much interested in the subject of a vaccine', advising the public that it had been very largely used, and on the whole appeared to be favourable. Although the death rate in Dublin nearly doubled during the epidemic (see Figure 13.1), Dublin did not fare as badly as many other cities, perhaps partly due to prompt and effective measures by Cameron and his office.

However, by 1918 the Public Health Committee had

decided that the time had come when Sir Charles Cameron should be relieved from the active work of the Department, and confine himself to consultative duties and analytical work in the City Laboratory, while Dr. Russell . . . should be held responsible for the discharge of the active duties of Medical and Executive Officer of Health.[36]

35 *Irish Independent*, 1 November 1918.
36 RDCD, 1921, Vol. 1, p. 371.

They reported that

in October 1918, a deputation from the Special Committee of Chairmen
and Deputy Chairmen of Committees interviewed Sir Charles, and as a
result he was granted leave—a medical certificate recommended a year's
leave of absence.[37]

This recommendation was not adopted by the Corporation until 3
March 1919, which explains why Cameron played such a prominent
role during the influenza pandemic. But now Cameron, the grand old
man of Irish public health, was preparing to bow out gracefully. His
diaries ceased in 1916, so the only record of his personal feelings on
taking a less prominent role is in his *Autobiography*, written in 1920,
where he acknowledges the contribution of Dr Russell in assisting
him as Medical Officer of Health, and of Bernard Fagan, who assisted
him as an additional Public Analyst.[38]

Death and funeral

Charles Cameron died in his house in Raglan Road on 27 February
1921. As *The Irish Times* put it 'he had been in feeble health for some
time, and the end was not unexpected.'[39] In its obituary the newspaper
forgot its somewhat critical reports of the 1913 Inquiry, and declared
that

for more than half-a-century he had charge of the Public Health
Department of the Dublin Corporation. His greatest services were
those rendered in connection with this department. The record of his
administration . . . represents an enormous amount of arduous labour
carried on during many years with extraordinary vigour and always
in a progressive spirit, his work produced abiding benefits in which all
sections of the community shared.[40]

His funeral took place on 2 March. His body was taken at 9 o' clock
from 27 Raglan Road to St Bartholemew's Church on nearby Clyde
Road, just off Pembroke Road, where he and his family had lived for
so many years. Cameron was laid to rest in Mount Jerome, in the grave
which already held his sons William and Mervyn, his mother and his
beloved wife Lucie. He had visited this grave devotedly for 38 years.
Nearby lay his sons Charlie and Ewen, and somewhere in the Canary

---

37 Ibid., p. 372.
38 Cameron, *Autobiography* (1920), op. cit., p. 147.
39 *The Irish Times* 28 February 1921
40 Ibid.

Isles his son Douglas. The horrors which Cameron saw and tried to remedy during his professional life were echoed by the tragedies of his personal life. And just as he never allowed the unending grind of his work to get him down, neither did he allow the crushing personal burdens to deflect him from that work.

Commenting on his death, *The Irish Times* remarked that 'he held a unique place in the life of Dublin. He had a genius for friendship, and his wit, his learning and his generosity endeared him to a very wide circle.'[41]

His funeral was large as would be expected for such a prominent personage, and it was particularly suitable that, among the usual 'with deepest sympathy' there was a preponderance of tributes that were to 'the kindest friend', 'love . . . for our truest and dearest friend' — tributes that confirm his reputation as a kindly and humane man.

Cameron, in common with other public health pioneers, has been undervalued in the history of medicine and public health. Partly this is because their labours were in administrative fields where the obscure operation of regulations can make so much difference; partly it is because their work was also the reverse of glamorous — the persistent eradication of one squalid nuisance after another.

However, some measure of culpability must lie with the era in which they served, which, while giving lip-service to public servants in the form of knighthoods and other honours, gave the most prominent recognition to different heros, those who expanded the bounds of Empire or who fought heroically on the battle-field. A typical example of this in Dublin's case is the statue in Merrion Square of Surgeon-Major T. H. Parkes, member of the intrepid Stanley expedition, and an archetypal Victorian hero. Parkes' medical career started in Dublin as a pupil of Charles Cameron, and his admiration for his former tutor was such that he carried a bottle of water from an African lake back to Dublin, especially for Cameron to analyse; the admiration was mutual — Cameron was instrumental in having the statue in Merrion Square erected to his former pupil.

There is no monument to Cameron or any other Medical Officer of Health, nor are any stirring poems written about their exploits. Yet these men pushed the boundaries of medical science and fought daily battles, often at risk to themselves, against a legion of deadly enemies in disease-ridden Victorian cities. They had to fight tangible opponents in the form of hostile councillors, landlords, ratepayers,

41 *The Irish Times* 28 February 1921

their own profession, and often the very public they were trying to help, and intangible enemies in the squalor and diseases they sought to eliminate, often finding hard-won gains eradicated by a sudden epidemic.

Those who laboured on the battlefields of city slums, fighting an enemy as ruthless as any found on foreign soil, were perhaps content with what recompense and recognition they received in their own lifetime—they were, after all, simply public servants, each of whom was devoted to his work, and to his individual city. Certainly Charles Cameron, among all his honours, claimed that he was most proud of being made an Honorary Freeman of Dublin, and of the statement that he had done 'more than a man's part' in eradicating disease in the city.[42] He would, no doubt, have concurred with the statement by his peer William Henry Duncan, who said 'we have done our duty in our generation'.[43]

However, true to his stated wish to 'die in harness',[44] he 'continued to exercise a large part of his principal professional activities up to the time of his death—a remarkable record of a very remarkable man'.[45]

It would be left to subsequent generations to finally solve Dublin's housing and public health problems, and they would do it in a different Ireland to that in which Cameron worked. As *The Irish Times*, with some prescience, wrote at the time of his death

> Others of course will take his place in the various organisations with which he was connected. His work will continue; but we never shall know another Sir Charles Cameron.[46]

42 *Irish Independent* 24 February 1911.
43 Frazer, op. cit., p. 102.
44 Cameron *Autobiography* (1920) p 147.
45 Dyer, (1932) op. cit., p. 37.
46 *The Irish Times*, 28 February 1921.

Cameron in the attire of a senior Freemason. His membership of the organisation was an important part of his personal and social life
(Grand Lodge of Antient Free and Accepted Masons of Ireland).

Appendixes

Appendix 1: *Memorandum on the Condition of Dwellings of the very Poor* by Sir Charles A. Cameron, Superintendent Medical Officer of Health for Dublin.

A large number of dwellings for the working classes have been erected by the Corporation of Dublin, by artizans' dwellings companies, by Lord Iveagh, and by several private persons and firms. With a few trifling exceptions the rents of these dwellings are 2s. to 7s. 6d. per week, and very few at the first-named figure.

There are thousands of people in Dublin who cannot afford to pay even 2s. a week for their dwellings. They occupy houses in courts, lanes, and alleys, and the lowest class tenements in the poorest localities.

The areas upon which large numbers of the very poor are located are often termed 'unhealthy', which, indeed, they are. Several of them have been cleared by the Corporation, and upon their sites new dwellings have been erected, but the people who were evicted from those unhealthy dwellings have not returned to occupy the new houses, the rent of which they could not afford to pay. They have sought refuge in the lowest class houses in other districts, and in process of time the districts to which they have migrated will become as unhealthy as were those from which they had been evicted.

There are in Dublin thousands of poor people who are quite unable to pay more than from one to two shillings per week for their dwellings. They comprise, amongst others, poor widows, with or without young children, peddlers, fish, fruit, and flower hawkers, charwomen, old men and women still capable of doing a little work, and the lowest class of porters and labourers. Many single men and women, and even families, earn less than 10s. per week. For the housing of such persons, neither artisans's dwellings companies nor ordinary builders care to cater. They live in the worst class of tenement houses, their immediate landlords being, as a rule, poor, and unable, even if willing, to keep their houses in good order and clean. These landlords rent houses from owners (many of whom are absentees, who take no active interest in their properties) and sublet them at the highest rent they can get. In my *Annual Report* on the health of Dublin for 1884, I gave a large number of tables showing the number of rooms and of inhabitants in several of the streets of Dublin, mainly consisting of tenement houses; also showing their valuation, rent, etc.

In four of these streets the average valuation of the houses was £15 11s. 9d. and the average rent from tenants £48 18s. 8d. Comparatively well-to-do and very poor people occupied, in many cases, the same house. The house, 36 Upper Mercer-street, valued at £18, was let to 11 families, whose combined rents amounted to £74 2s. Their occupants and earnings were as follows:-

Occupations	Weekly earnings.
Jeweller, 1	£1 8s 0d
Carpenters, 2	£1 14s 0d
Shoemaker, 1	£0 15s 0d
Bricklayer, 1	£1 12s 0d
Gardener, 1	£0 16s 0d
Porters, 3	12s. to £1 5s 0d
Job Coachman	Uncertain
Charwoman	£0 5s 0d

This tenement house was in fairly good order; but in many others the inhabitants were very poor, earning per family from 5s. to 10s. a week.

It is impossible to compel the landlords of the lowest class tenements to keep them in clean and good repair. Nearly 3,000 of the worst have been closed by magistrates' orders obtained by the Sanitary Authority, and many more would be closed if there were provision made for the reception of their ejected tenants—they cannot be turned out into the streets.

The homes of the very poor are the nurseries of infectious diseases, which spread from them into the houses of all classes. In the interest of the general welfare it is desirable to do something substantial for the improvement of the dwellings of these, the most dependent portion of the community. By providing them with plain but clean residences the amount of infection is decreased; sickness and consequent pauperism is lessened, and the health of the community, as a whole is exalted.

The condition of the dwellers in narrow courts and lanes, and in squalid, decayed houses in the poorer streets is, indeed, pitiable, and urgently demands a remedy. The influence of such dwellings upon these tenants cannot fail to be bad, morally and physically. As to the physical effects, I shall quote a single verse from Mr. Bedford Leno's poem:

As I gazed from out my window on the crowded courts below,
Where the sunshine seldom enters and winds seldom blow,
I beheld a flow'ret dying for the want of light and air,
And I said, 'How fares it brothers with the human flow'rets there?'

Public Health Office,
Cork-hill,
29 May 1897.

Appendix 2: Daily diet of the poorest classes—note entry for the woman in 'constant' employment

Name of Street	Occupation of Tenant	Rent per Week	Weekly Wages	Constant or Irregular Employment	Number in Family
16 Dame-court	Tailor	2s 6d	10s	Irregular	2
North Anne-st. (No. 18)	Bookmaker	3s	18s (average when working)	Irregular	6
Murphy's Cottages, St. Mary's-place	Labourer	3s	£1	Irregular	5
65 Bridgefoot-street	Charwoman	1s 6d	9s	Constant	3
Cottage at rere of Townsend-st.	Labourer	1s 6d	On an average of 14s	Very irregular	7 – father, mother and 5 children

Source: Sample from a larger table in Charles Cameron *How the Poor Live* (Dublin 1904) pp 16-21

Food used for Breakfast	Food used for Dinner	Food used for Supper or Tea	Name of Vegetables, if any
Tea and dry bread	Herrings, dry bread and tea	Sometimes porridge, "supper and dinner combined"	None used
Bread, butter and tea	Bacon, and sometimes eggs with bread and tea	Bread, butter and tea	Potatoes and cabbage
Bread, butter and tea	Bacon and vegetables	Bread, butter and tea	Potatoes and cabbage
Bread, butter and tea	Sun.—Bacon, potatoes and cabbage, 9d Mon.—Kalecannon, 2½d Tues.—Soup and bread, 4d Wed.—Fish and potatoes, 4½d Thurs.—Beef and potatoes, 8d Fri.—Bread and milk, 2½ Sat.—Eggs and potatoes, 4d	Tea, bread and butter	Potatoes and cabbage
Bread, butter and tea	Week-days—bread, butter and tea Sundays—Bacon	Bread, butter and tea	Cabbage and potatoes (on Sundays)

Bibliography

ARCHIVES

Dublin City Archives
Dublin Diocesan Archive
Grand Lodge Freemasons of Ireland
Major Rupert Stanley Memorial Masonic Lodge, No., 831 Belfast
National Archive of Ireland
National Library of Ireland
Royal College of Physicians of Ireland
Royal College of Surgeons in Ireland, Archives, Mercer Library
Royal Institute of Public Health, London
Royal Irish Academy

PARLIAMENTARY PAPERS

Municipal Boundaries Commission (Ireland) Part 1, Evidence from Dublin, Rathmines, etc. PP 1880, xxx, cd. 2725

Report of the Royal Commissioners appointed to inquire into the Sewerage and Drainage of the City of Dublin, and other matters connected therewith, together with Minutes of Evidence, Appendix, Index, etc. PP 1880, xxx, cd. 2605

Minutes of evidence of 3rd report of Her Majesty's Commissioners for inquiring into the Housing of the Working Classes (Ireland) PP 1884–5, xxxi, cd. 4547–1

Report of the Departmental Committee appointed by the Local Government Board for Ireland to inquire into the Housing Conditions of the Working Classes in Dublin (Dublin 1914) PP 1913, 1914 cd. 7273 (Evidence of Inquiry) and cd. 7317 (Report of Committee)

CONTEMPORARY BOOKS AND ARTICLES

Accum, F. *A Treatise on Adulterations of Food and Culinary Poisons* (London, 1820)

Anon *Dublin Main Drainage Scheme Souvenir Handbook 1906* (Dublin, 1906)

Brennan-Whitmore, W. J. *With the Irish in Frongoch* (Dublin, 1917)

Cameron, Charles A. *Chemistry of Agriculture, the food of plants: including the Composition, Properties, and Adulteration* (Dublin and London, 1857)

Cameron, Charles A. *Lectures on the Preservation of Health* (London and New York, 1868)

Cameron, Charles A. *A Manual of Hygiene, Public and Private and Compendium of Sanitary Laws, for the information and guidance of public health authorities, officers of health, and sanitarians generally* (Dublin and London, 1874)

Cameron, Charles A. *Short Poems Translated from the German* (Edinburgh, 1876)

Cameron, Charles A. 'On an Epidemic of Fever caused by Infected Milk', *Dublin Journal of Medical Science*, vol. LXVIII, No. 91, Third Series, Part 1, 1 July 1879, pp 1–25

Cameron, Charles A. 'Report on Public Health', *Dublin Journal of Medical Science*, vol. LXXIV, July to December, 1882, Part III, pp 481–99

Cameron, Charles A. *History of the Royal College of Surgeons in Ireland and of the Irish Schools of Medicine* (Dublin, 1886, 1916)

Cameron, Charles A. *Sanitary Prosecutions in Dublin and elsewhere 1892–5* [? location]

Cameron, Charles A. 'A History of Lodge No. XXV' *Irish Masonry Illustrated*, October 1901

Cameron, Charles A. *How the Poor Live* (Dublin, 1904)

Cameron, Charles A. *Reports 'upon the state of public health and the sanitary work, etc. performed in Dublin during the year…'* (1909–19)

Cameron, Charles A. *Reminiscences* (Dublin, 1913)

Cameron, Charles A. *A Brief History of Municipal Public Health Administration in Dublin* (Dublin and London, 1914)

Cameron, Charles A. 'Some Recollections of a Long Life in Dublin' *The Lady of the House* (Dublin, Christmas 1915)

Cameron, Charles A. *Autobiography* (Dublin, 1920)

Dawson, Charles 'The Dublin housing question sanitary and insanitary', *JSSISI* Vol. XIII, Part XCIII, 1912/1913 pp 90–5

Disraeli, Benjamin *Sybil, or The Two Nations* (London 1845)

Eason, Charles 'The tenement houses of Dublin: their condition and regulation', *JSSISI* Vol. X, Part LXXIV, 1898/1899, pp 383–98

Falkiner, Hon. F. R. 'Report on homes of the poor', *JSSISI* Vol. VIII, Part LIX, 1881/1882, pp 261–71

Falkiner, Dr Ninian M. 'The evolution of the Diploma of Public Health', *JSSISI* Vol. XIV, No 3, 1923-5, pp 158–65

Grimshaw, Thomas Wrigley *The House Accommodation of the Artisan and Labouring Classes in Ireland, with special reference to Dublin and other large towns*, (Dublin, 1885)

Harty, Spencer 'Some considerations on the working of the Artizans' Dwellings Acts, as illustrated in the case of the Coombe Area, Dublin' *JSSISI* Vol. VIII, Part LXII, 1883/1884 p 508

Jordan, Rev. Thomas 'The present state of the dwellings of the poor, chiefly in

Dublin', *JSSISI*, Vol II, Part VIII, 1857, pp 12–19

Lawson, William 'Remedies for Overcrowding in the City of Dublin', *JSSISI*, Vol XII, Part LXXXIX, 1908/1909, pp 230–48

Leyland, John *Contemporary Medical Men and their Professional Work, Vol ii* (Leicester, 1888)

MacDowell Cosgrave, E. *Dublin and County Dublin in the Twentieth Century, Contemporary Biographies* (Brighton and London, 1908)

Mapother, E. D. 'Address at the opening of the thirty-fourth session of the Statistical and Social Inquiry Society of Ireland', *JSSISI*, Vol. VIII, Part LVII 1880/1881, pp 85–106

Mapother, E. D. 'The sanitary state of Dublin', *JSSISI* Vol IV, Part XXVII, 1864 pp 62–76

Mapother, E. D. 'The differences between the statutes bearing on public health for England and Ireland', *JSSISI* Vol IV, Part XXX, 1865, pp 203–11

Mapother, E. D. 'The unhealthiness of Irish towns, and the want of sanitary legislation', *JSSISI* Vol IV, Part XXVI, 1865/1866, pp 250–75

Maunsell, Henry *Political Medicine; Being the Substance of a Discourse Lately Delivered before the Royal College of Surgeons in Ireland, on Medicine, Considered in its Relations to Government and Legislation* (Dublin, 1839)

Mearns, Andrew *The Bitter Cry of Outcast London: An Inquiry into the Condition of the Abject Poor* (London, 1883)

Neville, Parke *A Description of the Dublin Corporation Waterworks by the Engineer, Parke Neville, CE, MICE, FRIA, MRIA, etc, etc,* (Dublin, 1875)

Norwood, John 'On the working of the sanitary laws in Dublin, with suggestions for their amendment', *JSSISI* Vol VI, Part XLIII, 1872/1873, pp 230–42

Peter, A. *A Brief Account of the Magdalen Chapel, Leeson Street* (Dublin, 1907)

Pettigrew and Oulton *The Dublin Almanack and General Register of Ireland 1845* (Dublin 1846)

A. Thom *Thom's Directories* (Dublin 1846–)

Warburton, J., J. Whitelaw, R. Walsh, *The History of the City of Dublin, from the earliest accounts to the present time, etc.*, 2 vols., (London, 1818)

White, Francis *Report and Observations on the State of the Poor of Dublin* (Dublin, 1833)

Whitelaw, James *An Essay on the Population of Dublin, being the Result of an Actual Survey taken in 1798, with great care and precision, and arranged in a manner entirely new* (Dublin, 1805)

Willis, Thomas *Facts connected with the Social and Sanitary Condition of the Working Classes in the City of Dublin* (Dublin, 1845)

Wills, W. G. *In Memoriam Lucie Cameron* (Dublin, 1884)

Modern books and articles

Aalen, F. H. A. *The Iveagh Trust: the first hundred years, 1890–1990* (Dublin, 1990)

Aalen, F. H. A. and Kevin Whelan, (eds), *Health and Housing in Dublin c.1850 to 1921 in Dublin: from prehistory to present* (Dublin, 1992)

Allan, Adrian R. 'Duncan, William Henry (1805–1863)' *Oxford Dictionary of National Biography* (Oxford University Press, 2004)

Bannon, Michael J. (ed.), *A Hundred Years of Irish Planning, Volume 1, The Emergence of Irish Planning, 1880–1920* (Dublin, 1985)

Beckett, Ian F. W. 'Wolseley, Garnet Joseph, first Viscount Wolseley (1833–1913)' *Oxford Dictionary of National Biography*, (Oxford University Press, 2004)

Boylan, Henry *A Dictionary of Irish Biography*, Third Edition (Dublin, 1998)

Bradshaw, Percy Venner *Brother Savages and Guests: A History of the Savage Club, 1857–1957* (London, 1958)

Burke, Helen *The People and the Poor Law in Nineteenth Century Ireland* (Littlehampton, 1987)

Casey, Christine *Dublin, the City within the Grand and Royal Canals and the Circular Road with the Phoenix Park*, (New Haven and London, 2005)

Cooke, Jim 'Charles Dickens, A Dublin Chronicler' *Dublin Historical Record*, 1989, XLII, No. 3

Corcoran, Michael *'Our Good Health' a history of Dublin's water and drainage* (Dublin, 2005)

Cullen, M.J. *The Statistical Movement in Early Victorian Britain, the Foundations of Empirical Statistical Research* (New York, 1975)

Daly, Mary E. *Dublin—the Deposed Capital: A Social and Economic History 1860–1914* (Cork, 1984)

Daly, Mary E. 'Housing conditions and the genesis of housing reform in Dublin, 1880–1920' in Bannon, Michael J. (ed.), *A Hundred Years of Irish Planning, Volume 1, The Emergence of Irish Planning, 1880–1920* (Dublin, 1985)

Daly, Mary E. *The Spirit of Earnest Inquiry: the Statistical and Social Inquiry Society of Ireland, 1847–1997*, (Dublin, 1997)

Dyer, Bernard *The Society of Public Analysts and other Analytical Chemists, some reminiscences of its first fifty years* (Cambridge, 1932).

Dyos, H. J. and M. Wolff (eds), *The Victorian City: Images and Realities, 2 Vols.* (London and New York, 1973)

Feeney, J. K. *The Coombe Lying-in Hospital*, (Dublin, 1983)

Finer, S. E. *The Life and Times of Sir Edwin Chadwick*, (London, 1997)

Fleetwood, John F. *The History of Medicine in Ireland*, (Dublin, 1983)

Flinn, M. W. and T. C. Smout (eds), *Essays in Social History*, (London, 1974)

Fraser, Murray *John Bull's Other Homes: State Housing and British Policy in Ireland, 1883–1922* (Liverpool, 1996)

Frazer, W. M. *Duncan of Liverpool: Being an Account of the Work of Dr. W. H. Duncan, Medical Officer of Health for Liverpool, 1847–63* (London, 1947)

Gauldie, Enid *Cruel Habitation, A History of Working-Class Housing 1780–1918*, (London, 1974)

Geary, Laurence 'Cameron, Sir Charles Alexander (1830–1921)' *Oxford Dictionary of National Biography* (Oxford University Press, 2004)

Guha, Sumit 'The Importance of Social Intervention in England's Mortality Decline: The Evidence Reviewed' in *Social History of Medicine*, 1994, 7(1)

Gilbert, Bentley *The Evolution of National Insurance* (London, 1966)

Hamlin, Christopher *Public Health and Social Justice in the Age of Chadwick, Britain, 1800–1854*, (Cambridge, 1998)

Hamlin, Christopher 'Simon, Sir John (1816–1904)' *Oxford Dictionary of National Biography* (Oxford University Press, 2004)

Harkness, D. and M. O'Dowd (eds), *The Town in Ireland*, (Belfast, 1979)

Harris, Bernard 'Public Health, Nutrition, and the Decline of Mortality: The McKeown Thesis Revisited' in *Social History of Medicine*, 2004, 17(3)

Lambert, Royston *Sir John Simon 1816–1904 and English Social Administration* (London, 1963)

Lyons, J. B. *A Pride of Professors, The Professors of Medicine at the Royal College of Surgeons in Ireland 1813–1985*, (Dublin, 1999)

McDonagh, Oliver *O'Connell: The Life of Daniel O'Connell, 1775–1847* (London, 1991)

McKeown, Thomas *The Role of Medicine—Dream, Mirage or Nemesis* (London, 1976)

McKeown, Thomas *The Rise of Modern Population* (London, 1976)

Magee, Seán *Chart's Head of Household Surname Index* (Dublin 2001)

Morrissey, SJ, Thomas J. *William J. Walsh, Archbishop of Dublin, 1841–1921, No Uncertain Voice* (Dublin and Portland, Or., 2000)

Morrissey, SJ, Thomas J. 'The 1913 Lock-Out: Letters for the Archbishop' in *Studies* (Spring, 1986)

O'Brien, Joseph V. *Dear Dirty Dublin, A City in Distress, 1899–1916* (London, 1982)

O'Doherty, Mary '*Salus populi*—the endeavours of Edward Dillon Mapother (1835–1908)', *Jn. Irish Colleges of Physicians and Surgeons*, vol. 28, no. 3, July 1999

Ó Maitiú, Séamas *Dublin's Suburban Towns 1834–1930* (Dublin, 2003)

Prunty, Jacinta *Dublin Slums 1800–1925, A Study in Urban Geography* (Dublin,

1998)

Prunty, Jacinta *Managing the Dublin Slums, 1850–1922, The Sir John T. Gilbert Commemorative Lecture, 2002,* Dublin City Public Libraries (Dublin, 2004)

Robertson, Edna *Glasgow's Doctor James Burn Russell 1837–1904* (East Lothian, 1998)

Robins, Joseph *The Miasma: Epidemic and Panic in Nineteenth Century Ireland* (Dublin, 1995)

Robins, Joseph *Custom House People* (Dublin 1993)

Rosen, George 'Disease, Debility, and Death', in H. J. Dyos and Michael Wolff (eds), *The Victorian City,* Volume 2 (London and New York, 1973)

Sheard, Sally and Helen Power (eds), *Body and City, Histories of Urban Public Health* (Aldershot, 2000)

Smith, F. B. *The People's Health 1830–1910* (London, 1979)

Steele, David 'Sir John Gray (1816–1875)' *Oxford Dictionary of National Biography* (Oxford University Press, 2004)

Stewart, John *The Camerons: A History of the Clan Cameron* (Stirling, 1974)

Szreter, Simon 'Mortality and Public Health, 1815–1914' in *Refresh, Recent Findings of Research in Economic and Social History,* 14, Spring, 1992

Szreter, Simon 'Rethinking McKeown: The Relationship Between Public Health and Social Change', *American Journal of Public Health,* vol. 92, 5, 2002, pp 722–4

Szreter, Simon 'Szreter Responds' *American Journal of Public Health,* vol. 93, 7, 2003, pp 1032–3.

Turner, Roger 'Cameron, Archibald (1707–1753)' *Oxford Dictionary of National Biography* (Oxford University Press, 2004)

Widdess, J. D. H. *The Royal College of Surgeons in Ireland and its Medical School 1784–1984,* (Dublin, 1967)

Wohl, Anthony S. (ed) *Andrew Mearns—the Bitter Cry of Outcast London* (Leicester, 1970).

Wohl, Anthony S. 'Unfit for Human Habitation' in *The Victorian City,* Volume 2, H. J. Dyos and Michael Wolfe (eds) (London and New York, 1973)

Wohl, Anthony S. *The Eternal Slum, Housing and Social Policy in Victorian London* (London, 1977)

Wohl, Anthony S. *Endangered Lives, Public Health in Victorian Britain* (London, 1983)

Yeates, Pádraig *Lockout: Dublin 1913* (Dublin, 2000)

DISSERTATION

Jones, Stephanie 'Dublin reformed: the transformation of the municipal governance of a Victorian city, 1840–60' Ph.D. dissertation, University of Dublin, 2002

WEBSITES

http://www.groireland.ie/history.htm (General Register Office, Ireland)

http://www.belleek.ie/profile.asp

http://users.ox.ac.uk/~peter/workhouse/Ireland.shtml

http://www.rsc.org/Education/EiC/issues/2005Mar/Thefightagainstfood
adulteration.asp

http://www.lochiel.net/archives/arch.html

http://www.victorianlondon.org/publications/seven9.htm

Index

Jordan, Thomas, 35, 47, 62

Kelly, Thomas, 3, 195
Kerr's Porcelain Factory, 25
Kinahan, W. H., 58

laboratory, Royal College of Surgeons, 95
Lancet, 78, 79, 95
landlords, 55
Larcom, Thomas, 81
Larkin, Jim, 211
Lawson, William, 62
Ledwich School of Medicine, 31, 87
legal procedures to close houses, 151
Legislation 1848–1866, 68–75
Letheby, Dr Henry, 78, 80, 134
Liebig, Justus Von, 26, 29
Lister, Joseph, 138, 203
Littlejohn, Dr, MOH Edinburgh, 152
Local Government Board, 104, 213–214
Lock Hospital, 50
Lockout, Dublin 1913, 211–212
Lord Lieutenant, 53, 54, 81, 91, 92
Lord Mayor, 81, 83, 85

Magee's Court, 5, 6, 38, 208
Magdalen Chapel, Leeson Street, 118–119
Mapother, Edward Dillon, 45, 56, 61, 62, 66, 70, 71, 72, 73, 90, 92, 103, 104, 106–111
Masonic Female Orphan School, 148
Mearns, Andrew, 154–156
meat, diseased, 78, 93–94
milk, typhoid fever from, 95
Minchin, Dr 87
Mining Journal, 31
Mountjoy Barracks, 21
Moyers, George, 206
Municipal Boundaries Commission 1879, 56
Murphy, William Martin, 211

McBirney, David, 25
McNamara, Lucie (see Cameron, Lucie, wife)
McNamara, Rawdon, 205, 206

Nation newspaper, 84
Neville, Arthur, 60
Neville, Arthur Richards, 59
Neville, Parke, 58, 59–61, 73, 74
North Dublin Union, 92, 93
North William Street Convent, 6, 185, 187, 198
Norwood, John, 62, 68, 69, 74, 75

O'Brien, Timothy, 63
O'Leary, Mr, 87

Pall Mall Gazette, 155
Palmerstown/Chapelizod, 11
Parkes, T.H., 234
Paving Board, 53
Phoenix Park murders, 99
pinkeen in milk, 77
pleura-pneumonia in beef, 93–94
poisoning in Victorian era, 99
poor, attitudes to, 153–154
Poor Law Commission, 213
Powerscourt, Viscount, 170
Prince of Wales, 157, 161
Public Analyst, Dublin, 80–96
Public Health Inquiry 1900 and Report, 179–185, 212
Purdon, Edward, 206

Queen's College, Galway, 31

Redmond, Mr, 85
Reynolds, Mr, 84
Reynolds' Newspaper, 155
reformatories, report on, 212
Report 1914, 6
Roe, George, 58
Royal College of Physicians, 27
Royal College of Surgeons in Ireland, 31–32, 83, 105, 148, 203–204
Royal Irish Constabulary, 47, 211
Russell, James Burn, MOH Glasgow, 121, 135–146

Sackville Street, 211
Salisbury, Lord, 156, 157